IMPORTANT NOTICES AND DISCLAIMERS CON(

NFPA® codes, standards, recommended practices, and guides ("NI contained herein is one, are developed through a consensus standar(American National Standards Institute. This process brings together v ...g .... and interests to achieve consensus on fire and other safety issues. While the NFPA administers the process and establishes rules to promote fairness in the development of consensus, it does not independently test, evaluate, or verify the accuracy of any information or the soundness of any judgments contained in NFPA Standards.

The NFPA disclaims liability for any personal injury, property, or other damages of any nature whatsoever, whether special, indirect, consequential or compensatory, directly or indirectly resulting from the publication, use of, or reliance on NFPA Standards. The NFPA also makes no guaranty or warranty as to the accuracy or completeness of any information published herein.

In issuing and making NFPA Standards available, the NFPA is not undertaking to render professional or other services for or on behalf of any person or entity. Nor is the NFPA undertaking to perform any duty owed by any person or entity to someone else. Anyone using this document should rely on his or her own independent judgment or, as appropriate, seek the advice of a competent professional in determining the exercise of reasonable care in any given circumstances.

The NFPA has no power, nor does it undertake, to police or enforce compliance with the contents of NFPA Standards. Nor does the NFPA list, certify, test, or inspect products, designs, or installations for compliance with this document. Any certification or other statement of compliance with the requirements of this document shall not be attributable to the NFPA and is solely the responsibility of the certifier or maker of the statement.

REVISION SYMBOLS IDENTIFYING CHANGES FROM THE PREVIOUS EDITION

Text revisions are shaded. A Δ before a section number indicates that words within that section were deleted and a Δ to the left of a table or figure number indicates a revision to an existing table or figure. When a chapter was heavily revised, the entire chapter is marked throughout with the Δ symbol. Where one or more sections were deleted, a • is placed between the remaining sections. Chapters, annexes, sections, figures, and tables that are new are indicated with an N.

Note that these indicators are a guide. Rearrangement of sections may not be captured in the markup, but users can view complete revision details in the First and Second Draft Reports located in the archived revision information section of each code at www.nfpa.org/docinfo. Any subsequent changes from the NFPA Technical Meeting, Tentative Interim Amendments, and Errata are also located there.

REMINDER: UPDATING OF NFPA STANDARDS

Users of NFPA codes, standards, recommended practices, and guides ("NFPA Standards") should be aware that these documents may be superseded at any time by the issuance of a new edition, may be amended with the issuance of Tentative Interim Amendments (TIAs), or be corrected by Errata. It is intended that through regular revisions and amendments, participants in the NFPA standards development process consider the then-current and available information on incidents, materials, technologies, innovations, and methods as these develop over time and that NFPA Standards reflect this consideration. Therefore, any previous edition of this document no longer represents the current NFPA Standard on the subject matter addressed. NFPA encourages the use of the most current edition of any NFPA Standard [as it may be amended by TIA(s) or Errata] to take advantage of current experience and understanding. An official NFPA Standard at any point in time consists of the current edition of the document, including any issued TIAs and Errata then in effect.

To determine whether an NFPA Standard has been amended through the issuance of TIAs or corrected by Errata, visit the "Codes & Standards" section at www.nfpa.org.

ISBN: 978-145592971-9 (Print)
3 4 5 6 7 CW 28 27 26 25 24

ADDITIONAL IMPORTANT NOTICES AND DISCLAIMERS CONCERNING NFPA® STANDARDS

Updating of NFPA Standards

Users of NFPA codes, standards, recommended practices, and guides ("NFPA Standards") should be aware that these documents may be superseded at any time by the issuance of a new edition, may be amended with the issuance of Tentative Interim Amendments (TIAs), or be corrected by Errata. It is intended that through regular revisions and amendments, participants in the NFPA standards development process consider the then-current and available information on incidents, materials, technologies, innovations, and methods as these develop over time and that NFPA Standards reflect this consideration. Therefore, any previous edition of this document no longer represents the current NFPA Standard on the subject matter addressed. NFPA encourages the use of the most current edition of any NFPA Standard [as it may be amended by TIA(s) or Errata] to take advantage of current experience and understanding. An official NFPA Standard at any point in time consists of the current edition of the document, including any issued TIAs and Errata then in effect.

To determine whether an NFPA Standard has been amended through the issuance of TIAs or corrected by Errata, visit the "Codes & Standards" section at www.nfpa.org.

Interpretations of NFPA Standards

A statement, written or oral, that is not processed in accordance with Section 6 of the Regulations Governing the Development of NFPA Standards shall not be considered the official position of NFPA or any of its Committees and shall not be considered to be, nor be relied upon as, a Formal Interpretation.

Patents

The NFPA does not take any position with respect to the validity of any patent rights referenced in, related to, or asserted in connection with an NFPA Standard. The users of NFPA Standards bear the sole responsibility for determining the validity of any such patent rights, as well as the risk of infringement of such rights, and the NFPA disclaims liability for the infringement of any patent resulting from the use of or reliance on NFPA Standards.

NFPA adheres to the policy of the American National Standards Institute (ANSI) regarding the inclusion of patents in American National Standards ("the ANSI Patent Policy"), and hereby gives the following notice pursuant to that policy:

NOTICE: The user's attention is called to the possibility that compliance with an NFPA Standard may require use of an invention covered by patent rights. NFPA takes no position as to the validity of any such patent rights or as to whether such patent rights constitute or include essential patent claims under the ANSI Patent Policy. If, in connection with the ANSI Patent Policy, a patent holder has filed a statement of willingness to grant licenses under these rights on reasonable and nondiscriminatory terms and conditions to applicants desiring to obtain such a license, copies of such filed statements can be obtained, on request, from NFPA. For further information, contact the NFPA at the address listed below.

Law and Regulations

Users of NFPA Standards should consult applicable federal, state, and local laws and regulations. NFPA does not, by the publication of its codes, standards, recommended practices, and guides, intend to urge action that is not in compliance with applicable laws, and these documents may not be construed as doing so.

Copyrights

NFPA Standards are copyrighted. They are made available for a wide variety of both public and private uses. These include both use, by reference, in laws and regulations, and use in private self-regulation, standardization, and the promotion of safe practices and methods. By making these documents available for use and adoption by public authorities and private users, the NFPA does not waive any rights in copyright to these documents.

Use of NFPA Standards for regulatory purposes should be accomplished through adoption by reference. The term "adoption by reference" means the citing of title, edition, and publishing information only. Any deletions, additions, and changes desired by the adopting authority should be noted separately in the adopting instrument. In order to assist NFPA in following the uses made of its documents, adopting authorities are requested to notify the NFPA (Attention: Secretary, Standards Council) in writing of such use. For technical assistance and questions concerning adoption of NFPA Standards, contact NFPA at the address below.

For Further Information

All questions or other communications relating to NFPA Standards and all requests for information on NFPA procedures governing its codes and standards development process, including information on the procedures for requesting Formal Interpretations, for proposing Tentative Interim Amendments, and for proposing revisions to NFPA standards during regular revision cycles, should be sent to NFPA headquarters, addressed to the attention of the Secretary, Standards Council, NFPA, 1 Batterymarch Park, P.O. Box 9101, Quincy, MA 02269-9101; email: stds_admin@nfpa.org.

For more information about NFPA, visit the NFPA website at www.nfpa.org. All NFPA codes and standards can be viewed at no cost at www.nfpa.org/docinfo.

Copyright © 2022 National Fire Protection Association®. All Rights Reserved.

NFPA® 70B

Standard for

Electrical Equipment Maintenance

2023 Edition

This edition of NFPA 70B, *Standard for Electrical Equipment Maintenance*, was prepared by the Technical Committee on Electrical Equipment Maintenance and released by the Correlating Committee on National Electrical Code®. It was issued by the Standards Council on December 27, 2022, with an effective date of January 16, 2023, and supersedes all previous editions.

This edition of NFPA 70B was approved as an American National Standard on January 16, 2023.

Origin and Development of NFPA 70B

The National Electrical Code Committee had received several requests to include maintenance recommendations in the *National Electrical Code® (NEC®)*. The National Electrical Code Correlating Committee determined that the *NEC* was not the proper document in which to cover the maintenance of electrical equipment. However, the committee recognized that "lack of maintenance" frequently resulted in serious injuries and fatalities as well as high monetary damage. An ad hoc committee on electrical equipment maintenance was authorized by NFPA in 1967 to determine the need for the development of a document on the subject.

Equipment manufacturers typically provide maintenance needs for specific types of equipment, and general maintenance guidance was available from several sources. Therefore, it was determined that compiling that information into a single document under the NFPA process in the form of general guidelines was advantageous.

On June 27, 1968, NFPA authorized the establishment of the Committee on Electrical Equipment Maintenance with the following scope: "To develop suitable texts relating to preventive maintenance of electrical systems and equipment used in industrial-type applications with the view of reducing loss of life and property. The purpose is to correlate generally applicable procedures for preventive maintenance that have broad application to the more common classes of industrial electrical systems and equipment without duplicating or superseding instructions that manufacturers normally provide. Reports to the Association through the Correlating Committee of the National Electrical Code Committee."

In 1973, NFPA 70B-T, *Tentative Recommended Practice for Electrical Equipment Maintenance*, covered "Why an Electrical Preventive Maintenance (EPM) Program Pays Dividends," "What Is an Effective Electrical Preventive Maintenance Program?," and "Planning and Developing an Electrical Preventive Maintenance Program." The document was revised in 1974 to include a chapter on the fundamentals of electrical equipment maintenance, general maintenance requirements for various types of equipment, and a new appendix, "How to Instruct." The tentative recommended practice was adopted as NFPA 70B, *Recommended Practice for Electrical Equipment Maintenance*, in 1975.

For the 1977 edition, added chapters included Electronic Equipment, Ground-Fault Protection, Wiring Devices, and Maintenance of Electrical Equipment Subject to Long Intervals Between Shutdowns. New appendices addressed NEMA plug and receptacle configurations and guidelines for long-term maintenance.

In the 1983 edition, chapters on cable tray systems and on deenergizing and grounding of equipment to provide protection for maintenance personnel were added. An appendix covering equipment storage and maintenance during construction was also added.

The 1987 edition included distribution transformers as well as power transformers.

A chapter on uninterruptible power supply systems was added in the 1990 edition.

NFPA and National Fire Protection Association are registered trademarks of the National Fire Protection Association, Quincy, Massachusetts 02169.

Three new chapters were added to the 1994 edition to cover power system studies, power quality, and vibration analysis pertaining to rotating machinery. Other revisions were made to comply with the NFPA *Manual of Style*.

For the 1998 edition, the chapter on power quality was rewritten and expanded. Maintenance techniques for stationary batteries and infrared inspections were updated and revised. Special handling and disposal considerations were introduced, and employee training was focused to emphasize workplace safety.

The 2002 edition was restructured to comply with the *Manual of Style for NFPA Technical Committee Documents*. The scope was revised to include preventive maintenance for electronic and communications equipment. A chapter was added for grounding maintenance issues. A new section for gas insulated substations addressed the maintenance issues resulting from regulatory changes in the electrical utility industry.

The chapter on power quality was enhanced with information on the latest technology on voltage fluctuation. A new annex suggested maintenance intervals for electrical equipment.

The 2006 edition included a new chapter on safety placed up front to provide more complete and updated coverage, as well as to emphasize the importance of safety. An important part of maintenance is having a properly installed system with baseline performance data, and so a chapter on commissioning the electrical system at a new facility was added. With the industry trend shifted from routine maintenance to reliability-centered maintenance (RCM), a chapter on how to apply RCM and an extensive annex with detailed reliability data on many types of electrical equipment also was added.

The 2010 edition was reorganized to group like topics and equipment into a more logical arrangement. The chapter on testing and test methods centralized test procedures formerly located in the individual equipment chapters.

A section on emergency preparedness and electrical system and equipment restoration was added to Chapter 6 to respond to the concerns of electrical equipment owners and maintainers. Chapter 6 included new material covering outsourcing of electrical equipment maintenance. The requirements on personnel safety were revised to correlate with and directly reference *NFPA 70E*.

Significant material supporting reliability centered maintenance was added to Annex N.

Four new chapters were added to the 2013 edition: Chapter 32, Electrical Disaster Recovery; Chapter 33, Photovoltaic Systems; Chapter 34, Electrical Vehicle Charging Systems; and Chapter 35, Wind Power Electrical Systems and Associated Equipment.

For the 2016 edition, torque recommendations were added to assist in minimizing electrical issues associated with poor connections. Battery testing and maintenance recommendations were enhanced to provide greater detail regarding proper battery testing and safety considerations for persons performing battery maintenance.

The 2019 edition incorporated several editorial and stylistic updates to improve the consistency of the document.

The recommended practice has been converted to the *Standard for Electrical Equipment Maintenance* standard for the 2023 edition.

Correlating Committee on National Electrical Code®

Lawrence S. Ayer, *Chair*
Biz Com Electric, Inc., OH [IM]
Rep. Independent Electrical Contractors, Inc.

Ernest J. Gallo, Telcordia Technologies (Ericsson), NJ [UT]
Rep. Alliance for Telecommunications Industry Solutions

Palmer L. Hickman, Electrical Training Alliance, MD [L]
Rep. International Brotherhood of Electrical Workers

Richard A. Holub, The DuPont Company, Inc., DE [U]
Rep. American Chemistry Council

Dean C. Hunter, Minnesota Department of Labor & Industry, MN [E]

David H. Kendall, ABB Inc., TN [M]
Rep. National Electrical Manufacturers Association

John R. Kovacik, UL LLC, IL [RT]

Alan Manche, Schneider Electric, KY [M]

Roger D. McDaniel, Pinnacle Power Solutions, LLC., GA [UT]
Rep. Electric Light & Power Group/EEI

Christine T. Porter, Intertek Testing Services, WA [RT]

Timothy James Schultheis, T.S.B Inc., Schultheis Electric, PA [IM]
Rep. National Electrical Contractors Association

David A. Williams, Delta Charter Township, MI [E]
Rep. International Association of Electrical Inspectors

Alternates

Derrick L. Atkins, Minneapolis Electrical JATC, MN [L]
(Alt. to Palmer L. Hickman)

Trevor N. Bowmer, Bunya Telecom Consulting, LLC , ME [UT]
(Alt. to Ernest J. Gallo)

Donald R. Cook, Dewberry/Edmonds Engineering, AL [E]
(Alt. to David A. Williams)

Roland E. Deike, Jr., CenterPoint Energy, Inc., TX [UT]
(Alt. to Roger D. McDaniel)

William T. Fiske, Intertek Testing Services, NY [RT]
(Alt. to Christine T. Porter)

David L. Hittinger, Independent Electrical Contractors, VA [IM]
(Alt. to Lawrence S. Ayer)

Raymond W. Horner, Atkore International, IL [M]
(Alt. to David H. Kendall)

Peter D. Jackson, City of Bakersfield, California, CA [E]
(Alt. to Dean C. Hunter)

Michael J. Johnston, National Electrical Contractors Association, MD [IM]
(Alt. to Timothy James Schultheis)

Chad Kennedy, Schneider Electric, SC [M]
(Alt. to Alan Manche)

Robert D. Osborne, UL LLC, NC [RT]
(Alt. to John R. Kovacik)

Paul B. Sullivan, DuPont, SC [U]
(Alt. to Richard A. Holub)

Nonvoting

Timothy J. Pope, Canadian Standards Association, Canada [SE]
Rep. CSA/Canadian Electrical Code Committee

Rodger Reiswig, Johnson Controls, VA [M]

William R. Drake, Fairfield, CA [O]
(Member Emeritus)

D. Harold Ware, Libra Electric Company, OK [O]
(Member Emeritus)

Jeffrey S. Sargent, NFPA Staff Liaison

This list represents the membership at the time the Committee was balloted on the final text of this edition. Since that time, changes in the membership may have occurred. A key to classifications is found at the back of the document.

NOTE: Membership on a committee shall not in and of itself constitute an endorsement of the Association or any document developed by the committee on which the member serves.

Committee Scope: This Committee shall have primary responsibility for documents on minimizing the risk of electricity as a source of electric shock and as a potential ignition source of fires and explosions. It shall also be responsible for text to minimize the propagation of fire and explosions due to electrical installations.

Technical Committee on Electrical Equipment Maintenance

Rodney J. West, *Chair*
Schneider Electric, OH [M]

Abdelkader Abdelmoumene, Qatar Airways Group, Qatar [U]

Thomas H. Bishop, Electrical Apparatus Service Association, MO [IM]
Rep. Electrical Apparatus Service Association

William P. Cantor, TPI Corporation, PA [U]
Rep. IEEE-IAS/PES JTCC

Adria Corbett, CHUBB Group of Insurance Companies, NY [I]

Karl M. Cunningham, Self Employed, FL [M]
Rep. The Aluminum Association, Inc.

Paul Dobrowsky, Innovative Technology Services, NY [SE]

Randy Dollar, Siemens Industry, GA [M]
Rep. National Electrical Manufacturers Association

Thomas A. Domitrovich, Eaton Corporation, MO [M]

James B. Evans, Salisbury by Honeywell, OH [M]

Ryan Grimes, Toyota Motor Engineering & Manufacturing North America, Inc., KY [U]

Jeffrey Hall, UL LLC, NC [RT]

William R. Harris, General Motors Company, MI [U]

Palmer L. Hickman, Electrical Training Alliance, MD [L]
Rep. International Brotherhood of Electrical Workers

Mark C. Horne, Georgia Power Company, GA [U]
Rep. Electric Light & Power Group/EEI

David Huffman, Power Systems Testing Company, CA [IM]
Rep. InterNational Electrical Testing Association

Christel K. Hunter, Cerro Wire, NV [M]
Rep. Copper Development Association Inc.

Darrel Johnson, City of Jacksonville, NC [E]

Haley Masbruch, Danard Electric, Inc., WA [IM]
Rep. National Electrical Contractors Association

Ahmad A. Moshiri, Liebert Corporation, OH [M]

Robert Neary, SEA, Limited, MD [SE]

Thomas Warren Northcott, Jacobs Technology, TN [SE]

Paul B. Sullivan, DuPont, SC [U]

Kiley Taylor, National Renewable Energy Laboratory, CO [U]

Robert Urdinola, US Department of State, DC [U]

Marcelo E. Valdes, Asea Brown Boveri Ltd. (ABB), NC [M]
Rep. National Electrical Manufacturers Association

Jaime Ybarra, Tony Demaria Electric Inc., CA [IM]

Alternates

Gary Lee Babb, Chubb Insurance Company, IN [I]
(Alt. to Adria Corbett)

Scott A. Blizard, American Electrical Testing Company, Inc., MA [IM]
(Alt. to David Huffman)

Scott Brady, Eaton Corporation, AZ [M]
(Alt. to Thomas A. Domitrovich)

Aaron Butcher, SEA, Limited, OH [SE]
(Alt. to Robert Neary)

Dan Cooper, Toyota, KY [U]
(Alt. to Ryan Grimes)

Jeffrey A. Fecteau, UL LLC, AZ [RT]
(Alt. to Jeffrey Hall)

Charles Foland, National Renewable Energy Laboratory (NREL), CO [U]
(Alt. to Kiley Taylor)

Charles L. Kaufman, Miller Electric Manufacturing Company, WI [M]
(Alt. to Randy Dollar)

Christopher E. Kelly, JATC for Nassau & Suffolk Counties, NY [L]
(Alt. to Palmer L. Hickman)

Jack L. Lyons, National Electrical Manufacturers Association (NEMA), MA [M]
(Alt. to Marcelo E. Valdes)

Alan Manche, Schneider Electric, KY [M]
(Alt. to Rodney J. West)

Steve Park, Electrical Reliability SVCS, IN [M]
(Alt. to Ahmad A. Moshiri)

Timothy James Schultheis, T.S.B Inc., Schultheis Electric, PA [IM]
(Alt. to Haley Masbruch)

Ron Widup, Shermco Industries, TX [IM]
(Voting Alt.)

Christopher Coache, NFPA Staff Liaison

This list represents the membership at the time the Committee was balloted on the final text of this edition. Since that time, changes in the membership may have occurred. A key to classifications is found at the back of the document.

NOTE: Membership on a committee shall not in and of itself constitute an endorsement of the Association or any document developed by the committee on which the member serves.

Committee Scope: This Committee shall have the primary responsibility for documents relating to preventive maintenance of electrical, electronic, and communications systems and equipment used in industrial and commercial type applications with the view of: (1) reducing loss of life and property, and (2) improving reliability, performance, and efficiency in a cost-effective manner. The purpose is to provide generally applicable procedures for preventive maintenance that have broad application to the more common classes of industrial and commercial systems and equipment without duplicating or superseding instructions that manufacturers normally provide. This Committee shall report to Correlating Committee of the National Electrical Code.

Contents

Chapter 1 Administration 70B– 7
1.1 Scope. 70B– 7
1.2 Purpose. 70B– 7
1.3 Application. 70B– 7
1.4 Equivalency. 70B– 7
1.5 Units of Measurement. 70B– 7

Chapter 2 Referenced Publications 70B– 7
2.1 General. 70B– 7
2.2 NFPA Publications. (Reserved) 70B– 7
2.3 Other Publications. 70B– 7
2.4 References for Extracts in Mandatory Sections. 70B– 7

Chapter 3 Definitions 70B– 7
3.1 General. 70B– 7
3.2 NFPA Official Definitions. 70B– 8
3.3 General Definitions. 70B– 8

Chapter 4 General 70B– 10
4.1 General Requirements. 70B– 10
4.2 Electrical Maintenance Program (EMP). 70B– 10
4.3 Personnel. 70B– 11
4.4 Survey and Analysis. 70B– 11
4.5 Planned Inspections. 70B– 11
4.6 Acceptance Test Report. 70B– 11
4.7 Impact of Additions/Rework to Retrofitting
     Equipment. 70B– 11
4.8 Equipment Cleaning. 70B– 12

Chapter 5 Personnel Safety 70B– 12
5.1 Introduction. 70B– 12

Chapter 6 Single-Line Diagrams and System Studies . 70B– 12
6.1 Introduction. 70B– 12
6.2 Single-Line Diagrams. 70B– 12
6.3 Short-Circuit Studies. 70B– 12
6.4 Coordination Studies. 70B– 12
6.5 Load-Flow Studies. 70B– 12
6.6 Reliability Studies. 70B– 12
6.7 Incident Energy Analysis (Arc-Flash Study). 70B– 12
6.8 Electrical Maintenance-Related Design. 70B– 13

Chapter 7 Fundamental Tests 70B– 13
7.1 Fundamental Tests. 70B– 13
7.2 Bolted Bus Connections, Conductor
     Terminations, and Conductor Connectors. 70B– 13
7.3 Insulation Resistance Quality. 70B– 13
7.4 Infrared Thermography. 70B– 14

Chapter 8 Field Testing and Test Methods ... 70B– 14
8.1 Introduction. 70B– 14
8.2 Risk Assessment Special Considerations. 70B– 14
8.3 Testing Category Types. 70B– 14
8.4 Qualifications of Testing Personnel. 70B– 14
8.5 Test Equipment and Tools. 70B– 14
8.6 Test Record. 70B– 15
8.7 Condition of Maintenance Indication. 70B– 15

Chapter 9 Maintenance Intervals 70B– 15
9.1 Scope. 70B– 15
9.2 Frequency of Maintenance. 70B– 15
9.3 Equipment Condition Assessment. 70B– 15

**Chapter 10 Hazardous (Classified) Location Electrical
     Equipment** 70B– 20
10.1 General. 70B– 20

10.2 Maintenance Personnel for Hazardous
      (Classified) Locations. 70B– 20
10.3 Elimination of Hazardous Atmospheres. 70B– 20
10.4 Elimination of Ignition Sources. 70B– 20
10.5 Equipment Reassembly. 70B– 20
10.6 Conduit and Equipment Seals. 70B– 20
10.7 Bolts and Screws. 70B– 20
10.8 Handling of Equipment, Components, and
      Tools. 70B– 20
10.9 Field Modifications. 70B– 20

Chapter 11 Power and Distribution Transformers 70B– 20
11.1 Scope. 70B– 20
11.2 Frequency of Maintenance. 70B– 21
11.3 Periodic Maintenance Procedures. 70B– 21

Chapter 12 Substations and Switchgear 70B– 25
12.1 Scope. 70B– 25
12.2 Frequency of Maintenance. 70B– 25
12.3 Periodic Maintenance Procedures. 70B– 25

Chapter 13 Panelboards and Switchboards 70B– 29
13.1 Scope. 70B– 29
13.2 Frequency of Maintenance. 70B– 29
13.3 Periodic Maintenance Procedures. 70B– 29

Chapter 14 Busways 70B– 31
14.1 Scope. 70B– 31
14.2 Frequency of Maintenance. 70B– 31
14.3 Periodic Maintenance Procedures. 70B– 31

**Chapter 15 Circuit Breakers, Low- and Medium-
     Voltage** 70B– 34
15.1 Scope. 70B– 34
15.2 Frequency of Maintenance. 70B– 34
15.3 Periodic Maintenance Procedures for Low-
      Voltage Power Circuit (LVPCB), Molded Case
      Circuit Breaker (MCCB), and Insulated Case
      Circuit Breakers (ICCB). 70B– 34
15.4 Periodic Maintenance Procedures for Medium-
      Voltage Power Circuit Breakers. 70B– 35

Chapter 16 Fuses 70B– 42
16.1 Scope. 70B– 42
16.2 Frequency of Maintenance. 70B– 42
16.3 Periodic Maintenance Procedures. 70B– 42

Chapter 17 Switches 70B– 43
17.1 Scope. 70B– 43
17.2 Frequency of Maintenance. 70B– 43
17.3 Periodic Maintenance Procedures. 70B– 43

Chapter 18 Power Cables and Conductors 70B– 48
18.1 Chapter Scope. 70B– 48
18.2 Frequency of Maintenance. 70B– 48
18.3 Periodic Maintenance Procedures. 70B– 48

Chapter 19 Cable Tray 70B– 49
19.1 Scope. 70B– 49
19.2 Frequency of Maintenance. 70B– 49
19.3 Periodic Maintenance Procedures. 70B– 49

Chapter 20 Grounding and Bonding 70B– 50
20.1 Scope. 70B– 50
20.2 Frequency of Maintenance. 70B– 50
20.3 Periodic Maintenance Procedures. 70B– 50

Chapter 21 **Ground-Fault Circuit Interrupters and Ground-Fault Protection of Equipment Systems** **70B–** 51
21.1 Scope. **70B–** 51
21.2 Frequency of Maintenance. **70B–** 51
21.3 Periodic Maintenance Procedures. **70B–** 51

Chapter 22 **Lighting** **70B–** 54
22.1 Scope. **70B–** 54
22.2 Frequency of Maintenance. **70B–** 54
22.3 Periodic Maintenance Procedures. **70B–** 54

Chapter 23 **Lighting Control Systems (Reserved)** **70B–** 54

Chapter 24 **Wiring Devices** **70B–** 54
24.1 Scope. **70B–** 54
24.2 Frequency of Maintenance. **70B–** 54
24.3 Periodic Maintenance Procedures. **70B–** 54

Chapter 25 **Uninterruptible Power Supplies (UPS)** **70B–** 56
25.1 Scope. **70B–** 56
25.2 Frequency of Maintenance. **70B–** 56
25.3 Periodic Maintenance Procedures. **70B–** 56
25.4 Special Procedures. **70B–** 56

Chapter 26 **Electronic Equipment (Reserved)** **70B–** 58

Chapter 27 **Rotating Equipment** **70B–** 59
27.1 Scope. **70B–** 59
27.2 Frequency of Maintenance. **70B–** 59
27.3 Periodic Maintenance Procedures. **70B–** 59

Chapter 28 **Motor Control Equipment** **70B–** 61
28.1 Scope. **70B–** 61
28.2 Frequency of Maintenance. **70B–** 61
28.3 Periodic Maintenance Procedures. **70B–** 61

Chapter 29 **Portable Electrical Tools and Equipment** . **70B–** 63
29.1 Scope. **70B–** 63
29.2 Frequency of Maintenance. **70B–** 63
29.3 Periodic Maintenance Procedures. **70B–** 63

Chapter 30 **Photovoltaic Systems** **70B–** 64
30.1 Scope. **70B–** 64
30.2 Frequency of Maintenance. **70B–** 64
30.3 Documentation and Labeling. **70B–** 64
30.4 Periodic Maintenance Procedures. **70B–** 64

Chapter 31 **Wind Power Electric Systems and Associated Equipment** **70B–** 66
31.1 Scope. **70B–** 66
31.2 Frequency of Maintenance. **70B–** 66
31.3 Periodic Maintenance Procedures. **70B–** 66

Chapter 32 **Battery Energy Storage Systems** **70B–** 67
32.1 Scope. **70B–** 67
32.2 Frequency of Maintenance. **70B–** 67
32.3 Documentation. **70B–** 67

32.4 Periodic Maintenance Procedures. **70B–** 67

Chapter 33 **Electric Vehicle Power Transfer Systems and Associated Equipment** **70B–** 69
33.1 Scope. **70B–** 69
33.2 Frequency of Maintenance. **70B–** 69
33.3 Documentation. **70B–** 69
33.4 Periodic Maintenance Procedures. **70B–** 69

Chapter 34 **Public Pools, Fountains, and Similar Installations** **70B–** 70
34.1 Scope. **70B–** 70
34.2 Frequency of Maintenance. **70B–** 70
34.3 Periodic Maintenance Procedures. **70B–** 70

Chapter 35 **Protective Relays** **70B–** 71
35.1 Scope. **70B–** 71
35.2 Frequency of Maintenance. **70B–** 71
35.3 Periodic Maintenance Procedures. **70B–** 71

Chapter 36 **Stationary Standby Batteries** **70B–** 74
36.1 Scope. **70B–** 74
36.2 Frequency of Maintenance. **70B–** 74
36.3 Documentation. **70B–** 74
36.4 Periodic Maintenance Procedures. **70B–** 74
36.5 Special. (Reserved) **70B–** 74

Chapter 37 **Instrument Transformers (Reserved)** **70B–** 76

Chapter 38 **Control Power Transformers (Reserved)** . **70B–** 76

Annex A **Explanatory Material** **70B–** 76

Annex B **Suggestions for Inclusion in a Walk-Through Inspection Checklist** **70B–** 95

Annex C **Symbols** **70B–** 96

Annex D **Diagrams** **70B–** 100

Annex E **Forms** **70B–** 103

Annex F **NEMA Configurations** **70B–** 170

Annex G **Primary Contact Matrix** **70B–** 173

Annex H **Equipment Storage and Maintenance During Construction** **70B–** 175

Annex I **Reliability Centered Maintenance** **70B–** 177

Annex J **Power Quality** **70B–** 189

Annex K **Electrical Disaster Recovery** **70B–** 197

Annex L **Case Histories** **70B–** 200

Annex M **Informational References** **70B–** 204

Index **70B–** 208

NFPA 70B

Standard for

Electrical Equipment Maintenance

2023 Edition

IMPORTANT NOTE: This NFPA document is made available for use subject to important notices and legal disclaimers. These notices and disclaimers appear in all publications containing this document and may be found under the heading "Important Notices and Disclaimers Concerning NFPA Standards." They can also be viewed at www.nfpa.org/disclaimers or obtained on request from NFPA.

UPDATES, ALERTS, AND FUTURE EDITIONS: New editions of NFPA codes, standards, recommended practices, and guides (i.e., NFPA Standards) are released on scheduled revision cycles. This edition may be superseded by a later one, or it may be amended outside of its scheduled revision cycle through the issuance of Tentative Interim Amendments (TIAs). An official NFPA Standard at any point in time consists of the current edition of the document, together with all TIAs and Errata in effect. To verify that this document is the current edition or to determine if it has been amended by TIAs or Errata, please consult the National Fire Codes® Subscription Service or the "List of NFPA Codes & Standards" at www.nfpa.org/docinfo. In addition to TIAs and Errata, the document information pages also include the option to sign up for alerts for individual documents and to be involved in the development of the next edition.

NOTICE: An asterisk (*) following the number or letter designating a paragraph indicates that explanatory material on the paragraph can be found in Annex A.

A reference in brackets [ ] following a section or paragraph indicates material that has been extracted from another NFPA document. Extracted text may be edited for consistency and style and may include the revision of internal paragraph references and other references as appropriate. Requests for interpretations or revisions of extracted text shall be sent to the technical committee responsible for the source document.

Information on referenced publications can be found in Chapter 2 and Annex R.

Chapter 1   Administration

1.1 Scope. This standard covers the preventive maintenance of electrical, electronic, and communications systems and equipment.

1.2 Purpose. The purpose of this standard is to provide for the practical safeguarding of persons, property, and processes from the risks associated with failure, breakdown, or malfunction and a means to establish a condition of maintenance of electrical equipment and systems for safety and reliability.

N **1.3 Application.**

N **1.3.1** This standard applies to maintenance for electrical, electronic, and communications systems and equipment and is not intended to duplicate or supersede instructions provided by manufacturers. Systems and equipment covered are typical of those installed for industrial plants, institutional and commercial buildings, and large multifamily residential complexes.

N **1.3.2** Consumer appliances and equipment intended primarily for use in the home are not covered.

N **1.4 Equivalency.** Nothing in this standard is intended to prevent the use of systems, methods, or devices of equivalent or superior quality, effectiveness, and safety over those prescribed by this standard.

N **1.5 Units of Measurement.**

N **1.5.1 Primary Units.** Primary units of measurement are in accordance with the modernized metric system known as the International System of Units (SI), except where specific units are customary for industry practice.

N **1.5.2 Secondary Units and Conversions.**

N **1.5.2.1** Secondary units of measurement, where provided, are in accordance with US customary units (inch-pound units), except where specific units are customary for industry practice.

N **1.5.2.2** Where secondary units are not provided, converted values and converted trade sizes can be used.

N **1.5.2.3** Where extracted text contains values expressed in only one system of units, the values in the extracted text have been retained without conversion to preserve the values established by the responsible technical committee in the source document.

N **1.5.3 Unit Application and Enforcement.**

N **1.5.3.1** The values presented in this standard are expressed with a degree of precision that is appropriate for practical application and enforcement.

N **1.5.3.2*** Either the primary units or secondary units are acceptable for satisfying the requirements in this standard.

Chapter 2   Referenced Publications

2.1 General. The documents or portions thereof listed in this chapter are referenced within this standard and shall be considered part of the requirements of this document.

Δ **2.2 NFPA Publications. (Reserved)**

2.3 Other Publications.

Merriam-Webster's Collegiate Dictionary, 11th edition, Merriam-Webster, Inc., Springfield, MA, 2003.

2.4 References for Extracts in Mandatory Sections.

NFPA 70®, National Electrical Code®, 2023 edition.
NFPA 70E®, Standard for Electrical Safety in the Workplace®, 2021 edition.

Chapter 3   Definitions

Δ **3.1 General.**

N **3.1.1** The definitions contained in this chapter shall apply to the terms used in this standard.

N **3.1.2** Where terms are not defined in this chapter or within another chapter, they shall be defined using their ordinarily accepted meanings within the context in which they are used.

N **3.1.3** *Merriam-Webster's Collegiate Dictionary,* 11th edition, shall be the source for the ordinarily accepted meaning.

3.2 NFPA Official Definitions.

3.2.1* Approved. Acceptable to the authority having jurisdiction.

3.2.2* Authority Having Jurisdiction (AHJ). An organization, office, or individual responsible for enforcing the requirements of a code or standard, or for approving equipment, materials, an installation, or a procedure.

N 3.2.3 Labeled. Equipment or materials to which has been attached a label, symbol, or other identifying mark of an organization that is acceptable to the authority having jurisdiction and concerned with product evaluation, that maintains periodic inspection of production of labeled equipment or materials, and by whose labeling the manufacturer indicates compliance with appropriate standards or performance in a specified manner.

3.2.4* Listed. Equipment, materials, or services included in a list published by an organization that is acceptable to the authority having jurisdiction and concerned with evaluation of products or services, that maintains periodic inspection of production of listed equipment or materials or periodic evaluation of services, and whose listing states that either the equipment, material, or service meets appropriate designated standards or has been tested and found suitable for a specified purpose.

N 3.2.5 Shall. Indicates a mandatory requirement.

N 3.2.6 Standard. An NFPA standard, the main text of which contains only mandatory provisions using the word "shall" to indicate requirements and that is in a form generally suitable for mandatory reference by another standard or code or for adoption into law. Nonmandatory provisions are not to be considered a part of the requirements of a standard and shall be located in an appendix, annex, footnote, informational note, or other means as permitted in the NFPA manuals of style. When used in a generic sense, such as in the phrases "standards development process" or "standards development activities," the term "standards" includes all NFPA standards, including codes, standards, recommended practices, and guides.

3.3 General Definitions.

N 3.3.1* Adjustable Speed Drive. Power conversion equipment that provides a means of adjusting the speed of an electric motor. [**70**, 2023]

N 3.3.2 Appliance. Utilization equipment, generally other than industrial, that is fastened in place, stationary, or portable; is normally built in a standardized size or type; and is installed or connected as a unit to perform one or more functions such as clothes washing, air-conditioning, food mixing, deep frying, and so forth. [**70**, 2023]

3.3.3 Arc Flash Hazard. A source of possible injury or damage to health associated with the release of energy caused by an electric arc. [**70E**, 2021]

N 3.3.4 Bonded (Bonding). Connected to establish electrical continuity and conductivity. [**70**, 2023]

N 3.3.5 Bonding Conductor (Bonding Jumper). A conductor that ensures the required electrical conductivity between metal parts that are required to be electrically connected. [**70**, 2023]

N 3.3.6 Bonding Jumper, Equipment. The connection between two or more portions of the equipment grounding conductor. [**70**, 2023]

N 3.3.7 Busway. A raceway consisting of a metal enclosure containing factory-mounted, bare or insulated conductors, which are usually copper or aluminum bars, rods, or tubes. [**70**, 2023]

N 3.3.8 Cable Tray System. A unit or assembly of units or sections and associated fittings forming a structural system used to securely fasten or support cables and raceways. [**70**, 2023]

N 3.3.9* Circuit Breaker. A device designed to open and close a circuit by nonautomatic means and to open the circuit automatically on a predetermined overcurrent without damage to itself when properly applied within its rating. [**70**, 2023]

3.3.10 Commissioning. The process, procedures, and testing used to set up and verify the initial performance, operational controls, safety systems, and sequence of operation of electrical devices and equipment, prior to it being placed into active service. [**70**, 2023]

N 3.3.11 Condition of Maintenance. The state of the electrical equipment considering the manufacturers' instructions, manufacturers' recommendations, and applicable industry codes, standards, and recommended practices. [**70E**, 2021]

N 3.3.12 Continuous Monitoring. An uninterrupted method of data collection that utilizes permanently mounted counters, sensors, or controllers to measure a condition or state.

3.3.13 Coordination Study. A system planning process used to assist in selecting and setting protective devices to improve power system reliability.

3.3.14* Corona. An electrical discharge phenomenon occurring in gaseous substances, such as air.

N 3.3.15 Disconnecting Means. A device, or group of devices, or other means by which the conductors of a circuit can be disconnected from their source of supply. [**70**, 2023]

N 3.3.16* Electrical Maintenance Program (EMP). A managed program of inspecting, testing, monitoring, analyzing, and servicing electrical systems and equipment with the purpose of maintaining safe operations and production by reducing or eliminating system interruptions and equipment failures.

N 3.3.17 Electrically Safe Work Condition. A state in which an electrical conductor or circuit part has been disconnected from energized parts, locked/tagged in accordance with established standards, tested to verify the absence of voltage, and, if necessary, temporarily grounded for personnel protection. [**70E**, 2021]

N 3.3.18 EMP Coordinator. The individual responsible for coordinating the implementation and operation of the EMP.

N 3.3.19* Energy Storage System (ESS). One or more devices installed as a system capable of storing energy and providing electrical energy into the premises wiring system or an electric power production and distribution network. [**70**, 2023]

N 3.3.20 Equipment, Mobile (Mobile Equipment). Equipment with electrical components that is suitable to be moved only with mechanical aids or is provided with wheels for movement by a person(s) or powered devices. [**70**, 2023]

N **3.3.21* Fault Current, Available (Available Fault Current).** The largest amount of current capable of being delivered at a point on the system during a short-circuit condition. [**70**, 2023]

3.3.22 Ground. The earth. [**70**, 2023]

3.3.23 Grounded (Grounding). Connected (connecting) to ground or to a conductive body that extends the ground connection. [**70**, 2023]

3.3.24 Grounded Conductor. A system or circuit conductor that is intentionally grounded. [**70**, 2023]

3.3.25 Ground Fault. An unintentional, electrically conductive connection between an ungrounded conductor of an electrical circuit and the normally non–current-carrying conductors, metal enclosures, metal raceways, metal equipment, or earth. [**70**, 2023]

3.3.26* Ground-Fault Circuit Interrupter (GFCI). A device intended for the protection of personnel that functions to de-energize a circuit or portion thereof within an established period of time when a ground-fault current exceeds the values established for a Class A device. [**70**, 2023]

Δ **3.3.27* Ground-Fault Protection of Equipment.** A system intended to provide protection of equipment from damaging line-to-ground fault currents by operating to cause a disconnecting means to open all ungrounded conductors of the faulted circuit. This protection is provided at current levels less than those required to protect conductors from damage through the operation of a supply circuit overcurrent device. [**70**, 2023]

N **3.3.28 Grounding Conductor, Equipment (EGC).** A conductive path(s) that is part of an effective ground-fault current path and connects normally non–current-carrying metal parts of equipment together and to the system grounded conductor or to the grounding electrode conductor, or both. [**70**, 2023]

3.3.29 Grounding Electrode. A conducting object through which a direct connection to earth is established. [**70**, 2023]

3.3.30 Grounding Electrode Conductor. A conductor used to connect the system grounded conductor or the equipment to a grounding electrode or to a point on the grounding electrode system. [**70**, 2023]

3.3.31 Grounding Electrode System. The interconnection of grounding electrodes.

3.3.32 Grounding Terminal. A terminal, lug, or other provision provided on some equipment cases (enclosures) to connect the conductive portion of the enclosure to the equipment-grounding conductor.

Δ **3.3.33* Ground Loop.** Multiple intentional or unintentional connections from a conductive path to ground or the conductive body that serves in place of earth.

3.3.34 Harmonics. Voltages or currents whose frequencies are integer multiples of the fundamental system frequency.

3.3.35* Interharmonics. Voltages or currents whose frequencies are not integer multiples of the fundamental system frequency.

3.3.36* Long-Duration Undervoltage. A decrease of the supply voltage to less than 90 percent of the nominal voltage for a time duration greater than 1 minute.

N **3.3.37 Maintenance Interval.** The frequency of inspecting, testing, monitoring, analyzing, and servicing electrical equipment that is determined by the type, criticality, and condition of the equipment.

N **3.3.38 Motor Control Center.** An assembly of one or more enclosed sections having a common power bus and principally containing motor control units. [**70**, 2023]

3.3.39 Noise. Undesirable electrical signals in an electrical or electronic circuit.

Δ **3.3.39.1 *Noise, Common Mode.*** Undesirable electrical signals that exist between a circuit conductor and the grounding conductor.

N **3.3.40 Overcurrent.** Any current in excess of the rated current of equipment or the ampacity of a conductor. It may result from overload, short circuit, or ground fault. [**70**, 2023]

N **3.3.41 Overcurrent Protective Device, Branch-Circuit (Branch-Circuit Overcurrent Protective Device).** A device capable of providing protection for service, feeder, and branch circuits and equipment over the full range of overcurrents between its rated current and its interrupting rating. [**70**, 2023]

N **3.3.42 Overload.** Operation of equipment in excess of normal, full-load rating, or of a conductor in excess of its ampacity that, when it persists for a sufficient length of time, would cause damage or dangerous overheating. A fault, such as a short circuit or ground fault, is not an overload. [**70**, 2023]

N **3.3.43 Panelboard.** A single panel or group of panel units designed for assembly in the form of a single panel, including buses and automatic overcurrent devices, and equipped with or without switches for the control of light, heat, or power circuits; designed to be placed in a cabinet, enclosure, or cutout box placed in or against a wall, partition, or other support; and accessible only from the front. [**70**, 2023]

N **3.3.44 Portable Equipment.** Equipment with electrical components suitable to be moved by a single person without mechanical aids. [**70**, 2023]

N **3.3.45 Power Quality.** Electrical phenomena that can be used to quantify the quality of the electrical supply, including, but not limited to, voltage transients, voltage sags, voltage swells, voltage interruptions, voltage and current harmonics, voltage fluctuations resulting in light flicker, voltage and current unbalance, power frequency deviations, voltage and current interharmonics, and electrical noise (conducted or radiated).

N **3.3.46 Predictive Techniques.** Analytics, algorithms, or software that interpret and analyze data from input sources and provide recommendations to address identified problems.

Δ **3.3.47 Qualified Person.** One who has demonstrated skills and knowledge related to the construction and operation of electrical equipment and installations and has received safety training to identify the hazards and reduce the associated risk. [*70E*, 2021]

N **3.3.48* Reconditioned.** Electromechanical systems, equipment, apparatus, or components that are restored to operating conditions. This process differs from normal servicing of equipment that remains within a facility, or replacement of listed equipment on a one-to-one basis. [**70**, 2023]

3.3.49 Risk Assessment. An overall process that identifies hazards, estimates the likelihood of occurrence of injury or damage to health, estimates the potential severity of injury or damage to health, and determines if protective measures are required. [*70E*, 2021]

△ **3.3.50* Sag.** A decrease to between 10 percent and 90 percent of the normal voltage at the power frequency for durations of 0.5 cycle to 1 minute.

N **3.3.51* Service Point.** The point of connection between the facilities of the serving utility and the premises wiring. [**70**, 2023]

N **3.3.52* Servicing.** The process of following a manufacturer's set of instructions or applicable industry standards to analyze, adjust, or perform prescribed actions upon equipment with the intention to preserve or restore the operational performance of the equipment. [**70**, 2023]

N **3.3.53 Single-Line Diagram.** A diagram that shows, by means of single lines and graphic symbols, the course of an electric circuit or system of circuits and the component devices or parts used in the circuit or system. [*70E*, 2021]

N **3.3.54* Ground-Fault Circuit Interrupter, Special Purpose (SPGFCI). (Special-Purpose Ground-Fault Circuit Interrupter)** A device intended for the detection of ground-fault currents, used in circuits with voltage to ground greater than 150 volts, that functions to de-energize a circuit or portion of a circuit within an established period of time when a ground-fault current exceeds the values established for Class C, D, or E devices. [**70**, 2023]

N **3.3.55* Stationary Standby Battery.** A battery that spends the majority of the time on continuous float charge or in a high state of charge, in readiness for a discharge event.

3.3.56* Survey. The collection of accurate data on the electrical system and the evaluation of this data to obtain the necessary information for developing the EMP.

3.3.57 Sustained Voltage Interruption. The loss of the supply voltage to less than 10 percent on one or more phases for a period greater than 1 minute.

△ **3.3.58 Swell.** An increase to between 110 percent and 180 percent of the normal voltage at the power frequency for durations from 0.5 cycle to 1 minute.

N **3.3.59* Switchboard.** A large single panel, frame, or assembly of panels on which are mounted on the face, back, or both, switches, overcurrent and other protective devices, buses, and usually instruments. [**70**, 2023]

N **3.3.60* Switchgear.** An assembly completely enclosed on all sides and top with sheet metal (except for ventilating openings and inspection windows) and containing primary power circuit switching, interrupting devices, or both, with buses and connections. The assembly may include control and auxiliary devices. Access to the interior of the enclosure is provided by doors, removable covers, or both. [**70**, 2023]

N **3.3.61 Tests.**

N **3.3.61.1* *Acceptance Tests*.** Tests that are performed on new equipment prior to energization to determine whether the equipment complies with the purchase and design specifications.

N **3.3.61.2 *As-Found Tests*.** Tests performed on equipment before maintenance work is performed.

N **3.3.61.3 *As-Left Tests*.** Tests performed on equipment after maintenance work is performed.

N **3.3.61.4* *Enhanced Tests*.** Tests performed on equipment that is thought or known to be defective or equipment that has been subjected to conditions that could adversely affect its condition or operating characteristics.

N **3.3.61.5 *Standard Tests*.** Tests that are performed at regular intervals over the service life of equipment, typically in conjunction with maintenance on the equipment.

3.3.62 Transformer. Equipment, either single-phase or polyphase, that uses electromagnetic induction to convert current and voltage in a primary circuit into current and voltage in a secondary circuit. [**70**, 2023]

N **3.3.62.1 *Transformer, Power*.** A transformer rated greater than 500 kVA.

△ **3.3.63* Transients.** Very short duration, high amplitude excursions outside of the limits of the normal voltage and current waveform.

3.3.64 Unbalanced Voltages. Unequal voltage values on 3-phase circuits that can exist anywhere on the power distribution system.

N **3.3.65 Utilization Equipment.** Equipment that utilizes electric energy for electronic, electromechanical, chemical, heating, lighting, or similar purposes. [**70**, 2023]

N ## Chapter 4 General

N **4.1 General Requirements.**

N **4.1.1** Electrical equipment shall be maintained in accordance with the manufacturer's instructions and applicable codes and standards.

N **4.1.2** This standard is not intended to duplicate or supersede manufacturer's instructions.

N **4.1.3** In the absence of manufacturer's instructions, equipment shall be maintained in accordance with industry consensus standards.

N **4.2 Electrical Maintenance Program (EMP).**

N **4.2.1 General.** The equipment owner shall implement and document an overall EMP that directs activity appropriate to the safety and operational risks.

N **4.2.2 Inspection.**

N **4.2.2.1** The EMP shall include elements to verify that electrical equipment or systems have been inspected to comply with applicable installation codes and standards.

N **4.2.2.2** Equipment-specific maintenance tasks shall be developed utilizing the information gathered during the inspection.

N **4.2.3 Condition of Maintenance.** The EMP shall include elements that consider current condition of maintenance of electrical equipment and systems as well as the potential safety and operational risks to maintenance and operational personnel.

N **4.2.4 EMP Principles.** The EMP shall identify the principles upon which it is based and the goals to be achieved.

Shaded text = Revisions.   △ = Text deletions and figure/table revisions.   • = Section deletions.   *N* = New material.

***N* 4.2.4.1** The EMP shall be designed to function in conjunction with the applicable electrical safety program.

N* 4.2.4.2 The EMP shall include the following elements:

(1) An electrical safety program that addresses the condition of maintenance
(2) Identification of personnel responsible for implementing each element of the program
(3) Survey and analysis of electrical equipment and systems to determine maintenance requirements and priorities
(4) Developed and documented maintenance procedures for equipment
(5) A plan of inspections, servicing, and suitable tests
(6) A maintenance, equipment, and personnel documentation and records-retention policy
(7) A process to prescribe, implement, and document corrective measures based on collected data
(8) A process for incorporating design for maintainability in electrical installations
(9) A program review and revision process that considers failures and findings for continuous improvement

***N* 4.2.5 EMP Controls.** The EMP shall identify the controls by which it is measured and monitored.

***N* 4.2.6 Incident Investigations.** The EMP shall include a method to utilize all associated reports for feedback and EMP refinement, including the following:

(1) Electrical safety incidents
(2) Equipment malfunctions
(3) Unintended operations or alarms
(4) Operation of protective devices

***N* 4.2.7 EMP Audit.** The EMP shall be audited at intervals not to exceed 5 years to verify that the principles and procedures of the EMP comply with this standard.

***N* 4.3 Personnel.**

***N* 4.3.1 EMP Coordinator.** The EMP shall identify an EMP coordinator.

***N* 4.3.2 Maintenance Personnel.** Personnel assigned to EMP duties shall be qualified for the assigned tasks.

***N* 4.3.3 Electrical Maintenance Training.** A qualified person responsible for conducting electrical maintenance shall be trained in the specific maintenance tasks, test methods, test equipment, PPE usage (as applicable), and hazards associated with the electrical equipment or system being serviced.

***N* 4.3.3.1** A person who is undergoing on-the-job training for the purpose of obtaining the skills and knowledge necessary to be considered a qualified person, and who in the course of such training demonstrates an ability to perform specific duties safely at his or her level of training, and who is under the direct supervision of a qualified person shall be considered to be a qualified person for the performance of those specific duties.

***N* 4.3.3.2** The employer shall determine through regular supervision or through inspections conducted on at least an annual basis that each employee is complying with the electrical maintenance procedures and testing required by this standard.

***N* 4.3.3.3** A person responsible for conducting electrical maintenance shall be provided additional training (or retraining) if any of the following conditions exists:

(1) The supervision or annual inspections indicate the person is not complying with the maintenance procedures and testing requirements.
(2) New technology, new types of equipment, or changes in procedures necessitate the use of maintenance procedures and testing requirements different from those that the person would normally use.
(3) The person needs to review tasks that are performed less often than once per year.
(4) The person needs to review maintenance procedures and testing requirements that they do not normally use during regular job duties.
(5) The person's job duties change.
(6) A new edition of this standard is adopted that includes changes applicable to the person's job duties.

***N* 4.3.3.4** Training shall be documented in accordance with the following:

(1) Documentation shall be issued when the person demonstrates proficiency in the electrical maintenance procedures and testing requirements.
(2) Documentation shall be retained for the duration of the person's employment.
(3) Documentation shall specify the content of the training, the person's name, and the dates of training.

***N* 4.4 Survey and Analysis.**

***N* 4.4.1** The EMP coordinator shall determine the scope of the work to be performed and develop a prioritized plan for the electrical maintenance of the electrical equipment or system.

***N* 4.4.2** Electrical equipment and systems shall be evaluated to determine the appropriate scope and frequency of maintenance.

***N* 4.4.3** Environmental, physical, or operating conditions of a specific installation shall be considered in determining the frequency of electrical maintenance.

***N* 4.5 Planned Inspections.** The following considerations shall be reviewed during development of planned inspections:

(1) Potential of equipment failure to endanger or threaten personnel safety
(2) Manufacturer's recommended service and maintenance practices and procedures
(3) Operating environment
(4) Operating load conditions and equipment rating
(5) Failure and repair of equipment causing extensive downtime and lost production dollars
(6) Equipment condition
(7) Production and operating schedules
(8) Failure history
(9) Inspection history

***N* 4.6 Acceptance Test Report.** A copy of the acceptance test reports, if available, shall be included with the maintenance records.

***N* 4.7 Impact of Additions/Rework to Retrofitting Equipment.**

N* 4.7.1 Safety certifications shall be maintained for repaired or rebuilt equipment.

N* 4.7.2 When repairing, rebuilding, or remanufacturing equipment, the work shall be conducted by a qualified person or organization to assure that no changes are made to the equip-

Shaded text = Revisions.   Δ = Text deletions and figure/table revisions.   • = Section deletions.   *N* = New material.

2023 Edition

ment that might prevent the equipment from meeting the applicable performance and safety requirements.

N **4.7.3** Refurbished or remanufactured equipment shall be marked to identify it as such.

N **4.8* Equipment Cleaning.** Electrical equipment cleaning shall be a part of the EMP.

N **4.8.1 Cleaning Personnel.**

N **4.8.1.1** Electrical equipment cleaning shall be performed by personnel who are familiar with the cleaning materials required and methodologies necessary for effective removal of contaminants, debris, and other foreign materials that compromise electrical equipment performance.

N **4.8.1.2** The persons assigned to the task of electrical equipment cleaning shall be trained in the following:

(1) Potential damage to the equipment from cleaning procedures
(2) Potential personal injury
(3) Specific cleaning procedures
(4) Equipment not to be cleaned

N **Chapter 5 Personnel Safety**

N **5.1 Introduction.**

N **5.1.1** Electrical maintenance shall be performed only by qualified persons.

N **5.1.2*** Electrical safety-related work practices shall be instituted and followed, in accordance with applicable state, federal, or local codes and standards, to identify the hazards and reduce the associated risks.

N **Chapter 6 Single-Line Diagrams and System Studies**

N **6.1 Introduction.**

N **6.1.1*** System studies shall be completed in accordance with this chapter.

N **6.1.2** Single-line diagrams shall be maintained in accordance with this chapter.

N **6.2 Single-Line Diagrams.** Up-to-date single-line diagrams shall be the primary reference for system studies.

N **6.2.1** Single-line diagrams shall be maintained in a legible condition.

N **6.2.2** Single-line diagrams shall be kept accurate.

N **6.2.3** Single-line diagram shall indicate the date of the last revision.

N **6.2.4** When single-line diagrams are not available, the facility or equipment owner shall be responsible for providing an equally effective means of obtaining the necessary information.

N **6.3* Short-Circuit Studies.**

N **6.3.1** Where a short-circuit study does not exist, one shall be created, as necessary to support the arc-flash risk assessment and equipment evaluations.

N **6.3.2** The short-circuit study shall be updated when changes occur in the electrical distribution system that could affect the results of the study.

N **6.3.3** The short-circuit study shall be reviewed for accuracy at intervals not to exceed 5 years.

N **6.3.4** The most recent study shall be made available to the EMP coordinator.

N **6.3.5** When the short-circuit study is updated, an electrical equipment rating evaluation shall be completed for the equipment within the scope of the study.

N **6.4* Coordination Studies.**

N **6.4.1** A coordination study shall be created as necessary to support risk assessments and the intended system design goals.

N **6.4.2** The coordination study shall be updated when changes occur in the electrical distribution system that could affect the results of the study.

N **6.4.3** The coordination study shall be reviewed for accuracy at intervals not to exceed 5 years.

N **6.4.4** The most recent study shall be made available to the EMP coordinator.

N **6.4.5** When the coordination study is updated, the electrical equipment overcurrent protective devices and equipment ratings shall be reviewed and verified for the equipment within the scope of the study.

N **6.5* Load-Flow Studies.**

N **6.5.1** If a load-flow study is needed to allow maintenance to be performed, the load-flow study shall be updated when changes occur that could affect the results of the study.

N **6.5.2** The load-flow study shall be reviewed for accuracy at intervals not to exceed 5 years.

N **6.5.3** The most recent study shall be made available to the EMP coordinator.

N **6.6* Reliability Studies.**

N **6.6.1** A reliability study shall be conducted as necessary on critical or important facility electrical systems to identify equipment and circuit configurations that can lead to unplanned outages.

N **6.6.2** Spare parts shall be monitored and inspected periodically to ensure that they will be available when needed.

N **6.6.3** The reliability study shall be reviewed for accuracy at intervals not to exceed 5 years.

N **6.6.4** The study shall be kept current and revised whenever a significant change to the electrical system has been made.

N **6.7* Incident Energy Analysis (Arc-Flash Study).**

N **6.7.1** The incident energy analysis shall be updated when changes occur in the electrical distribution system that could affect the results of the analysis.

N **6.7.2** The analysis shall be reviewed for accuracy at intervals not to exceed 5 years.

N **6.7.3** The most recent study shall be made available to the EMP coordinator.

Shaded text = Revisions. Δ = Text deletions and figure/table revisions. • = Section deletions. *N* = New material.

N 6.8* Electrical Maintenance-Related Design. Where a recognized hazard presents an increased risk during maintenance, a study shall be conducted to develop design options that could be implemented to reduce risk.

N

Chapter 7 Fundamental Tests

N 7.1 Fundamental Tests. The fundamental test procedures described in this chapter shall be used where required elsewhere in this standard.

N 7.2 Bolted Bus Connections, Conductor Terminations, and Conductor Connectors.

N 7.2.1 The quality of undisturbed bolted electrical bus connections, conductor terminations, and conductor connectors shall be verified using one or more of the methods described in 7.2.1.1 through 7.2.1.4.

N 7.2.1.1 Infrared Thermographic Inspection of Electrical Connections. Infrared thermographic inspection of electrical connections and terminations shall be performed in accordance with Section 7.4.

N 7.2.1.2 Thermal Sensors. Permanently mounted thermal sensors shall be permitted to monitor the temperature of electrical connections and terminations.

N 7.2.1.3 Contact Resistance Test.

N 7.2.1.3.1 A calibrated tester shall be used to obtain contact resistance test values.

N 7.2.1.3.2 Where contact resistance tests are used, the resistance values shall not exceed the maximum values published by the manufacturer.

N 7.2.1.3.3 If contact resistance values exceed the maximum values published by the manufacturer, the cause for the excess values shall be investigated.

N 7.2.1.4 Torque Verification.

N 7.2.1.4.1 When using a calibrated torque wrench to confirm the torque of previously installed threaded hardware, the retightening value shall not exceed 90 percent of the manufacturer's specified initial torque value.

N 7.2.1.4.2 Where initial threaded hardware torque value data is not available, torque values shall be in accordance with Table 7.2.1.4.2(a), Table 7.2.1.4.2(b), or Table 7.2.1.4.2(c).

N 7.2.2 Newly Installed Threaded Hardware Torque Values.

N 7.2.2.1 Newly installed threaded hardware connections shall be torqued to the manufacturer's published data.

N 7.2.2.2 Where the manufacturer's data is not available, torque values shall be in accordance with Table 7.2.1.4.2(a), Table 7.2.1.4.2(b), or Table 7.2.1.4.2(c) based on the hardware used.

N 7.3 Insulation Resistance Quality.

N 7.3.1 For equipment rated up to 1000 volts, the quality of electrical insulation (insulation resistance) shall be verified using a dc insulation resistance test set.

N 7.3.1.1 Insulation Resistance Testing. The applied test voltage shall not exceed the value specified by the manufacturer.

N Table 7.2.1.4.2(a) Bolt-Torque Values for Electrical Connections, US Standard Fasteners — Cadmium or Zinc Plated

Bolt Diameter (in.)	Torque (Pound-Feet)
$\frac{1}{4}$	6
$\frac{5}{16}$	11
$\frac{3}{8}$	20
$\frac{7}{16}$	32
$\frac{1}{2}$	48
$\frac{9}{16}$	70
$\frac{5}{8}$	96
$\frac{3}{4}$	160
$\frac{7}{8}$	240
1.0	370

Notes:
(1) Consult the manufacturer for equipment supplied with metric fasteners.
(2) The table is based on national coarse thread pitch.
(3) The grade is SAE 5.
(4) The minimum tensile (strength) is 105,000 lbf/in.[2]

N Table 7.2.1.4.2(b) Bolt-Torque Values for Electrical Connections, US Standard Fasteners — Silicon Bronze

Bolt Diameter (in.)	Torque (Pound-Feet)	
	Nonlubricated	Lubricated
$\frac{5}{16}$	15	10
$\frac{3}{8}$	20	15
$\frac{1}{2}$	40	25
$\frac{5}{8}$	55	40
$\frac{3}{4}$	70	60

Notes:
(1) Consult the manufacturer for equipment supplied with metric fasteners.
(2) This table is based on national coarse thread pitch.
(3) This table is based on bronze alloy bolts having a minimum 70,000 lb/in.[2] tensile strength.

N Table 7.2.1.4.2(c) Bolt-Torque Values for Electrical Connections, US Standard Fasteners — Aluminum

Bolt Diameter (in.)	Torque (Pound-Feet), Lubricated
$\frac{5}{16}$	10
$\frac{3}{8}$	14
$\frac{1}{2}$	25
$\frac{5}{8}$	40
$\frac{3}{4}$	60

Notes:
(1) Consult the manufacturer for equipment supplied with metric fasteners.
(2) This table is based on national coarse thread pitch.
(3) This table is based on aluminum alloy bolts having a minimum 55,000 lb/in.[2] tensile strength.

Shaded text = Revisions. △ = Text deletions and figure/table revisions. • = Section deletions. **N** = New material.

2023 Edition

N 7.3.1.1.1 Where manufacturer's value is not available, test voltage shall be in accordance with appropriate industry standard.

N 7.3.1.1.2 The test instrument used to perform an insulation-resistance test shall be calibrated.

N 7.3.2 For equipment rated in excess of 1000 volts, the electrical insulation quality test method shall be determined by the EMP.

N 7.3.2.1 The test method shall be one or more of the following:

(1) dc insulation resistance
(2) ac or dc dielectric withstand testing
(3) dc overpotential (hipot) testing
(4) ac insulation power factor/dissipation factor testing
(5) Very low frequency (VLF) testing
(6) Damped alternating current (DAC) voltage test
(7) Acoustical ultrasonic testing
(8) Partial discharge (PD) testing

N 7.4 Infrared Thermography.

N 7.4.1 Infrared thermography shall be used when required to verify temperature differences (ΔT) of the following:

(1) Similar electrical components under similar loading
(2) Comparison between electrical components and ambient air temperatures

N 7.4.2 All accessible and necessary covers shall be removed prior to infrared thermography inspection to provide a clear line of sight to the equipment being scanned.

N 7.4.3 Temperature differences between the area of concern and the reference area shall be documented.

N 7.4.4 Infrared thermography inspections shall be performed at normal circuit loading.

N 7.4.5 Where normal circuit loading is not feasible, circuit loading of not less than 40 percent of nominal circuit loading shall be permitted.

N 7.4.6 Circuit loading characteristics shall be documented and retained for future reference.

N **Chapter 8 Field Testing and Test Methods**

N 8.1 Introduction. Field testing and test methods shall be conducted in accordance with this chapter to assess the overall condition of electrical equipment and systems and to accomplish the following objectives:

(1) Ascertain the ability of the device under test to continue to perform its function as designed
(2) Determine whether any corrective maintenance or replacement is necessary
(3) Document the condition of the equipment over its service life
(4) Provide results to ascertain the overall condition of maintenance of the device under test

N 8.2 Risk Assessment Special Considerations. Where the following special considerations are present, a risk assessment shall be performed to identify hazards and determine if additional protective measures are required prior to beginning work:

(1) Electrical, as follows:

(a) X-ray
(b) Overpotential
(2) Mechanical, as follows:

(a) Stored energy
(b) Mass energy
(3) Chemical, as follows:

(a) SF_6 gas fault by-products
(b) Electrolytes
(4) Environmental, as follows:

(a) Asbestos
(b) SF_6 gas
(c) Insulating fluids, as follows:

(i) PCBs
(ii) Tetrachloroethylene

N 8.3* Testing Category Types. Electrical maintenance testing tasks shall be identified as one of the following category types:

(1) Category 1 — Online standard test
(2) Category 1A — Online enhanced test
(3) Category 2 — Offline standard test
(4) Category 2A — Offline enhanced test

WARNING: Testing of electrical equipment while it is connected to the source of supply introduces additional hazards to the worker. Workers should understand the hazards and risks of the test being performed.

N 8.3.1 Category 1 — Online Standard Test. Online standard tests shall include testing procedures performed while the electrical equipment or device is connected to the source of supply.

N 8.3.2 Category 1A — Online Enhanced Test. Online enhanced tests shall include certain testing procedures performed while the electrical equipment or device is connected to the source of supply and that are not typically performed in normal electrical maintenance activities and that provide additional diagnostic information. *(See A.8.3.)*

N 8.3.3 Category 2 — Offline Standard Test. Offline standard tests shall include testing procedures performed while the electrical equipment or device is disconnected from the source of supply or is connected to an external test voltage source of supply.

N 8.3.4 Category 2A — Offline Enhanced Test. Offline enhanced tests shall include certain testing procedures performed while the electrical equipment or device is disconnected from the source of supply or is connected to an external test voltage source of supply and that are not typically performed in normal electrical maintenance activities and that provide additional diagnostic information. *(See A.8.3.)*

N 8.4 Qualifications of Testing Personnel.

N 8.4.1 Testing personnel shall be qualified to operate the test equipment used in the type of test to be performed.

N 8.4.2 Testing personnel shall be qualified to perform the test procedure on the specific equipment to be tested.

N 8.5 Test Equipment and Tools.

N 8.5.1 The test equipment shall be maintained in satisfactory mechanical and electrical condition.

N 8.5.2 The test equipment shall be applied in accordance with the manufacturer's specifications.

N **8.5.3*** Test equipment that provides measurements shall be calibrated.

N **8.5.4** Calibration information shall be readily available for all test equipment.

N **8.5.5** Test equipment calibration intervals shall be appropriate to ensure the accuracy of the test instrument with consideration for the conditions of use.

N **8.5.6** Proper tools, instruments, and other test equipment shall be used when performing maintenance activities.

N **8.6 Test Record.**

N **8.6.1** A test record shall be created for all field tests of electrical equipment.

N **8.6.2** Test records shall contain the following minimum information:

(1) Identification of the testing person and organization
(2) Identification of the equipment under test
(3) Nameplate or label data from the equipment under test
(4) Environmental conditions, such as humidity and temperature, that could affect the results of the tests or calibrations
(5) Date of the test
(6) Indication of test performed
(7) Indication of pass/fail criteria, where applicable
(8) Indication of as-found and as-left test results, where applicable
(9) Test operator's comments or recommendations, where applicable

N **8.7* Condition of Maintenance Indication.** Information shall be made readily available to communicate the condition of maintenance.

N **8.7.1 Conditions of Maintenance.**

N **8.7.1.1 Serviceable.** Equipment that passes all tests and is electrically and mechanically sound shall be designated as serviceable.

N **8.7.1.2* Limited Service.** Equipment that has problems that are not detrimental to the protective operation or design characteristics of the equipment shall be designated as limited service.

N **8.7.1.3* Nonserviceable.** Equipment that has a problem that is detrimental to the proper electrical or mechanical operation of the equipment shall be designated as nonserviceable.

Chapter 9 Maintenance Intervals

N **9.1 Scope.** This chapter identifies the required frequency of maintenance for electrical equipment.

N **9.1.1* Continuous Monitoring and Predictive Techniques.**

N **9.1.1.1*** Continuous monitoring or predictive techniques shall be permitted to be used as a consideration when determining maintenance intervals.

N **9.1.1.2*** Continuous monitoring or predictive techniques shall be based on manufacturer's recommendations or accepted industry practices.

N **9.1.2 Maintenance Frequency Modifications.**

N **9.1.2.1** Once the initial frequency for inspection and tests has been established based on the intervals listed in Table 9.2.2 and the equipment condition assessment, this frequency shall be adhered to for at least two maintenance cycles unless unexpected failures occur.

N **9.1.2.1.1** For equipment that has unexpected failures, the cause of the failure shall be used to determine if the maintenance interval for the equipment needs to be reduced.

N **9.1.2.1.2*** If more than two inspections are completed without requiring additional service, the equipment owner shall be permitted to resume the original inspection period.

N **9.1.2.2** If more than two inspections are completed without detecting equipment problems, the maintenance cycle shall be permitted to be extended to longer intervals than listed in Table 9.2.2.

N **9.2 Frequency of Maintenance.**

N **9.2.1*** The manufacturer's recommendations shall be followed for each of the maintenance scopes specified in this standard for the required intervals.

N **9.2.2*** Where the manufacturer's recommendations are not provided or available and failure, breakdown, or malfunction of the equipment will present an unacceptable risk for personnel or the environment, equipment maintenance shall be performed at not greater than the intervals specified in Table 9.2.2, in accordance with the equipment condition assessment in Section 9.2, and as modified by the other parts of this chapter.

N **9.2.2.1** The intervals in Table 9.2.2 shall only be required if referenced by a specific section in another chapter.

N **9.2.2.2** The maintenance interval for electrical equipment shall be permitted to be altered based on the potential risk to personnel or facility operations due to a failure of the equipment to operate as expected.

N **9.2.2.3** Any deviations from the maintenance intervals described in Table 9.2.2 to extend the maintenance interval and the justification for the deviation shall be documented in the EMP.

N **9.3 Equipment Condition Assessment.** The equipment condition shall be the highest condition category in accordance with 9.3.1, 9.3.2, and 9.3.3 as determined by the owner or their designee.

N **9.3.1 Physical Condition of Electrical Equipment.** Equipment that is included in the electrical EMP shall be assessed for current equipment condition in accordance with 9.3.1.1 through 9.3.1.3.

N **9.3.1.1** Equipment Physical Condition 1 shall be assigned where all the following criteria apply:

(1) The equipment appears in like new condition.
(2) The enclosure is clean, free from moisture intrusion, and tight.
(3) No unaddressed notification from the continuous monitoring system has occurred.
(4) There are no active recommendations from predictive techniques.
(5) Previous maintenance has been performed in accordance with the EMP.

N Table 9.2.2 Maintenance Intervals

Product	Scope of Work	Equipment Condition Assessment		
		Condition 1	Condition 2	Condition 3
All equipment	Infrared thermography	12 months	12 months	6 months
Battery ESSs	Visual inspection	60 months	36 months	12 months
	Cleaning	60 months	36 months	12 months
	Lubrication		Reserved	
	Mechanical servicing		Reserved	
	Electrical testing	60 months	36 months	12 months
Busways	Visual inspection	60 months	60 months	12 months
	Cleaning	60 months	36 months	12 months
	Lubrication	60 months	36 months	12 months
	Mechanical servicing	60 months	36 months	12 months
	Electrical testing	60 months	36 months	12 months
	Special	60 months	36 months	12 months
Cable trays	Visual inspection	12 months	12 months	6 months
	Cleaning	60 months	36 months	12 months
	Lubrication	60 months	36 months	12 months
	Mechanical servicing	60 months	36 months	12 months
	Electrical testing	60 months	36 months	12 months
Electric vehicle power transfer systems	Visual inspection	60 months	36 months	12 months
	Mechanical inspection	60 months	36 months	12 months
	Electrical testing	60 months	36 months	12 months
Electronic equipment			Reserved	
Fuses	Visual inspection	60 months	36 months	12 months
	Cleaning	60 months	36 months	12 months
	Lubrication	60 months	36 months	12 months
	Mechanical servicing	60 months	36 months	12 months
	Electrical testing	60 months	36 months	12 months
GFCIs	Visual inspection	12 months	12 months	6 months
	Cleaning	60 months	36 months	12 months
	Lubrication	60 months	36 months	12 months
	Mechanical servicing		Reserved	
Grounding and bonding	Visual inspection	12 months	12 months	6 months
	Cleaning		Reserved	
	Lubrication		Reserved	
	Mechanical servicing		Reserved	
	Electrical testing	60 months	36 months	36 months
High-voltage substation insulators	Visual inspection	12 months	12 months	6 months
	Corona detection	12 months	6 months	4 months
	Maintenance and testing	60 months	36 months	12 months
Lighting	Visual inspection	60 months	36 months	12 months
	Cleaning	60 months	36 months	12 months
	Servicing	60 months	36 months	12 months

(continues)

     Shaded text = Revisions.   △ = Text deletions and figure/table revisions.   • = Section deletions.   **N** = New material.

N Table 9.2.2   *Continued*

Product	Scope of Work	Equipment Condition Assessment		
		Condition 1	Condition 2	Condition 3
Lighting control systems			Reserved	
Low-voltage ground-fault protection systems	Visual inspection	12 months	12 months	6 months
	Cleaning	60 months	36 months	12 months
	Lubrication		Reserved	
	Mechanical servicing	60 months	36 months	12 months
	Electrical testing	60 months	36 months	12 months
Medium-voltage ground-fault protection systems	Visual inspection	12 months	12 months	6 months
	Cleaning	60 months	36 months	12 months
	Lubrication		Reserved	
	Mechanical servicing	60 months	36 months	12 months
	Electrical testing	60 months	36 months	12 months
Medium-voltage power circuit breakers	Visual inspection	60 months	36 months	12 months
	Cleaning	60 months	36 months	12 months
	Lubrication	60 months	36 months	12 months
	Mechanical servicing	60 months	36 months	12 months
	Electrical testing	60 months	36 months	12 months
Molded-case/insulated-case/low-voltage power circuit breakers	Visual inspection	60 months	36 months	12 months
	Cleaning	60 months	36 months	12 months
	Lubrication	60 months	36 months	12 months
	Mechanical servicing	60 months	36 months	12 months
	Electrical testing	60 months	36 months	12 months
Motor control equipment	Visual inspection	60 months	36 months	12 months
	Cleaning	60 months	36 months	12 months
	Lubrication	60 months	36 months	12 months
	Mechanical servicing	60 months	36 months	12 months
	Electrical testing	60 months	36 months	12 months
Panelboards and switchboards	Visual inspection	60 months	36 months	12 months
	Cleaning	60 months	36 months	12 months
	Lubrication	60 months	36 months	12 months
	Mechanical inspections	60 months	36 months	12 months
	Electrical testing	60 months	36 months	12 months
Photovoltaic systems	Visual inspection	60 months	36 months	12 months
	Cleaning		Reserved	
	Lubrication		Reserved	
	Mechanical servicing		Reserved	
	Electrical testing	60 months	36 months	12 months
Portable electrical tools and equipment	Visual inspection	Before each use	Before each use	Before each use
	Cleaning	Before each use	Before each use	Before each use
	Lubrication	In accordance with the manufacturer's instructions	In accordance with the manufacturer's instructions	In accordance with the manufacturer's instructions
	Mechanical servicing	In accordance with the manufacturer's instructions	In accordance with the manufacturer's instructions	In accordance with the manufacturer's instructions

(continues)

Shaded text = Revisions.   △ = Text deletions and figure/table revisions.   • = Section deletions.   N = New material.

N Table 9.2.2 *Continued*

		Equipment Condition Assessment		
Product	**Scope of Work**	**Condition 1**	**Condition 2**	**Condition 3**
	Electrical testing	3 months	3 months	3 months
Power and distribution transformers	Visual inspection	12 months	12 months	6 months
	Cleaning	60 months	36 months	12 months
	Lubrication		Reserved	
	Mechanical servicing	60 months	36 months	12 months
	Electrical testing	60 months	36 months	12 months
Power cables	Visual inspection	60 months	36 months	12 months
	Cleaning	60 months	36 months	12 months
	Mechanical servicing	Reserved	Reserved	
	Electrical testing	60 months	36 months	12 months
Power-factor correction capacitors	Visual inspection	60 months	36 months	12 months
	Cleaning	60 months	36 months	12 months
	Lubrication		Reserved	
	Mechanical servicing	60 months	36 months	12 months
	Electrical testing	60 months	36 months	12 months
	Special		Reserved	
Protective relays, electromechanical	Visual inspection	36 months	24 months	12 months
	Cleaning	36 months	24 months	12 months
	Lubrication		Reserved	
	Mechanical servicing	36 months	24 months	12 months
	Electrical testing	36 months	24 months	12 months
Protective relays, solid state and microprocessor	Visual inspection	60 months	36 months	12 months
	Cleaning	60 months	36 months	12 months
	Lubrication		Reserved	
	Mechanical servicing	60 months	36 months	12 months
	Electrical testing	60 months	36 months	12 months
Public pools, fountains, and similar installations			Reserved	
Rotating equipment	Visual inspection	60 months	36 months	12 months
	Cleaning	60 months	36 months	12 months
	Lubrication	60 months	36 months	12 months
	Mechanical servicing	60 months	36 months	12 months
	Electrical testing	60 months	36 months	12 months
Stationary standby batteries	Visual inspection	60 months	36 months	12 months
	Cleaning	60 months	36 months	12 months
	Mechanical servicing		Reserved	
	Electrical testing	60 months	36 months	12 months
Substations	Visual inspection	12 months	12 months	6 months
	Cleaning	60 months	36 months	12 months
	Lubrication	60 months	36 months	12 months
	Mechanical servicing	60 months	36 months	12 months
	Electrical testing	60 months	36 months	12 months
	Special	60 months	36 months	12 months
	Mechanical checks	60 months	36 months	12 months

(continues)

Shaded text = Revisions. Δ = Text deletions and figure/table revisions. • = Section deletions. N = New material.

N **Table 9.2.2** *Continued*

| Product | Scope of Work | Equipment Condition Assessment | | |
		Condition 1	Condition 2	Condition 3
Switches	Visual inspection	60 months	36 months	12 months
	Cleaning	60 months	36 months	12 months
	Lubrication	60 months	36 months	12 months
	Mechanical servicing	60 months	36 months	12 months
	Electrical testing	60 months	36 months	12 months
Switchgear	Visual inspection	12 months	12 months	6 months
	Cleaning	60 months	36 months	12 months
	Lubrication	60 months	36 months	12 months
	Mechanical servicing	60 months	36 months	12 months
	Electrical testing	60 months	36 months	12 months
	Special	60 months	36 months	12 months
Uninterruptible power supplies	Visual inspection	6 months	3 months	1 month
	Cleaning	12 months	6 months	3 months
	Lubrication		Reserved	
	Mechanical servicing	12 months	6 months	3 months
	Electrical testing	12 months	6 months	3 months
	Special procedures	24 months	24 months	24 months
Wind power electric systems	Visual inspection	60 months	36 months	12 months
	Cleaning	60 months	36 months	12 months
	Lubrication		Reserved	
	Mechanical servicing	60 months	36 months	12 months
	Electrical testing	60 months	36 months	12 months
Wiring devices	Visual inspection	12 months	3 months	1 month
	Cleaning	60 months	36 months	12 months
	Lubrication		Reserved	
	Mechanical servicing	60 months	36 months	12 months
	Electrical testing	60 months	36 months	12 months

N **9.3.1.2** Equipment Physical Condition 2 shall be assigned where all of 9.3.1.1 apply, and where any of the following criteria apply:

(1) Maintenance results deviate from past results or have indicated more frequent maintenance in accordance with manufacturer's published data.
(2) The previous maintenance cycle has revealed issues requiring the repair or replacement of major equipment components.
(3) There have been notifications from the continuous monitoring system since the prior assessment.
(4) There are active recommendations from predictive techniques.

N **9.3.1.3** Equipment Physical Condition 3 shall be assigned where changes in operation are noted or where any of the following criteria applies:

(1) The equipment has missed the last two successive maintenance cycles in accordance with the EMP.

(2) The previous two maintenance cycles have revealed issues requiring the repair or replacement of major equipment components.
(3) There is an active or unaddressed notification from the continuous monitoring system.
(4) There are urgent actions identified from predictive techniques.

N **9.3.1.4 Nonserviceable Equipment.**

N **9.3.1.4.1** Equipment that poses an imminent risk of injury or negative health effects to personnel shall be designated as nonserviceable in accordance with 8.7.1.3.

N **9.3.1.4.2** Access to nonserviceable equipment by unqualified persons shall be restricted.

N **9.3.1.5 Nonconforming Equipment.** Equipment exhibiting characteristics that do not conform to any of the above conditions shall be identified as requiring corrective measures before returning it to a normal operating condition.

Shaded text = Revisions.   Δ = Text deletions and figure/table revisions.   • = Section deletions.   *N* = New material.

2023 Edition

N 9.3.2* Criticality Condition of Equipment.

N 9.3.2.1* Criticality Condition 1 or Criticality Condition 2 shall be permitted to be assigned where the failure of the equipment or system will not endanger personnel.

N 9.3.2.2 Criticality Condition 3 shall be assigned where the failure of the equipment or system will endanger personnel.

N 9.3.3 Operating Environment Condition of Equipment.

N 9.3.3.1 Operating Environment Condition 1 or Operating Environment Condition 2 shall be permitted to be assigned where the equipment is used in an operating environment for which it is rated.

N 9.3.3.2 Operating Environment Condition 3 shall be assigned where the equipment is used in an environment with harsh chemicals, contaminants, or extreme operating conditions for which it is not specifically rated or evaluated.

N   Chapter 10   Hazardous (Classified) Location Electrical Equipment

N 10.1* General. Electrical equipment designed for use in hazardous (classified) locations shall be maintained through regular inspections, testing, and servicing, as recommended by the manufacturer.

N 10.1.1 Documentation shall be readily available to identify the classification, group, temperature code specification, and extent of the classified area.

N 10.1.2* Repairs and maintenance, including access to and removal of components, shall not be performed inside the hazardous (classified) area unless a documented risk assessment to determine the risk of igniting an explosive atmosphere is conducted by a qualified person.

N 10.1.3 Electrical maintenance documentation shall identify where the maintenance is to be performed and what precautions are necessary.

N 10.1.4 A thorough inspection shall be performed after any maintenance work to ensure the equipment is restored to a safe operational condition.

N 10.2 Maintenance Personnel for Hazardous (Classified) Locations.

N 10.2.1 Maintenance shall be performed only by qualified persons who are trained in safe maintenance practices and the special considerations necessary to maintain electrical equipment for use in the specific class of hazardous (classified) locations.

N 10.2.2* Qualified persons shall be trained to evaluate and eliminate ignition sources and to identify the need for special tools, procedures, equipment, tests, and protective clothing.

N 10.3 Elimination of Hazardous Atmospheres. For maintenance involving permanent electrical installations, the following procedures shall be followed:

(1) Hazardous vapors, dust, or fibers/flyings shall be removed from the area.

(2) Enclosed or trapped hazardous vapors shall be cleared.

(3) Atmosphere shall be tested to confirm it is within safe limits for the required maintenance.

N 10.4 Elimination of Ignition Sources.

N 10.4.1* An electrically safe work condition shall be established, and all other ignition sources abated before maintenance is performed.

N 10.4.2 Before opening any enclosure, time shall be allowed for parts to cool and electrical charges to dissipate, as identified in the risk assessment or manufacturer's instructions.

N 10.4.3 Bonding jumpers shall be applied as required to dissipate and prevent static electrical charges.

N 10.5 Equipment Reassembly.

N 10.5.1 Electrical equipment designed for use in hazardous (classified) locations shall be fully reassembled with original components or approved replacement components before the hazardous atmosphere is reintroduced.

N 10.5.2 Covers shall not be interchanged unless identified for the purpose.

N 10.5.2.1* Prior to reinstalling covers, they shall be checked for proper closure of mating joints and seals.

N 10.5.2.2 Mating joints or seals that do not make a proper closure shall be repaired or replaced in accordance with the manufacturer's instructions.

N 10.6 Conduit and Equipment Seals.

N 10.6.1 An approved system of conduit and equipment seals shall be maintained.

N 10.6.2* Corrective action shall be taken on any seal that is found to be damaged or missing.

N 10.7 Bolts and Screws. Where bolts or screws used to secure an electrical equipment cover require torqueing to meet installation specifications, the bolts or screws shall be maintained with the torque specified by the manufacturer.

N 10.7.1 All bolts and screws shall be replaced with original components or as specified by the manufacturer.

N 10.8* Handling of Equipment, Components, and Tools. Electrical equipment used in hazardous (classified) locations shall not be subjected to damage from tools that pry, impact, or abrade components.

N 10.8.1 Where grease, paint, or dirt must be cleaned from machined joints, a nonmetallic bristle brush, an acceptable noncorrosive solvent, or other methods recommended by the manufacturer shall be used.

N 10.8.2 Prior to replacing a cover on an enclosure designed to prevent flame propagation upon an explosion, mating surfaces shall be cleaned and lubricated in accordance with the manufacturer's instructions.

N 10.9* Field Modifications. Field modifications of equipment and parts shall be limited to those changes acceptable to the manufacturer and, where required, approved by the AHJ.

N   Chapter 11   Power and Distribution Transformers

N 11.1 Scope.

N 11.1.1 This chapter identifies electrical maintenance requirements for power and distribution transformers.

Shaded text = Revisions.   Δ = Text deletions and figure/table revisions.   • = Section deletions.   **N** = New material.

1.1.2 This chapter does not apply to control power and instrument transformers.

1.2 Frequency of Maintenance. The periodic maintenance procedures specified in Section 11.3 shall be performed in accordance with the frequencies specified in Chapter 9, unless otherwise specified in Table 11.2.

1.3 Periodic Maintenance Procedures.

1.3.1 Visual Inspections. Transformers shall be visually inspected in accordance with Table 11.3.1.

1.3.2 Cleaning.

1.3.2.1 Transformers shall be cleaned to remove buildup of accumulated dirt and debris.

N 11.3.2.2 Transformer bushings and any accessible insulators and conductors shall be wiped clean to remove surface buildup of contaminants.

N 11.3.3 Lubrication. (Reserved)

N 11.3.4 Mechanical Servicing. Transformers shall be mechanically serviced in accordance with Table 11.3.4.

N 11.3.5* Electrical Testing. Transformers shall be electrically tested in accordance with Table 11.3.5.

N 11.3.6 Special. (Reserved)

Table 11.2 Frequency of Maintenance

Scope of Work	Equipment Condition Assessment			Notes
	Condition 1	Condition 2	Condition 3	
Sample insulating fluid and tests	12 months	12 months	6 months	See 11.3.5.

N Table 11.3.1 Transformer Visual Inspections

No.	Task	Dry Type, Air-Cooled		Liquid-Filled Test Type*	Notes
		Small, Windings, ≤600 Volts, ≤167 kVA 1-ph, ≤500 kVA 3-ph Test Type*	Large, Windings, >600 Volts, >167 kVA 1-ph, >500 kVA 3-ph Test Type*		
1	Bolted connections	2	2	2	
2	Cooling devices	2	2	2	
3	Liquid level gauge(s) and alarm(s)	NA	NA	2	
4	Neutral grounding impedance devices	2	2	2	
5	Nitrogen bottle pressure system	NA	NA	2	
6	Pressure relief device(s)	NA	NA	2	
7	Sudden pressure relay(s)	NA	NA	2	
8	Tank over/under pressure gauge and alarms	NA	NA	2	
9	Transformer enclosure	1 or 2	1 or 2	1 or 2	Ensure ventilation and equipment enclosure integrity has not been compromised.

NA: Not applicable.
*Types specified in accordance with Section 8.3, as follows: Type 1 = online standard test; Type 1A = online enhanced test; Type 2 = offline standard test; Type 2A = offline enhanced test.

N Table 11.3.4 Transformer Mechanical Servicing

No.	Task	Test Type*			Notes
		Dry Type, Air-Cooled			
		Small, Windings ≤600 V ≤167 kVA 1-ph, ≤500 kVA 3-ph	Large, Windings >600 V >167 kVA 1-ph, >500 kVA 3-ph	Liquid-Filled	
1	Bolted connection	2	2	2	
1A	Verify tightness of accessible bolted electrical connections	2	2	2	
1B	Verify as-left tap connections are as specified	2	2	2	
2	Inspect anchorage, alignment, and grounding	2	2	2	
3	Cooling devices	2	2	2	
4	Transformer enclosures, ventilation filters, and screens inspected and replaced or cleaned, as needed	2	2	NA	
5	Control cabinets connections and cleaning	2	2	2	

NA: Not applicable.

*Types specified in accordance with Section 8.3, as follows: Type 1 = online standard test; Type 1A = online enhanced test; Type 2 = offline standard test; Type 2A = offline enhanced test.

Shaded text = Revisions.   △ = Text deletions and figure/table revisions.   • = Section deletions.   *N* = New material.

2023 Edition

N **Table 11.3.5 Transformer Electrical Tests**

| No. | Task | Dry Type, Air-Cooled | | Liquid-Filled Test Type* | Notes |
		Small, Windings, ≤600 Volts, ≤167 kVA 1-ph, ≤500 kVA 3-ph Test Type*	Large, Windings, >600 Volts, >167 kVA 1-ph, >500 kVA 3-ph Test Type*		
1	Core insulation resistance	NA	2A	2A	
2	Excitation current on each phase	NA	2	2	
3	Insulation power factor	NA	2	2	
4	Insulation power factor tip-up	NA	2A	NA	
5	Main insulation resistance	2	2	2	
6	Neutral grounding impedance devices	NA	2	2	
7	Online partial discharge on MV/HV windings	NA	1A	1A	
8	Insulation power factor on each bushing	NA	NA	2†	
9	Sweep frequency response analysis	NA	NA	2A	
10	Turns ratio on all load tap changer (LTC) taps	NA	NA	2A	
11	Turns ratio on all no-load tap changer (NLTC) taps	2A	2A	2A	
12	Turns ratio on designated tap	2	2	2	
13	Winding resistance at designated tap	2A	2A	2	
14	Bolted connection resistance	2	2	2	
15	Applied voltage test	NA	2A	NA	
16	Sample insulating fluid and test for: Dielectric breakdown Acid neutralization number Specific gravity Interfacial tension Color Visual condition Water content Power factor Dissolved gas analysis Furan analysis	NA NA NA NA NA NA NA NA NA NA	NA NA NA NA NA NA NA NA NA NA	1 or 2 1 or 2 1 or 2 1 or 2 1 or 2 1 or 2 1 or 2 1, 1A or 2, 2A 1, 1A or 2, 2A	
17	Sweep frequency response analysis	NA	NA	2A	
18	Percent oxygen in insulating blanket	NA	NA	2A	
19	Testing of transformer alarms, including temperature, liquid level, nitrogen bottle pressure, tank over/ under pressure, sudden pressure	NA	NA	2	

NA: Not applicable.
*Types specified in accordance with Section 8.3, as follows: Type 1 = online standard test; Type 1A = online enhanced test; Type 2 = offline standard test; Type 2A = offline enhanced test.
†Transformers applied at voltages greater than 1000 volts.

Shaded text = Revisions.   △ = Text deletions and figure/table revisions.   • = Section deletions.   **N** = New material.

Chapter 12 Substations and Switchgear

12.1 Scope.

12.1.1 This chapter identifies electrical maintenance requirements for substations, switchgear, and surrounding areas, whether fenced or in rooms.

12.1.2* This chapter does not address requirements of individual components of substations and switchgear that are addressed in the chapters for those components.

12.2 Frequency of Maintenance. The periodic maintenance procedures specified in Section 12.3 shall be performed in accordance with the frequencies specified in Chapter 9, unless otherwise specified in this chapter.

12.3 Periodic Maintenance Procedures.

12.3.1* Visual Inspection. Substations and switchgear shall be visually inspected in accordance with Table 12.3.1.

12.3.2 Cleaning. Electrical equipment surfaces, enclosures, insulating materials, and surrounding areas shall be kept clean to prevent a buildup of contaminants that negatively affect performance, reduce life expectancy, or create a safety hazard.

12.3.3 Lubrication. Terminating devices, mechanical parts, or operating parts that open, close, insert, and trip a circuit breaker, switch, or protective device shall be lubricated as required per the manufacturer's instruction manual.

N 12.3.4* Mechanical Servicing. Substation and switchgear shall be mechanically serviced in accordance with Table 12.3.4.

N 12.3.5* Electrical Testing. Substations and switchgear shall be electrically tested in accordance with Table 12.3.5.

N 12.3.6 Special.

N 12.3.6.1 Miscellaneous Equipment.

N 12.3.6.1.1* The availability and condition of required dedicated maintenance or operational tools and other test equipment shall be inspected.

N 12.3.6.1.2 If found to be defective, the dedicated maintenance or operational tools or other test equipment shall be taken out of service, replaced, or repaired, according to the manufacturer's specifications.

N 12.3.6.2 Auxiliary Apparatus. Area lighting, exit and emergency lighting, room HVAC or ventilation systems, and other auxiliary apparatus shall be checked for proper operation.

N   **Table 12.3.1 Substation and Switchgear Visual Inspections**

No.	Task	1000 Volts or Below Test Type*	Greater than 1000 Volts Test Type*	Notes
1	Inspect external physical condition	1	1	This includes condition and integrity of applied labels.
2	Inspect anchorage and grounding	1	1	Document if anchorage is not appropriate in accordance with current seismic requirements so improvements can be considered.
3	Ensure maintenance devices and tools are available for equipment servicing	1	1	
4	Verify circuit breakers, fuses, protective relays, and other type of overload elements are the right sizes and types and correspond to the drawings and the power system studies	1 or 2	1 or 2	Verify against plans, drawings, and pertinent records, as well as against evidence of current load levels. Some devices might be able to be checked while panel doors are closed.
5	For connected communicating addressable devices, verify the device addresses are set in accordance with documentation	1 or 2	1 or 2	Confirm addressing or correct device association where protective devices or the human-machine interface (HMI) are connected to multiple devices via a communication network.
6	Verify instrument transformer ratios are correct as installed	2A	2A	
7	Inspect insulators for damage or contaminated surfaces	2	2	
8	Verify air filters or screens are clean and in place	1 or 2	1 or 2	
9	Check all ventilation openings for obstructions and correct operation of any flap or automatic cover intended to assist in arc resistant ratings	2	2	
10	Inspect arc resistant equipment to ensure all doors are secured and in place	1 or 2	1 or 2	
11	Verify switch phase barriers are in place and in good condition	2	2	
12	For individual components, refer to the appropriate chapter(s) of this standard	NA	NA	
13	Visually inspect environmental controls, where provided	1 or 2	1 or 2	Includes, but is not limited to, fans, heaters, thermostats and humidity control equipment and settings.

NA: Not applicable.
*Types specified in accordance with Section 8.3, as follows: Type 1 = online standard test; Type 1A = online enhanced test; Type 2 = offline standard test; Type 2A = offline enhanced test.

Table 12.3.4 Substation and Switchgear Mechanical Servicing

No.	Task	1000 Volts or Below Test Type*	Greater than 1000 Volts Test Type*	Notes
1	Check circuit breakers and switches — mechanical operation	2	2	See manufacturer's instructions, Chapter 15, and Chapter 17.
2	Check bolted connection resistance	2	2	See Chapter 7.
3	Verify lubrication on moving current-carrying parts and sliding surfaces	2	2	See manufacturer's instructions.
4	Verify mechanical interlock systems for correct sequencing	2	2	
5	Verify mechanical systems for correct sequencing, including shutters, racking mechanisms, and similar	2	2	
6	Verify mechanical indicating devices are functional	2	2	
7	Verify filters or screens are clean and in place	1 or 2	1 or 2	Include filters and screens in the room related to the substation or switchgear.
8	Verify fuse holders provide mechanical support and contact integrity	2	2	
9	For individual components, refer to the appropriate chapter(s) of this standard	NA	NA	

NA: Not applicable.

*Types specified in accordance with Section 8.3, as follows: Type 1 = online standard test; Type 1A = online enhanced test; Type 2 = offline standard test; Type 2A = offline enhanced test.

Shaded text = Revisions.   Δ = Text deletions and figure/table revisions.   • = Section deletions.   *N* = New material.

2023 Edition

N Table 12.3.5 Substation and Switchgear Electrical Tests

No.	Task	1000 Volts or Below Test Type*	Greater than 1000 Volts Test Type*	Notes
1	Inspect electrical connections for high resistance	2	2	See Section 7.2.
2	Perform ground resistance test	2	2	See 20.3.5. Perform point-to-point test to determine the resistance between the main grounding system and substation/switchgear frames, system neutral, or derived neutral points. Perform fall-of-potential or alternative test on the grounding electrode system.
3	Measure insulation resistance	2	2	
4	Measure insulation resistance of control wiring	2A	2A	
5	Test protective devices and systems	2	2	For surge protective devices, surge arresters, and arc-energy reduction systems, see the manufacturer's instructions.
6	Perform system operational tests	2	2	Include emergency or standby sources of power systems to ensure they are available when needed, automatic throw-overs, paralleling controls, interlock systems, or any other operational or maintenance-related control that might be installed.
7	Perform dielectric withstand test	NA	2A	
8	Perform online partial discharge (PD) survey	NA	1A	
9	Where environmental controls are provided, check for correct operating condition	1 or 2	1 or 2	Includes, but is not limited to, fans, heaters, thermostats and humidity control equipment and settings.
10	Test control power transformers, instrument transformers, and metering to ensure correct operation	1 or 2	1 or 2	
11	Verify operation of communications systems	1 or 2	1 or 2	
12	For individual components, refer to the appropriate chapter(s) of this standard	NA	NA	

NA: Not applicable.
*Types specified in accordance with Section 8.3, as follows: Type 1 = online standard test; Type 1A = online enhanced test; Type 2 = offline standard test; Type 2A = offline enhanced test.

N **Chapter 13 Panelboards and Switchboards**

N **13.1 Scope.**

N **13.1.1*** This chapter identifies electrical maintenance requirements for panelboards and switchboards rated 1000 V or below.

N **13.1.2*** This chapter does not address requirements of individual components of panelboards and switchboards that are addressed in the chapters for those components.

N **13.2 Frequency of Maintenance.** The periodic maintenance procedures specified in Section 13.3 shall be performed in accordance with the frequencies specified in Chapter 9, unless otherwise specified in this chapter.

N **13.3 Periodic Maintenance Procedures.**

N **13.3.1 Visual Inspection.** Panelboards and switchboards shall be visually inspected in accordance with Table 13.3.1.

N **13.3.2 Cleaning.** Bus insulation, cable insulation, terminals or terminations, electrical equipment surfaces, enclosures, and insulating materials shall be kept in a clean and contaminant-free state.

N **13.3.3 Lubrication.** Terminating devices, mechanical parts, and operating parts that exist to open, close, insert, and trip a circuit breaker, switch, or protective device shall be lubricated as required in accordance with the manufacturer's instructions.

N **13.3.4 Mechanical Servicing.** Panelboards and switchboards shall be mechanically serviced in accordance with Table 13.3.4.

N **13.3.5 Electrical Testing.** Panelboards and switchboards shall be electrically tested in accordance with Table 13.3.5.

N **13.3.6 Special. (Reserved)**

N **Table 13.3.1 Panelboard and Switchboard Visual Inspections**

No.	Task	Test Type*	Notes
1	Inspect external physical condition	1	This includes condition and integrity of applied labels.
2	Inspect anchorage and grounding	1	
3	Verify circuit breakers, fuses, and overload elements are the right sizes and types and correspond to the drawings and power system studies	2	
4	For connected communicating addressable devices, verify the device addresses are set in accordance with documentation	2	Confirm addressing or correct device association where protective devices or the human machine interface (HMI) are connected to multiple devices via a communication network.
5	Verify instrument transformer ratios are correct	2	
6	Inspect insulators for damage or contaminated surfaces	2	
7	Verify filters are clean and in place	2	
8	Ensure maintenance devices and tools are available for equipment servicing	1	
9	Verify phase barriers are in place	2	
10	Visually inspect environmental controls, where provided	1 or 2	Includes, but is not limited to, fans, heaters, thermostats and humidity control equipment and settings.
11	For individual components, refer to the appropriate chapter(s) of this standard	NA	

NA: Not applicable.

*Types specified in accordance with Section 8.3, as follows: Type 1 = online standard test; Type 1A = online enhanced test; Type 2 = offline standard test; Type 2A = offline enhanced test.

Shaded text = Revisions.   Δ = Text deletions and figure/table revisions.   • = Section deletions.   N = New material.

2023 Edition

N   **Table 13.3.4 Panelboard and Switchboard Mechanical Servicing**

No.	Task	Test Type*	Notes
1	Inspect mechanical condition	2	
2	Ensure maintenance devices and tools are available for equipment servicing	1 or 2	
3	Inspect anchorage and grounding	2	
4	Mechanically operate circuit breakers and switches	2	
5	Inspect bolted connection integrity	2	See Chapter 7.
6	Verify lubrication on moving current-carrying parts and sliding surfaces	2	See the manufacturer's instructions.
7	Verify mechanical interlock systems for correct sequencing	2	
8	Verify mechanical indicating devices are functional	2	
9	Verify filters are clean and in place	2	
10	Verify fuse holders provide mechanical support and contact integrity	2	
11	For individual components, refer to the appropriate chapter(s) of this standard	NA	

NA: Not applicable.
*Types specified in accordance with Section 8.3, as follows: Type 1 = online standard test; Type 1A = online enhanced test; Type 2 = offline standard test; Type 2A = offline enhanced test.

Shaded text = Revisions.   Δ = Text deletions and figure/table revisions.   • = Section deletions.   **N** = New material.

N **Table 13.3.5 Panelboard and Switchboard Electrical Testing**

No.	Task	Test Type*	Notes
1	Check electrical hardware connections	NA	See Chapter 7.
2	Measure insulation resistance of the main bus	2	
3	Measure insulation resistance of control wiring	2A	
4	Test protective devices and systems	2	For surge protective devices, surge arresters, and arc-fault energy reduction systems, see the manufacturer's instructions.
5	Perform system operational tests	1 or 2	Includes emergency or standby power systems.
6	Test control power transformers, instrument transformers, and metering to ensure correct operation	2	
7	For individual components, refer to the appropriate chapter(s) of this standard	NA	
8	Where environmental controls are provided, check for correct operating condition	1 or 2	Includes, but is not limited to, fans, heaters, thermostats, and humidity control equipment and settings.

NA: Not applicable.

*Types specified in accordance with Section 8.3, as follows: Type 1 = online standard test; Type 1A = online enhanced test; Type 2 = offline standard test; Type 2A = offline enhanced test.

N

Chapter 14   Busways

N **14.1* Scope.** This chapter identifies electrical maintenance requirements for busways and associated fittings.

N **14.2 Frequency of Maintenance.** The periodic maintenance procedures in Section 14.3 shall be performed in accordance with the frequencies in Chapter 9, unless otherwise specified in this chapter.

N **14.3 Periodic Maintenance Procedures.**

N **14.3.1* Visual Inspection.** Busways shall be visually inspected in accordance with Table 14.3.1.

N **14.3.2* Cleaning.**

N **14.3.2.1*** Accumulations of dust, dirt, and debris shall be removed from busways using a brush, vacuum cleaner, or clean, lint-free rags.

N **14.3.2.2** Compressed air shall not be used to remove dust, dirt, or debris from busways or associated fittings.

N **14.3.3* Lubrication.**

N **14.3.3.1** Operating mechanisms and interlocks on plug-in units shall be lubricated in accordance with the manufacturer's instructions.

N **14.3.3.2** Where no manufacturer's instructions are available, non-current-carrying mechanisms and interlocks shall be lubricated with a clean, light grease.

N **14.3.3.3** Excess lubrication shall be wiped off to avoid accumulation of foreign material.

N **14.3.3.4** Where plug-in units are relocated, electrical plug-in connections on plug-in units shall be lubricated in accordance with the manufacturer's instructions with a conductive lubricant labeled for use on electrical power connections.

N **14.3.4 Mechanical Servicing.** Busways shall be mechanically serviced in accordance with Table 14.3.4.

N **14.3.5* Electrical Testing.** Busways shall be electrically tested in accordance with Table 14.3.5.

N **14.3.6 Special. (Reserved)**

Shaded text = Revisions.   Δ = Text deletions and figure/table revisions.   • = Section deletions.   *N* = New material.

2023 Edition

N **Table 14.3.1 Busway Visual Inspections**

No.	Task	Busways Rated 600 Volts or Less Test Type*	Busways Rated Over 600 Volts Test Type*	Notes
1	Visually inspect the physical condition of the busway and associated fittings	1	1	Look for evidence of moisture contamination, corrosion, and excessive buildup of dust, dirt, or debris.
2	Visually inspect anchorage, hangers, and alignment of busway system	1	1	Look for loose connections and twisting or bending of lifted supports.
3	Visually inspect all areas near electrical joints, terminations, and connections	2	2	Visually check connections to be certain that they are clean and secure and show no signs of overheating or discoloration.
4	Examine outdoor busway to ensure that weepholes are not obstructed and that the joint shield is installed correctly	1	1	
5	Inspect ventilation openings on busway and associated fittings	1	1	
6	Look for signs of deterioration of visible seals and gaskets	1	1	Outdoor and drip-resistant busways can contain seals and gaskets.
7	For individual components, refer to the appropriate chapter(s) of this standard	NA	NA	

*Types specified in accordance with Section 8.3, as follows: Type 1 = online standard test; Type 1A = online enhanced test; Type 2 = offline standard test; Type 2A = offline enhanced test.

   Shaded text = Revisions.   ∆ = Text deletions and figure/table revisions.   • = Section deletions.   N = New material.

N Table 14.3.4 Busway Mechanical Servicing

No.	Task	Busways Rated 600 Volts or Less Test Type*	Busways Rated Over 600 Volts Test Type*	Notes
1	Adjust or repair anchorage or hangers to ensure support of the busway	2	2	
2	Exercise plug-in unit operating mechanisms and external operators to confirm they operate to their full ON and OFF positions	2	NA	
3	Confirm operation of mechanical interlocks and locking means of plug-in units	2	NA	
4	Clean ventilation openings and weep holes	2	2	
5	Inspect forced-air cooling system	NA	2	Verify operation of forced-air cooling that could be included in metal enclosed bus systems.
6	Inspect for loose, open, or missing covers or doors on busways and associated fittings	2	2	Inspect all plug-in openings, plug-in units, and joints between busway sections. Some covers are not designed to be removed for inspection.
7	For individual components, refer to the appropriate chapter(s) of this standard	NA	NA	

NA: Not applicable.
*Types specified in accordance with Section 8.3, as follows: Type 1 = online standard test; Type 1A = online enhanced test; Type 2 = offline standard test; Type 2A = offline enhanced test.

N Table 14.3.5 Busway Electrical Tests

No.	Task	Busways Rated 600 Volts or Less Test Type*	Busways Rated Over 600 Volts Test Type*	Notes
1	Perform bus resistance tests	1 or 2	1 or 2	See Chapter 7.
2	Perform insulation resistance tests	2	2	See A.14.3.5 for additional information.
3	Perform a dielectric withstand voltage test	NA	2	See A.14.3.5 for additional information.
4	Where environmental controls are provided, check for correct operating condition	1 or 2	1 or 2	Includes, but is not limited to, fans, heaters, thermostats, and humidity control equipment and settings.
5	Perform insulation power-factor or dissipation-factor tests	NA	2A	
6	Perform online partial-discharge survey	NA	1A	

NA: Not applicable.
*Types specified in accordance with Section 8.3, as follows: Type 1 = online standard test; Type 1A = online enhanced test; Type 2 = offline standard test; Type 2A = offline enhanced test.

Shaded text = Revisions. Δ = Text deletions and figure/table revisions. • = Section deletions. *N* = New material.

2023 Edition

N　Chapter 15　Circuit Breakers, Low- and Medium-Voltage

N 15.1 Scope.

N 15.1.1 This chapter identifies electrical maintenance requirements for the following circuit breakers and their enclosures:

(1) Molded-case circuit breakers (MCCBs) rated less than or equal to 1000 V ac
(2) Insulated-case circuit breakers (ICCBs) rated less than or equal to 1000 V ac
(3) Low-voltage power circuit breakers (LVPCBs) rated less than or equal to 1000 V ac
(4) Medium-voltage power circuit breakers (MVPCBs) rated greater than 1000 V ac to less than or equal to 69 kV ac

N 15.2 Frequency of Maintenance. The periodic maintenance procedures in Section 15.3 and Section 15.4 shall be performed in accordance with the frequencies in Chapter 9, unless otherwise specified in this chapter.

N 15.3 Periodic Maintenance Procedures for Low-Voltage Power Circuit (LVPCB), Molded Case Circuit Breaker (MCCB), and Insulated Case Circuit Breakers (ICCB).

N 15.3.1 Visual Inspections. A visual inspection shall be conducted in accordance with Table 15.3.1.

N 15.3.2 Cleaning.

N 15.3.2.1 Electrical equipment surfaces, enclosures, and insulating materials shall be kept in a clean and contaminant-free state.

N　Table 15.3.1 MCCB, ICCB, and LVPCB Visual Inspections

No.	Task	MCCB Test Type*	ICCB Test Type*	LVPCB Test Type*	Notes
1	Verify ratings for proper system application.	1 or 2	1 or 2	1 or 2	
2	Inspect insulating materials and frame for evidence of physical damage, cracks from stresses of operation, or contamination.	2	2	2	
3	Inspect wiring, bus, cables, and connections for damaged insulation, broken leads, tightness of connections, proper crimping, and overall general condition, including corrosion.	2	2	2	
4	Inspect visible current-carrying parts and control devices if applicable for signs of overheating or deterioration.	2	2	2	
5	Inspect arc chutes for cracks or excessive erosion if applicable.	NA	2	2	
6	Check for cracks or lack of visual indication for all associated indicating status devices.	1 or 2	1 or 2	1 or 2	
7	Check all markings on the circuit breaker are legible.	1 or 2	1 or 2	1 or 2	
8	Inspect operating mechanism.	NA	2	2	
9	Check main contact over travel and arcing contact engagement.	NA	2	2	
10	Check condition of main and arcing contacts.	NA	2	2	
11	Check insulating links/push rods and interphase barriers for cracks and defects.	NA	2	2	

NA: Not applicable.
*Types specified in accordance with Section 8.3, as follows: 1 = online standard test, 1A = online enhanced test, 2 = offline standard test, 2A = offline enhanced test.

N 15.3.2.2 If contamination such as dust, dirt, soot, grease, or moisture is found, cleaning shall be performed in accordance with Table 15.3.2.2.

N 15.3.3 Lubrication. Moving and sliding surfaces shall be lubricated in accordance with Table 15.3.3.

N 15.3.4 Mechanical Servicing. Circuit breakers shall be mechanically serviced in accordance with Table 15.3.4.

N 15.3.5* Electrical Testing. Circuit breakers shall be electrically tested in accordance with Table 15.3.5.

N 15.3.6 Special. (Reserved)

N 15.4 Periodic Maintenance Procedures for Medium-Voltage Power Circuit Breakers. Medium-voltage power circuit breakers shall be maintained in accordance with this section.

N 15.4.1 Circuit breakers shall be visually inspected in accordance with Table 15.4.1.

N 15.4.2 Cleaning. Electrical equipment surfaces, enclosures, and insulating materials shall be kept in a clean and contaminant-free state in accordance with Table 15.4.2.

N 15.4.3 Lubrication. Moving and sliding surfaces shall be lubricated in accordance with Table 15.4.3.

N 15.4.4 Mechanical Servicing. Circuit breakers shall be mechanically serviced in accordance with Table 15.4.4.

N 15.4.5 Electrical Testing. Circuit breakers shall be electrically tested in accordance with Table 15.4.5.

N 15.4.6 Special. (Reserved)

N Table 15.3.2.2 MCCB, ICCB, and LVPCB Cleaning

No.	Task	MCCB Test Type*	ICCB Test Type*	LVPCB Test Type*	Notes
1	Clean insulating surfaces of the circuit breaker using a lint-free dry cloth, brush, or vacuum cleaner (avoid blowing material into the circuit breaker or into surrounding equipment)	2	2	2	
2	Clean contact surfaces in accordance with the manufacturer's instructions	NA	2	2	
3	Clean circuit breaker interior frame	NA	2	2	

NA: Not applicable.
*Types specified in accordance with Section 8.3, as follows: Type 1 = online standard test; Type 1A = online enhanced test; Type 2 = offline standard test; Type 2A = offline enhanced test.

N Table 15.3.3 MCCB, ICCB, and LVPCB Lubrication

No.	Task	MCCB Test Type*	ICCB Test Type*	LVPCB Test Type*	Notes
1	Apply a thin coating of conductive lubricant to exposed contacts as specified by the manufacturer	NA	2	2	
2	Apply nonconductive lubricant as needed to mechanism parts as specified by the manufacturer	NA	2	2	
3	Apply conductive lubricant to pivot points, as well as moving and sliding surfaces as specified by the manufacturer	NA	2	2	

NA: Not applicable.
*Types specified in accordance with Section 8.3, as follows: Type 1 = online standard test; Type 1A = online enhanced test; Type 2 = offline standard test; Type 2A = offline enhanced test.

N **Table 15.3.4 MCCB, ICCB, and LVPCB Mechanical Servicing**

No.	Task	MCCB Test Type*	ICCB Test Type*	LVPCB Test Type*	Notes
1	Check all accessible electrical hardware connections for correct torque	2	2	2	See Chapter 7.
2	Operate the circuit breaker three times	2	2	2	
3	Verify operation and alignment of mechanical safety interlocks, where applicable	2	2	2	
4	Verify correct operation of shutter assemblies on draw-out circuit breakers	2	2	2	
5	Measure and record trip bar force	NA	2A	2A	

NA: Not applicable.

*Types specified in accordance with Section 8.3, as follows: Type 1 = online standard test; Type 1A = online enhanced test; Type 2 = offline standard test; Type 2A = offline enhanced test.

N **Table 15.3.5 MCCB, ICCB, and LVPCB Electrical Tests**

No.	Task	MCCB† 250 Amperes and Less Frame Test Type*	MCCB† Over 250 Amperes Frame Test Type*	ICCB Test Type*	LVPCB Test Type*	Notes
1	Perform infrared thermography	1	1	1	1	
2	Measure contact resistance of each switching pole	2A	2	2	2	
3	Perform insulation-resistance tests, phase-to-phase and phase-to-ground with circuit breaker closed and across each open pole	2A	2	2	2	
4	Operate circuit breaker auxiliary and control devices such as local and remote-control switches, shunt trips coils, close coils, motors, auxiliary switches, and under-voltage coils	2	2	2	2	
5	Verify the calibration of all functions of the trip unit by means of the manufacturer's specified test set for circuit breakers equipped with electronic trip units	2A	2	2	2	
6	Perform inverse time trip test at 300% of rated continuous current of thermal magnetic circuit breakers	2A	2	NA	NA	
7	Perform inverse time trip test at 300% of rated continuous current of electronic trip circuit breakers	2A	2A	2A	2A	
8	Perform the instantaneous overcurrent trip test for thermal-magnetic circuit breakers by "run-up" or "pulse" method	2A	2	NA	2	
9	Perform the instantaneous overcurrent trip test for electronic trip breakers by "run-up" or "pulse" method	2A	2A	2A	2A	
10	Perform rated hold-in test	2A	2A	2A	2A	
11	Test current-limiter resistance	2	2	2	2	
12	Check status of rating plug battery	2	2	2	2	
13	Perform millivolt drop test	2A	2A	2A	2A	
14	Test arc reduction technology in accordance with the manufacturer's instructions	2	2	2	2	

NA: Not applicable.

*Types specified in accordance with Section 8.3, as follows: Type 1 = online standard test; Type 1A = online enhanced test; Type 2 = offline standard test; Type 2A = offline enhanced test.

†The rating of adjustable-trip circuit breakers shall be the maximum setting possible.

Shaded text = Revisions.   Δ = Text deletions and figure/table revisions.   • = Section deletions.   *N* = New material.

2023 Edition

N **Table 15.4.1 Medium-Voltage Power Circuit Breakers Visual Inspections**

No.	Task	Air Magnetic Circuit Breakers Test Type*	Vacuum Circuit Breakers Test Type*	Gas Insulated Circuit Breakers Test Type*	Oil Circuit Breakers Test Type*	Notes
1	Verify ratings for proper system application	1 or 2	1 or 2	1 or 2	1 or 2	
2	Inspect insulating materials and frame for evidence of physical damage, cracks from stresses of operation, or contamination	2	2	2	2	
3	Inspect wiring, bus, cables, and connections for damaged insulation, broken leads, tightness of connections, proper crimping, and overall general condition including corrosion	2	2	2	2	
4	Inspect visible current-carrying parts and control devices, if applicable, for signs of overheating or deterioration	2	2	2	2	
5	Inspect each arc chute for cracks or excessive erosion	2	NA	NA	NA	
6	Inspect ground contact, secondary disconnect, close and trip interlocks, levering latch, mechanism-operated contact (MOC), and truck-operated contact (TOC) switches, and all other interlocks	2	2	2	2	
7	Check all markings on the circuit breaker are legible	1 or 2	1 or 2	1 or 2	1 or 2	
8	Inspect contact erosion indicator mark on vacuum interrupter moving stem	NA	2	NA	NA	Some manufacturers have visual inspections to determine contact erosion.
9	Inspect contact	NA	2	NA	NA	Some manufacturers have visual inspections to determine contact wipe.
10	Verify correct oil level	NA	NA	NA	2	
11	Check for oil leaks	NA	NA	NA	2	
12	Visually inspect bushings for cracks, chips, loss of porcelain, evidence of corona damage, or other physical damage	2	2	2	2	
13	Check for low gas pressure	NA	NA	2A	NA	

NA: Not applicable.

*Types specified in accordance with Section 8.3, as follows: Type 1 = online standard test; Type 1A = online enhanced test; Type 2 = offline standard test; Type 2A = offline enhanced test.

Table 15.4.2 Medium-Voltage Power Circuit Breakers Cleaning

No.	Task	Air Magnetic Circuit Breakers Test Type*	Vacuum Circuit Breakers Test Type*	Gas Insulated Circuit Breakers Test Type*	Oil Circuit Breakers Test Type*	Notes
1	Clean insulating surfaces of the circuit breaker using a lint-free dry cloth, brush, or vacuum cleaner (avoid blowing material into the circuit breaker or into surrounding equipment)	2	2	NA	NA	For vacuum circuit breakers, follow the manufacturer's instructions to avoid shock due to inherent capacitance from the technology used in the circuit breaker.
2	Clean contact surfaces	2	NA	NA	2	

NA: Not applicable.

*Types specified in accordance with Section 8.3, as follows: Type 1 = online standard test; Type 1A = online enhanced test; Type 2 = offline standard test; Type 2A = offline enhanced test.

Table 15.4.3 Medium-Voltage Power Circuit Breakers Lubrication

No.	Task	Air Magnetic Circuit Breakers Test Type*	Vacuum Circuit Breakers Test Type*	Gas Insulated Circuit Breakers Test Type*	Oil Circuit Breakers Test Type*	Notes
1	Apply a thin coating of conductive lubricant to exposed contacts as specified by the manufacturer	2	2	2	2	
2	Apply nonconductive lubricant as needed to mechanism parts as specified by the manufacturer	2	2	2	2	
3	Apply conductive lubricant to pivot points, as well as moving and sliding surfaces, as specified by the manufacturer	2	2	2	2	

*Types specified in accordance with Section 8.3, as follows: Type 1 = online standard test; Type 1A = online enhanced test; Type 2 = offline standard test; Type 2A = offline enhanced test.

Shaded text = Revisions.   △ = Text deletions and figure/table revisions.   ● = Section deletions.   *N* = New material.

2023 Edition

N **Table 15.4.4 Medium-Voltage Power Circuit Breakers Mechanical Servicing**

No.	Task	Air Magnetic Circuit Breakers Test Type*	Vacuum Circuit Breakers Test Type*	Gas Insulated Circuit Breakers Test Type*	Oil Circuit Breakers Test Type*	Notes
1	Check all accessible electrical hardware connections for proper torque	2	2	2	2	See Chapter 7.
2	Replace any barriers and parts that have been removed for maintenance	2	2	2	2	
3	Close and open the circuit breaker	2	2	2	2	
4	Verify operation and alignment of mechanical safety interlocks, where applicable	2	2	2	2	
5	Verify the proper operation of all circuit breaker/cell accessories, shutters, auxiliary switches, cell MOC and TOC switches, and key interlocks	2	2	2	2	
6	Verify proper operation of all cell status indicators	2	2	2	2	
7	Charge closing spring and close manually	2	2	2	2	
8	Measure and record trip bar force	2A	2A	2A	2A	
9	Perform gas leakage detection	NA	NA	2	NA	
10	Inspect pneumatic and hydraulic fittings and connections for leaks	2	2	2	2	

NA: Not applicable.

*Types specified in accordance with Section 8.3, as follows: Type 1 = online standard test; Type 1A = online enhanced test; Type 2 = offline standard test; Type 2A = offline enhanced test.

Shaded text = Revisions.   Δ = Text deletions and figure/table revisions.   • = Section deletions.   *N* = New material

N Table 15.4.5 Medium-Voltage Power Circuit Breakers Electrical Tests

No.	Task	Air Magnetic Circuit Breaker Test Type*	Vacuum Circuit Breaker Test Type*	Gas Insulated Circuit Breaker Test Type*	Oil Insulated Circuit Breaker Test Type*	Notes
1	Inspect electrical connections for high resistance	1 or 2	1 or 2	1 or 2	1 or 2	See Section 7.2.
2	Measure contact resistance of each switching pole	2	2	2	2	
3	Perform insulation-resistance tests, phase-to-phase and phase-to-ground with circuit breaker closed and across each open pole	2	2	2	2	
4	Verify control power for close and trip functions	2	2	2	2	
5	Perform trip and close tests with control switch	2	2	2	2	
6	Verify operating mechanism charge, anti-pump, and trip-free functions	2	2	2	2	
7	Perform vacuum integrity test by ac overpotential across each vacuum bottle	NA	2	NA	NA	
8	Verify proper operation of space heaters, if equipped	2	2	2	2	
9	Perform an ac overpotential test one pole at a time with the other poles and structure grounded	2A	2A	2A	2A	
10	Perform an ac overpotential test on control wiring	2A	2A	2A	2A	**WARNING:** Do not perform this test on wiring connected to solid-state components.
11	Verify blow-out coil continuity	2	NA	NA	NA	
12	Perform circuit breaker motion analysis	2A	2A	2	2	
13	Perform circuit breaker contact timing test	2	2	2	2	
14	Perform trip/close coil current signature analysis	2A	2A	2A	2A	
15	Perform pickup test on trip and/or close coil	2A	2A	2A	2A	
16	Measure power/dissipation factor	2A	NA	2A	2	

NA: Not applicable.

*Types specified in accordance with Section 8.3, as follows: Type 1 = online standard test; Type 1A = online enhanced test; Type 2 = offline standard test; Type 2A = offline enhanced test.

Shaded text = Revisions.　△ = Text deletions and figure/table revisions.　• = Section deletions.　**N** = New material.

2023 Edition

N **Chapter 16   Fuses**

N **16.1 Scope.** This chapter identifies electrical maintenance requirements for fuses to protect branch, feeder and service conductors.

N **16.2 Frequency of Maintenance.** The periodic maintenance procedures specified in Section 16.3 shall be performed in accordance with the frequencies specified in Chapter 9, unless otherwise specified in this chapter.

N **16.3 Periodic Maintenance Procedures.**

N **16.3.1* Visual Inspections.** Fuses shall be visually inspected in accordance with Table 16.3.1.

N **16.3.2 Cleaning.** If contamination is present, fuses shall be cleaned in accordance with Table 16.3.2.

N **16.3.3 Lubrication. (Reserved)**

N **16.3.4 Mechanical Servicing.** Fuses shall be mechanically serviced in accordance with Table 16.3.4.

N **16.3.5* Electrical Testing.** Fuses shall be electrically tested in accordance with Table 16.3.5.

N **16.3.6 Special. (Reserved)**

N **Table 16.3.1 Fuse Visual Inspections**

No.	Task	1000 Volts or Less Test Type*	Greater than 1000 Volts Test Type*	Notes
1	Check for discoloration of fuse terminals and clips caused by heat	1 or 2	1 or 2	
2	Check fuse indicating device status, if applicable	1 or 2	1 or 2	
3	Confirm that fuses, in any one circuit, have the same catalog number to ensure that they have the same current rating, voltage rating, interrupting rating, time delay, and type (e.g., UL class)	1 or 2	1 or 2	
4	Confirm that all fuses match the most recent short-circuit, coordination, and arc flash studies	1 or 2	1 or 2	
5	Where current-limiting fuses are required, confirm that correct rejection-type mountings are used so that the current-limiting fuses cannot be replaced by non-current-limiting fuses	2	2	
6	Verify ratings for correct system application	1 or 2	1 or 2	
7	Inspect insulators for breaks, cracks, tracking, corona, burns, or overheating	NA	2	
8	Inspect contact surfaces for pitting or burning, alignment, and contact pressure	NA	2A	
9	Examine the fuse unit, fuse tube, and renewable element, if used, for evidence of corrosion and wear	NA	2	
10	Inspect bolts, nuts, washers, pins, and terminal connectors to ensure they are in place, in good condition, and properly installed	NA	2	
11	Inspect seals of vented expulsion type fuses	NA	2	

NA: Not applicable.
*Types specified in accordance with Section 8.3, as follows: Type 1 = online standard test; Type 1A = online enhanced test; Type 2 = offline standard test; Type 2A = offline enhanced test.

Shaded text = Revisions.   Δ = Text deletions and figure/table revisions.   • = Section deletions.   N = New material.

Table 16.3.2 Fuse Cleaning

No.	Task	1000 Volts or Less Test Type*	Greater than 1000 Volts Test Type*	Notes
1	Clean fuse terminals and clips that have become corroded or oxidized	2	2	
2	Clean insulators of accumulated dust and foreign matter	NA	2	

NA: Not applicable.
*Types specified in accordance with Section 8.3, as follows: Type 1 = online standard test; Type 1A = online enhanced test; Type 2 = offline standard test; Type 2A = offline enhanced test.

Table 16.3.4 Fuse Mechanical Servicing

No.	Task	1000 Volts or Less Test Type*	Greater than 1000 Volts Test Type*	Notes
1	Check fuse holder terminations for tightness	2	2	See Chapter 7.
2	Verify that each fuseholder has adequate mechanical support	NA	2	

NA: Not applicable.
*Types specified in accordance with Section 8.3, as follows: Type 1 = online standard test; Type 1A = online enhanced test; Type 2 = offline standard test; Type 2A = offline enhanced test.

Table 16.3.5 Fuse Electrical Tests

No.	Task	1000 Volts or Less Test Type*	Greater than 1000 Volts Test Type*	Notes
1	Perform infrared thermography	1	1	When equipment has infrared viewing port or is accessible while in operation.
2	Measure fuse connection resistance	2A	2	
3	Measure fuse resistance	2A	2	

*Types specified in accordance with Section 8.3, as follows: Type 1 = online standard test; Type 1A = online enhanced test; Type 2 = offline standard test; Type 2A = offline enhanced test.

Chapter 17   Switches

17.1 Scope.

17.1.1 This chapter identifies electrical maintenance requirements for the following:

(1) Enclosed and dead-front (safety) switches, bolted-pressure switches (BPS), high-pressure contact switches (HPC), automatic transfer switches, bypass-isolation switches, and other transfer switch equipment rated 1000 volts or less

(2) Switches used in metal-enclosed load interrupter switchgear and automatic transfer switches, bypass-isolation switches, and other transfer switch equipment rated over 1000 volts

17.2 Frequency of Maintenance. The periodic maintenance procedures specified in Section 17.3 shall be performed in accordance with the frequencies specified in Chapter 9, unless otherwise specified in this chapter.

N 17.3* Periodic Maintenance Procedures.

N 17.3.1 Visual Inspection. Switches shall be visually inspected in accordance with Table 17.3.1.

N 17.3.2 Cleaning. If contamination is present, switches shall be cleaned in accordance with Table 17.3.2.

N 17.3.3* Lubrication. Switches shall be lubricated in accordance with Table 17.3.3 and the manufacturer's published instructions.

N 17.3.4 Mechanical Servicing. Switches shall be mechanically serviced in accordance with Table 17.3.4.

N 17.3.5* Electrical Testing. Switches shall be electrically tested in accordance with Table 17.3.5.

N 17.3.6 Special. (Reserved)

Shaded text = Revisions.   Δ = Text deletions and figure/table revisions.   • = Section deletions.   N = New material.

2023 Edition

N **Table 17.3.1 Switch Visual Inspections**

No.	Task	1000 Volts or Less Test Type*	Greater than 1000 Volts Test Type*	Notes
1	Inspect doors and latches for fit, dents, corrosion, and missing hardware	1 or 2	1 or 2	
2	Inspect insulating materials and switch base for evidence of physical damage, cracks from stresses of operation, or contamination	2	2	
3	Inspect wiring, bus, cables, and connections for damaged insulation, broken leads, tightness of connections, crimping, and overall general condition, including corrosion	2	2	
4	Check that exposed switch contacts, both moving and stationary, are free from environmental contamination	2	NA	
5	Inspect visible current-carrying parts and control devices, if applicable, for signs of overheating or deterioration	2	2	
6	Check that fuses are secured	2	2	
7	Examine switches with exposed contacts for evidence of high short-circuit closing operation	2	NA	
8	Check the main body of the switch blades and the arcing contacts for arc erosion	2	2	Mild pitting and burning is permitted.
9	Inspect each arc chute for cracks or excessive erosion	NA	2	

NA: Not applicable.
*Types specified in accordance with Section 8.3, as follows: Type 1 = online standard test; Type 1A = online enhanced test; Type 2 = offline standard test; Type 2A = offline enhanced test.

Table 17.3.2 Switch Cleaning

No.	Task	1000 Volts or Less Test Type*	Greater than 1000 Volts Test Type*	Notes
1	Clean the switch and barriers	2	2	
2	Clean exposed switch contacts with a multi-purpose precision lubricant before lubricating	2	NA	
3	Wipe contact surfaces with a lint-free cleaning cloth	2	NA	
4	Wipe contact surfaces with a noncorrosive cleaning agent	NA	2	
5	Clean insulators	NA	2	

NA: Not applicable.
*Types specified in accordance with Section 8.3, as follows: Type 1 = online standard test; Type 1A = online enhanced test; Type 2 = offline standard test; Type 2A = offline enhanced test.

Table 17.3.3 Switch Lubrication

No.	Task	1000 Volts or Less Test Type*	Greater than 1000 Volts Test Type*	Notes
1	Apply a thin coating of conductive lubricant to exposed switch contacts.	2	NA	Enclosed and dead-front (safety) switches do not require lubrication.
2	Apply nonconductive lubricant as needed to mechanism parts as specified by the manufacturer.	2	NA	
3	Apply conductive lubricant to pivot points, as well as moving and sliding surfaces.	NA	2	

NA: Not applicable.
*Types specified in accordance with Section 8.3, as follows: 1 = online standard test, 1A = online enhanced test, 2 = offline standard test, 2A = offline enhanced test.

N   **Table 17.3.4 Switch Mechanical Servicing**

No.	Task	1000 Volts or Less Test Type*	Greater than 1000 Volts Test Type*	Notes
1	If accessible, verify main blade alignment, penetration, travel stops, and mechanical operation	2	2	
2	Check all accessible electrical hardware connections	2	2	See Chapter 7.
3	Operate the switch three times to work the lubricant between the contacts	2	NA	
4	Verify operation and alignment of mechanical interlocks	2	2	
5	Verify the contact pressure is within specification using a force gauge or other device that measures forces	NA	2	
6	With the door closed and latched, close and open the switch three times to confirm the switch and operator lever is operating; view switch position through the window after each operation, where available; when open, verify that switch blades have cleared the arc chutes; when closed, verify that the switch blades are inside the arc chutes and vertical; if they are not, perform alignment adjustments per the manufacturer's instructions	NA	2	

NA: Not applicable.
*Types specified in accordance with Section 8.3, as follows: Type 1 = online standard test; Type 1A = online enhanced test; Type 2 = offline standard test; Type 2A = offline enhanced test.

N **Table 17.3.5 Switch Electrical Tests**

No.	Task	1000 Volts or Less Test Type*	Greater than 1000 Volts Test Type*	Notes
1	Perform infrared thermography	1A	1	
2	Measure contact resistance of each switching pole	2A	2	
3	Perform insulation-resistance tests, phase-to-phase and phase-to-ground with switch closed and across each open pole	2A	2	
4	Functional tests only for switches with motor operators: Verify control power for close and trip functions Verify the electrical operation of switch Perform trip and close tests Verify operation of the switch from local switches or terminal blocks	2	2	
5	Functional tests only for switches with shunt trip capabilities	2	2	
6	Measure the resistance between the line and load terminal pads on each phase	NA	2	
7	Verify operation of space heaters, if equipped	NA	2	
8	Perform overpotential test one pole at a time with the other poles and structure grounded	NA	2A	
9	Perform overpotential test on control wiring	NA	2A	**WARNING:** Do not perform this test on wiring connected to solid-state components.
10	Test arc reduction technology in accordance with the manufacturer's instructions	2	2	
11	Perform functional tests for automatic transfer switches, bypass switches, and other transfer switch equipment	1A or 2A	1A or 2A	

NA: Not applicable.

*Types specified in accordance with Section 8.3, as follows: Type 1 = online standard test; Type 1A = online enhanced test; Type 2 = offline standard test; Type 2A = offline enhanced test.

Shaded text = Revisions.   Δ = Text deletions and figure/table revisions.   • = Section deletions.   *N* = New material.

2023 Edition

N **Chapter 18 Power Cables and Conductors**

N **18.1* Chapter Scope.**

N **18.1.1** This chapter identifies electrical maintenance requirements for power cables and conductors operating at 1000 volts or less and those that are purpose-built, multilayered, and operating at over 1000 volts.

N **18.1.1.1** This chapter applies to circuit cables and conductors between the service point or other power supply source and the final branch-circuit overcurrent device.

N **18.1.1.2** This chapter does not apply to the cables and conductors between the final overcurrent device protecting the circuit and the outlet(s).

N **18.2 Frequency of Maintenance.** The periodic maintenance procedures in Section 18.3 shall be performed in accordance with the frequencies in Chapter 9, unless otherwise specified in this chapter.

N **18.3 Periodic Maintenance Procedures.**

N **18.3.1* Visual Inspections.** Readily accessible and visible portions of power cables and conductors shall be visually inspected in accordance with Table 18.3.1.

N **18.3.2 Cleaning.** Cable and conductor insulation, jackets, sheaths, terminals or terminations, enclosures, and insulating materials shall be kept clean to prevent a buildup of contaminants that can negatively affect performance, reduce life expectancy, or create a safety hazard.

N **18.3.3 Lubrication.** Terminating devices, elbows, or T-bodies shall be lubricated in accordance with the manufacturer's instructions.

N **18.3.4 Mechanical Servicing. (Reserved)**

N **18.3.5* Electrical Testing.** Power cables and conductors shall be electrically tested in accordance with Table 18.3.5.

N **18.3.6 Special. (Reserved)**

N **Table 18.3.1 Power Cable and Conductor Visual Inspections**

No.	Task	Test Type*	Notes
1	Physical condition, including operating environment	1 or 2	Damage or deterioration, supports or restraints, bending radius, excessive tension, signs of overheating, corrosion, swelling or soft spots
2	Correct labeling or identification	1 or 2	Phasing, cable ID, multiple sources, hazard, other warning labels
3	Grounding/bonding	1 or 2	Damage, missing or loose terminations, clearance from energized parts, protection from physical damage
4	Vaults containing cables	1 or 2	Damage, concrete deterioration, drainage
5	Cable and conductor terminations	1 or 2	Oil or compound leaks, cracks or damaged bodies, cleanliness, terminations
6	Aerial installations	1 or 2	Damage, deteriorating supports, suspension systems, pinched or damaged insulation at dead ends, animal or bird infestation
7	Raceway	1 or 2	Damage or deterioration, abrasion or wear, continuity, tight joints, missing or loose bonding jumpers, corrosion
8	Barriers, guards, and assemblies	1 or 2	Damage or signs of deterioration, arcing, tracking, supports and mounting hardware

*Types specified in accordance with Section 8.3, as follows: Type 1 = online standard test; Type 1A = online enhanced test; Type 2 = offline standard test; Type 2A = offline enhanced test.

Shaded text = Revisions.   **Δ** = Text deletions and figure/table revisions.   • = Section deletions.   *N* = New material.

N Table 18.3.5 Power Cable and Conductor Electrical Tests

No.	Task	1000 Volts or Less Test Type*	Over 1000 Volts Test Type*	Notes
1	Airborne ultrasonic acoustic emissions	NA	1A	
2	Insulation resistance	2A	NA	For cables and conductors 1000 volts or less.
3	Insulation resistance:			For cables and conductors over 1000 volts.
	Very low frequency (VLF <1 Hz)	NA	2	
	Overpotential test (hi-pot)	NA	2	
	Dissipation factor/tan delta	NA	2	
	Partial discharge	NA	1 or 2	
	Power frequency	NA	2	
	Oscillating wave	NA	2	
4	Connection quality	1 or 2	1 or 2	Millivolt drop, digital low-resistance ohmmeter, infrared thermography. Circuits tested are based on criticality of the circuit.

NA: Not applicable.
*Types specified in accordance with Section 8.3, as follows: Type 1 = online standard test; Type 1A = online enhanced test; Type 2 = offline standard test; Type 2A = offline enhanced test.

N   **Chapter 19   Cable Tray**

N **19.1 Scope.** This chapter identifies electrical maintenance requirements for cable tray systems, including ladder, ventilated trough, ventilated channel, solid bottom, and other similar structures.

N **19.2 Frequency of Maintenance.** The periodic maintenance procedures in Section 19.3 shall be performed in accordance with the frequencies in Chapter 9, unless otherwise specified in this chapter.

N **19.3 Periodic Maintenance Procedures.**

N **19.3.1 Visual Inspections.** Cable tray shall be visually inspected in accordance with Table 19.3.1.

N **19.3.2 Cleaning.** Cable trays and the cables within shall be kept clean to prevent a buildup of contaminants that can negatively affect performance, reduce life expectancy, or create a safety hazard.

N **19.3.3 Lubrication. (Reserved)**

N **19.3.4 Mechanical Servicing. (Reserved)**

N **19.3.5 Electrical Testing.** Metal cable trays shall be electrically tested in accordance with Table 19.3.5.

N **19.3.6 Special. (Reserved)**

N **Table 19.3.1 Cable Tray Visual Inspections**

No.	Task	Test Type*	Notes
1	Verify equipment grounding and bonding for the following:		
	Cable tray	1 or 2	
	Transition raceways	1 or 2	
2	Check for overfilling	1 or 2	
3	Inspect for the following:		
	Incorrect cables (small, not TC listed)	1A or 2A	
	Cable damage	1A or 2A	
	Cables support damage	1 or 2	
	Intrusive items (e.g., pipes, hangers)	1 or 2	
4	Inspect for the following:		
	Spacing of cables, for cables that have minimum spacing requirements	1 or 2	
	Cable tie-downs	1 or 2	
	Supports of cable trays	1 or 2	
	Damaged tray or supports	1 or 2	
	Expansion joints in sufficient distances	1 or 2	

*Types specified in accordance with Section 8.3, as follows: Type 1 = online standard test; Type 1A = online enhanced test; Type 2 = offline standard test; Type 2A = offline enhanced test.

N **Table 19.3.5 Metal Cable Tray Electrical Tests**

No.	Task	Test Type*	Notes
1	Perform infrared thermography	1A	Check for inductive heating of the cable tray.
2	Test cable tray effective ground fault current path for continuity	1A	

*Types specified in accordance with Section 8.3, as follows: Type 1 = online standard test; Type 1A = online enhanced test; Type 2 = offline standard test; Type 2A = offline enhanced test.

N ## Chapter 20 Grounding and Bonding

N **20.1 Scope.** This chapter identifies electrical maintenance requirements for grounding and bonding of electrical systems.

N **20.2 Frequency of Maintenance.** The periodic maintenance procedures specified in Section 20.3 shall be performed in accordance with the frequencies specified in Chapter 9, unless otherwise specified in this chapter.

N **20.3 Periodic Maintenance Procedures.**

N **20.3.1* Visual Inspections.** Grounding and bonding shall be visually inspected in accordance with Table 20.3.1.

N **20.3.2 Cleaning. (Reserved)**

N **20.3.3 Lubrication. (Reserved)**

N **20.3.4 Mechanical Servicing. (Reserved)**

N **20.3.5* Electrical Testing.** Grounding and bonding shall be electrically tested in accordance with Table 20.3.5.

N **20.3.6 Special. (Reserved)**

N **Table 20.3.1 Grounding and Bonding Visual Inspections**

No.	Task	Test Type*	Notes
1	Inspect physical and mechanical condition of accessible and visible components and connections	2	
2	Inspect anchorage	2	

*Types specified in accordance with Section 8.3, as follows: Type 1 = online standard test; Type 1A = online enhanced test; Type 2 = offline standard test; Type 2A = offline enhanced test.

N **Table 20.3.5 Grounding and Bonding Electrical Testing**

No.	Task	Test Type*	Notes
1	Measure bolted or mechanical connection resistance	2A	
2	For ground rod electrode systems, perform fall-of-potential test to measure grounding rod to earth resistance	2A	
3	Perform point-to-point test to verify equipment is bonded together	2A	
4	Perform substation grounding electrode system and substation grid integrity test by injecting current in accordance with industry practices	2A	
5	Measure voltage between the equipment grounding conductor and the grounded conductor	1A	
6	Measure current magnitude on the equipment grounding conductor	1A	

*Types specified in accordance with Section 8.3, as follows: Type 1 = online standard test; Type 1A = online enhanced test; Type 2 = offline standard test; Type 2A = offline enhanced test.

N **Chapter 21 Ground-Fault Circuit Interrupters and Ground-Fault Protection of Equipment Systems**

N **21.1* Scope.** This chapter identifies electrical maintenance requirements for ground-fault circuit interrupter (GFCI) protection for personnel, special-purpose GFCI (SPGFCI), and ground-fault protection of equipment for solidly grounded systems.

N **21.2 Frequency of Maintenance.** The periodic maintenance procedures specified in Section 21.3 shall be performed in accordance with the frequencies specified in Chapter 9, unless otherwise specified in this chapter.

N **21.3 Periodic Maintenance Procedures.**

N **21.3.1* Ground-Fault Circuit Interrupters (GFCIs) and Special-Purpose GFCIs (SPGFCIs).**

N **21.3.1.1 Visual Inspections.** (Reserved)

N **21.3.1.2 Cleaning.** (Reserved)

N **21.3.1.3 Lubrication.** (Reserved)

N **21.3.1.4 Mechanical Servicing.** (Reserved)

N **21.3.1.5 Electrical Testing.** GFCIs shall be electrically tested in accordance with the manufacturer's instructions using either the integral push-to-test button or an external test set.

N **21.3.1.6 Special.** (Reserved)

N **21.3.2* Low-Voltage Ground-Fault Protection Systems.**

N **21.3.2.1 Visual Inspections.** Low-voltage ground-fault protection systems shall be visually inspected in accordance with Table 21.3.2.1.

N **21.3.2.2 Cleaning.** If contamination is found, low-voltage ground-fault protection systems shall be cleaned in accordance with Table 21.3.2.2.

N **21.3.2.3 Lubrication.** (Reserved)

N **21.3.2.4 Mechanical Servicing.** Low-voltage ground-fault protection systems shall be mechanically serviced in accordance with Table 21.3.2.4.

N **21.3.2.5 Electrical Testing.** Low-voltage ground-fault protection systems shall be electrically tested in accordance with Table 21.3.2.5.

N **21.3.2.6 Special.** (Reserved)

N **21.3.3 Medium-Voltage Ground-Fault Protection Systems.**

N **21.3.3.1 Visual Inspections.** Medium-voltage ground-fault protection systems shall be visually inspected in accordance with Table 21.3.3.1.

N **21.3.3.2 Cleaning.** If contamination is present, medium-voltage ground-fault protection systems shall be cleaned in accordance with Table 21.3.3.2.

N **21.3.3.3 Lubrication.** (Reserved)

N **21.3.3.4 Mechanical Servicing.** Medium-voltage ground-fault protection systems shall be mechanically serviced in accordance with Table 21.3.3.4.

N **21.3.3.5 Electrical Testing.** Medium-voltage ground-fault protection systems shall be electrically tested in accordance with Chapter 35.

N **21.3.3.6 Special.** (Reserved)

Shaded text = Revisions.   Δ = Text deletions and figure/table revisions.   • = Section deletions.   N = New material.

2023 Edition

N Table 21.3.2.1 Low-Voltage Ground-Fault Protection Systems Visual Inspections

No.	Task	Circuit Breaker Trip Units or Switches with Integral Ground-Fault Protection Test Type*	Circuit Breakers or Switches with External Ground-Fault Protection Test Type*	Notes
1	Verify ground connection is made on the source side of the neutral disconnect link and any ground fault sensors	2	2	
2	For zero-sequence systems, verify all phase and neutral conductors pass through the sensor in the same direction, and that grounding conductors do not pass through the sensor	NA	2	
3	Verify sensor, wiring, and ground-fault components are not damaged	NA	2	

NA: Not applicable.
*Types specified in accordance with Section 8.3, as follows: Type 1 = online standard test; Type 1A = online enhanced test; Type 2 = offline standard test; Type 2A = offline enhanced test.

N Table 21.3.2.2 Low-Voltage Ground-Fault Protection System Cleaning

No.	Task	Circuit Breaker Trip Units or Switches with Integral Ground-Fault Protection Test Type*	Circuit-Breakers or Switches with External Ground-Fault Protection Test Type*	Notes
1	Clean the relay case and cover	NA	2	
2	Clean sensors and associated ground faults protection system components	NA	2	

NA: Not applicable.
*Types specified in accordance with Section 8.3, as follows: Type 1 = online standard test; Type 1A = online enhanced test; Type 2 = offline standard test; Type 2A = offline enhanced test.

N Table 21.3.2.4 Low-Voltage Ground-Fault Protection System Mechanical Servicing

No.	Task	Circuit Breaker Trip Units or Switches with Integral Ground-Fault Protection Test Type*	Circuit Breakers or Switches with External Ground-Fault Protection Test Type*	Notes
1	Inspect bolted electrical connections	NA	2	
2	Verify correct operation of the self-test panel/trip unit functions	2	2	

NA: Not applicable.
*Types specified in accordance with Section 8.3, as follows: Type 1 = online standard test; Type 1A = online enhanced test; Type 2 = offline standard test; Type 2A = offline enhanced test.

Shaded text = Revisions. Δ = Text deletions and figure/table revisions. • = Section deletions. N = New material.

Table 21.3.2.5 Low-Voltage Ground-Fault Protection System Electrical Testing

No.	Task	Circuit Breaker Trip Units or Switches with Integral Ground-Fault Protection Test Type*	Circuit Breakers or Switches with External Ground-Fault Protection Test Type*	Notes
1	Measure system neutral-to-ground resistance with the neutral disconnect link removed, and verify no downstream grounds exist on the neutral	2	2	
2	Verify reduced control voltage tripping ability at 55% for ac systems and 80% for dc systems	NA	2A	

NA: Not applicable.
*Types specified in accordance with Section 8.3, as follows: Type 1 = online standard test; Type 1A = online enhanced test; Type 2 = offline standard test; Type 2A = offline enhanced test.

Table 21.3.3.1 Medium-Voltage Ground-Fault Protection Systems Visual Inspections

No.	Task	Circuit Breaker Trip Units or Switches with Integral Ground-Fault Protection Test Type*	Circuit Breakers or Switches with External Ground-Fault Protection Test Type*	Notes
1	Verify ground connection is made on the source side of the neutral disconnect link and any ground fault sensors	2	2	
2	For zero-sequence systems, verify all phase and neutral conductors pass through the sensor in the same direction, and that grounding conductors either do not pass through the sensor or pass back through the sensor	NA	2	

NA: Not applicable.
*Types specified in accordance with Section 8.3, as follows: Type 1 = online standard test; Type 1A = online enhanced test; Type 2 = offline standard test; Type 2A = offline enhanced test.

Table 21.3.3.2 Medium-Voltage Ground-Fault Protection System Cleaning

No.	Task	Circuit Breaker Trip Units or Switches with Integral Ground-Fault Protection Test Type*	Circuit-Breakers or Switches with External Ground-Fault Protection Test Type*	Notes
1	Clean sensors and associated ground-fault protection system components	NA	2	

NA: Not applicable.
*Types specified in accordance with Section 8.3, as follows: Type 1 = online standard test; Type 1A = online enhanced test; Type 2 = offline standard test; Type 2A = offline enhanced test.

Shaded text = Revisions.   Δ = Text deletions and figure/table revisions.   • = Section deletions.   *N* = New material.

2023 Edition

N **Table 21.3.3.4 Medium-Voltage Ground-Fault Protection System Mechanical Servicing**

No.	Task	Circuit Breaker Trip Units or Switches with Integral Ground-Fault Protection Test Type*	Circuit Breakers or Switches with External Ground-Fault Protection Test Type*	Notes
1	Inspect bolted electrical connections	NA		2
2	Verify correct operation of the self-test panel/trip unit functions	2		2

NA: Not applicable.

*Types specified in accordance with Section 8.3, as follows: Type 1 = online standard test; Type 1A = online enhanced test; Type 2 = offline standard test; Type 2A = offline enhanced test.

N   **Chapter 22   Lighting**

N **22.1 Scope.** This chapter identifies electrical maintenance requirements for luminaires and lighting systems.

N **22.2 Frequency of Maintenance.** The periodic maintenance procedures in Section 22.3 shall be performed in accordance with the frequencies in Chapter 9, unless otherwise specified in this chapter.

N **22.3 Periodic Maintenance Procedures.**

N **22.3.1 Visual Inspections.** An inspection of the readily visible portion of the luminaire shall be conducted to check the physical condition.

N **22.3.2 Cleaning.** Luminaires shall be kept clean to prevent a buildup of contaminants that negatively affect performance, reduce life expectancy, or create a safety hazard.

N **22.3.3* Maintenance Program.** A maintenance program for any lighting system shall include the following elements:

(1) Periodic inspections
(2) Criteria for determining group or spot replacement options to maintain the required illuminance levels
(3) Repair and replacement strategy
(4) Assessment of illuminance levels

N **22.3.4 Servicing.** Servicing shall include inspections of the luminaire system for the following conditions, where applicable:

(1) Aiming or orientation
(2) Pole and pole base condition
(3) Safety chains and/or supports
(4) Socket condition and luminaire mounting hardware when replacing lamps

(5) Compatibility of replacement lamps with existing luminaire

N   **Chapter 23   Lighting Control Systems (Reserved)**

N   **Chapter 24   Wiring Devices**

N **24.1* Scope.** This chapter identifies electrical maintenance requirements for receptacles and attachment plugs, pin-and-sleeve devices, heavy-duty industrial-type plugs, cord connectors, and receptacles rated not more than 600 volts.

N **24.2 Frequency of Maintenance.** The periodic maintenance procedures specified in Section 24.3 shall be performed in accordance with the frequencies specified in Chapter 9, unless otherwise specified in this chapter.

N **24.3 Periodic Maintenance Procedures.**

N **24.3.1 Visual Inspections.** Wiring devices shall be visually inspected in accordance with Table 24.3.1.

N **24.3.2 Cleaning.** Wiring devices shall be cleaned in accordance with Table 24.3.2.

N **24.3.3 Lubrication. (Reserved)**

N **24.3.4 Mechanical Servicing.** Wiring devices shall be mechanically serviced in accordance with Table 24.3.4.

N **24.3.4.1** Cracked, bent, or broken spring doors or covers are to be replaced.

N **24.3.5 Electrical Testing.** Wiring devices shall be electrically tested in accordance with Table 24.3.5.

Table 24.3.1 Wiring Device Visual Inspections

No.	Task	Test Type*	Notes
1	Check for worn, cracked, or distorted housing	2A	Repair or replace as needed.
2	Pins or contacts are burned, bent, pitted, missing, or discolored	2A	Repair or replace as needed.
3	Securement method for flexible wiring is intact	2A	Repair or replace as needed.
4	Check for corrosion of housing, contacts, and pins	2A	Repair or replace as needed.
5	Confirm gaskets are intact	2A	Replace as needed.

*Types specified in accordance with Section 8.3, as follows: Type 1 = online standard test; Type 1A = online enhanced test; Type 2 = offline standard test; Type 2A = offline enhanced test.

Table 24.3.2 Wiring Device Cleaning

No.	Task	Plug Test Type*	Receptacle Test Type*	Notes
1	Clean current-carrying parts and housing faces of foreign material or corrosion	2A	2A	
2	Clean exterior surfaces to maintain visibility of nameplate ratings	2A	2A	

*Types specified in accordance with Section 8.3, as follows: Type 1 = online standard test; Type 1A = online enhanced test; Type 2 = offline standard test; Type 2A = offline enhanced test.

Table 24.3.4 Wiring Device Cleaning

No.	Task	Test Type*	Notes
1	Confirm secure mating of plug and receptacle components.	2	Replace components with loose contact mating.
2	Confirm cable gland nut is secure and retains cable.	2	Tighten as needed, assuring no damage to the flexible cord jacket.
3	Confirm tightness of all wiring terminals.	2	Wiring terminal discoloration is indication of possible inadequate wire securement.

*Types specified in accordance with Section 8.3, as follows: 1 = online standard test, 1A = online enhanced test, 2 = offline standard test, 2A = offline enhanced test.

Table 24.3.5 Wiring Device Electrical Servicing

No.	Task	Test Type*	Notes
1	Confirm grounding and bonding for correct installation and secure connection	2A	
2	Confirm proper polarity of contacts	1A or 2A	

*Types specified in accordance with Section 8.3, as follows: Type 1 = online standard test; Type 1A = online enhanced test; Type 2 = offline standard test; Type 2A = offline enhanced test.

Shaded text = Revisions.   △ = Text deletions and figure/table revisions.   • = Section deletions.   N = New material.

2023 Edition

N   Chapter 25   Uninterruptible Power Supplies (UPS)

N 25.1 Scope.

N 25.1.1* This chapter identifies electrical maintenance requirements for uninterruptible power supplies (UPS) rated 600 volts or less ac or dc.

N 25.1.2 This chapter does not apply to a UPS that contains no serviceable components.

N 25.2 Frequency of Maintenance.

N 25.2.1 The periodic maintenance procedures specified in Section 25.3 shall be performed in accordance with the frequencies specified in Chapter 9, unless otherwise specified in this chapter.

N 25.2.2 The special procedures specified in Section 25.4 shall be performed in accordance with the frequencies specified in Section 25.4 and the EMP.

N 25.3 Periodic Maintenance Procedures.

N 25.3.1 Visual Inspections. UPS shall be visually inspected in accordance with Table 25.3.1.

N 25.3.2 Cleaning. If contamination is present, UPS shall be cleaned in accordance with Table 25.3.2.

N 25.3.3 Lubrication. Rotary-type UPS shall be lubricated in accordance with Table 25.3.3.

N 25.3.4 Mechanical Servicing. UPS shall be mechanically serviced in accordance with Table 25.3.4.

N 25.3.5 Electrical Testing. UPS shall be electrically tested in accordance with Table 25.3.5.

N 25.4 Special Procedures.

N 25.4.1 Equipment Software Upgrades and Revisions. Equipment software upgrades and revisions shall be performed as needed.

N 25.4.2 Load Transfer and Load Testing. System tests shall be performed in accordance with the following:

(1) When warranted by special circumstances, such as repeated failure of a system to pass routine maintenance checks

(2) Periodically, where the desired degree of reliability justifies the procedure

N   Table 25.3.1 UPS Visual Inspections

No.	Task	Static Test Type*	Rotary Test Type*	Notes
1	Inspect doors and latches for fit, dents, corrosion, and missing hardware	1	1	
2	Check fans for operation	1	1	
3	Inspect wiring, bus, cables, and connections for damaged insulation, broken leads, tightness of connections, crimping, and overall general condition including corrosion	2	2	
4	Inspect capacitors for swelling and discoloration	2	NA	
5	Check visible current-carrying parts and control devices, if applicable, for signs of overheating or deterioration	2	2	
6	Inspect rectifier and inverter assembly	2	NA	Inspect for signs of overheating or deterioration.
7	Inspect static switch module	2	NA	Inspect for signs of overheating or deterioration.
8	Inspect interface, control, I/O boards, and dc capacitor boards	2	2	Inspect for signs of overheating or deterioration.
9	For individual components, refer to the appropriate chapter(s) of this standard	NA	NA	

NA: Not applicable.
*Types specified in accordance with Section 8.3, as follows: Type 1 = online standard test; Type 1A = online enhanced test; Type 2 = offline standard test; Type 2A = offline enhanced test.

Table 25.3.2 UPS Cleaning

No.	Task	Static Test Type*	Rotary Test Type*	Notes
1	Replace the air filters and verify the vents are clear	2	2	
2	Vacuum enclosure	2	2	
3	Clean exposed switch contacts with a multipurpose precision lubricant before lubricating	2	2	
4	Wipe contact surfaces with a lint-free cleaning cloth	2	2	
5	Wipe contact surfaces with a noncorrosive cleaning agent	2	2	
6	Clean insulators	2	NA	

NA: Not applicable.
*Types specified in accordance with Section 8.3, as follows: Type 1 = online standard test; Type 1A = online enhanced test; Type 2 = offline standard test; Type 2A = offline enhanced test.

Table 25.3.3 UPS Lubrication

No.	Task	Static Test Type*	Rotary Test Type*	Notes
1	Lubricate rotating equipment	NA	2	

NA: Not applicable.
*Types specified in accordance with Section 8.3, as follows: Type 1 = online standard test; Type 1A = online enhanced test; Type 2 = offline standard test; Type 2A = offline enhanced test.

Table 25.3.4 UPS Mechanical Servicing

No.	Task	Static Test Type*	Rotary Test Type*	Notes
1	Verify operation and alignment of mechanical safety interlocks	2	2	
2	Check electrical hardware connections	2	2	
3	Perform mechanical servicing for system circuit breakers	2	2	
4	Transfer systems	2	2	
5	For individual components, refer to the appropriate chapter(s) of this standard	NA	NA	

NA: Not applicable.
*Types specified in accordance with Section 8.3, as follows: Type 1 = online standard test; Type 1A = online enhanced test; Type 2 = offline standard test; Type 2A = offline enhanced test.

Shaded text = Revisions.   Δ = Text deletions and figure/table revisions.   • = Section deletions.   *N* = New material.

2023 Edition

N Table 25.3.5 UPS Electrical Tests

No.	Task	Static Test Type*	Rotary Test Type*	Notes
1	Perform infrared thermography of lug terminals	1	1	Conduct on annual basis.
2	Measure the neutral output current during peak loads	1A	1A	Conduct every 3 months or when new equipment is added to the system
3	Record all operating parameters, such as frequency, voltage, and current, at the bypass switch, input, output, batteries, and modules, where applicable	1	1	
4	Test static transfer from normal to bypass and back to normal	1	1	
5	Electrical interlock systems, alarms, and indicator circuits	2	2	
6	Perform operational test on all alarms and emergency shutdowns, where applicable	2	2	
7	For individual components, refer to the appropriate chapter(s) of this standard	NA	NA	

NA: Not applicable.
*Types specified in accordance with Section 8.3, as follows: Type 1 = online standard test; Type 1A = online enhanced test; Type 2 = offline standard test; Type 2A = offline enhanced test.

N 25.4.2.1 System Test Conditions.

N 25.4.2.1.1 The UPS shall be placed under load using a load bank during the tests described in 25.4.2.

N 25.4.2.1.2 If the UPS has batteries, the batteries shall be fully charged prior to the tests described in 25.4.2.

N 25.4.2.1.3 While the tests described in 25.4.2 are conducted, critical loads shall be placed on isolation bypass, if available, or connected to another source.

N 25.4.2.1.4 Manual and automatic load transfers from UPS to bypass shall be tested.

N 25.4.2.1.5 Each module shall be individually load-tested to verify that it is functioning prior to parallel load testing.

N 25.4.2.1.6 Simultaneous input and output readings of voltage, current, and frequency shall be recorded.

N 25.4.2.1.7 The external power source shall be removed and reapplied to verify output stability.

N 25.4.2.1.8 Voltage and frequency measurements of UPS operation during load testing shall be performed.

N 25.4.2.1.9 The results of the tests described in 25.4.2 shall be recorded.

N 25.4.2.2 Output Stability.

N 25.4.2.2.1* The load shall be adjusted in steps to determine the performance of the UPS when significant load changes occur.

N 25.4.2.2.2 The voltage regulation and frequency stability shall be within the manufacturer's specifications.

N 25.4.2.2.3 Low Battery Voltage Shutdown.

N 25.4.2.2.3.1 Where applicable, UPS ac input power shall be removed while the system is supplying 100 percent power to a load bank.

N 25.4.2.2.3.2 The elapsed time until low battery voltage shutdown occurs shall be recorded and compared with specifications.

N 25.4.2.2.3.3 Voltage, current, and frequency shall be recorded during tests.

N 25.4.2.2.3.4 Upon restoration of UPS input power, the battery shall be verified as recharging properly.

N   Chapter 26 Electronic Equipment (Reserved)

Chapter 27 Rotating Equipment

N 27.1* Scope. This chapter identifies electrical maintenance requirements for rotating equipment (machines) and their ancillary devices.

N 27.2 Frequency of Maintenance. The periodic maintenance procedures in Section 27.3 shall be performed in accordance with the frequencies in Chapter 9, unless otherwise specified in this chapter.

N 27.3 Periodic Maintenance Procedures.

N 27.3.1* Visual Inspections. Rotating equipment shall be visually inspected in accordance with Table 27.3.1.

N 27.3.2* Cleaning.

N 27.3.2.1 Electrical equipment surfaces, enclosures, and insulating materials shall be kept clean to prevent a buildup of contaminants that negatively affect performance, reduce life expectancy, or create a safety hazard.

N 27.3.2.2* After cleaning, apparatus shall be dried before being placed in operation if tests indicate that the insulation resistance is below the recommended level.

N 27.3.3* Lubrication.

N 27.3.3.1 Bearings, couplings, and auxiliary devices shall be lubricated as needed.

N 27.3.3.2 Where equipped, lubrication systems shall be maintained in accordance with the manufacturer's instructions.

N 27.3.4* Mechanical Servicing. Rotating equipment shall be mechanically serviced in accordance with Table 27.3.4.

N 27.3.5* Electrical Testing. Rotating equipment shall be electrically tested in accordance with Table 27.3.5.

N 27.3.6* Special. (Reserved)

Table 27.3.1 Rotating Equipment Visual Inspections

| | | Test Type* | | | | | |
| | | Low-Voltage Machines | | | Medium-Voltage Machines | | |
No.	Task	≤200 hp	>200 hp	dc Machines	Induction	Synchronous	Notes
1	Application	1 or 2	1 or 2	1 or 2	1 or 2	1 or 2	Ensure the machinery is installed in accordance with the manufacturer's listing and labeling and applicable codes/standards.
2	Physical condition	1 or 2	1 or 2	1 or 2	1 or 2	1 or 2	
3	Indicating device status	1 or 2	1 or 2	1 or 2	1 or 2	1 or 2	
4	Labeling	1 or 2	1 or 2	1 or 2	1 or 2	1 or 2	
5	Grounding/bonding	1 or 2	1 or 2	1 or 2	1 or 2	1 or 2	
6	Machinery alignment	1 or 2	1 or 2	1 or 2	1 or 2	1 or 2	Intended where signs of misalignment exist.

NA: Not applicable.

*Types specified in accordance with Section 8.3, as follows: Type 1 = online standard test; Type 1A = online enhanced test; Type 2 = offline standard test; Type 2A = offline enhanced test.

Table 27.3.4 Mechanical Servicing

| | | Test Type* | | | | | |
| | | Low-Voltage Machines | | | Medium-Voltage Machines | | |
No.	Task	<=200 hp	>200 hp	dc Machines	Induction	Synchronous	Notes
1	Integrity of accessible bolted connections	2	2	2	2	2	
2	Cooling system operation, as applicable	2	2	2	2	2	
3	Mechanical operation	2	2	2	2	2	
4	Machine guards and assemblies	2	2	2	2	2	

NA: Not applicable.

*Types specified in accordance with Section 8.3, as follows: Type 1 = online standard test; Type 1A = online enhanced test; Type 2 = offline standard test; Type 2A = offline enhanced test.

Shaded text = Revisions.   △ = Text deletions and figure/table revisions.   • = Section deletions.   N = New material.

2023 Edition

N Table 27.3.5 Rotating Equipment Electrical Tests

No.	Task	Low-Voltage Machines			Medium-Voltage Machines		Notes
		≤200 hp Test Type*	>200 hp Test Type*	dc Machines Test Type*	Induction Test Type*	Synchronous Test Type*	
1	Bolted connection resistance	2A	2A	2A	2	2	
2	Stator/armature winding DAR	2A	2A	2A	2	2	ac stator or dc armature
3	Wound rotor/field winding DAR	2A	2A	2A	2	2	ac wound rotor, synchronous dc rotor, dc fields
4	Stator/armature winding polarization index (PI)	2A	2A	2A	2	2	
5	Wound rotor/field winding PI	2A	2A	2A	2A	NA	
6	Stator winding dc dielectric withstand (overpotential)	2A	2A	2A	2A	2A	
7	Wound rotor/field winding dc dielectric withstand (overpotential)	2A	2A	2A	2A	2A	
8	Stator/armature winding resistance	2A	2A	2A	2	2	
9	Wound rotor/field winding resistance	2A	2A	2A	2	2	
10	Stator winding insulation power factor	NA	NA	NA	2A	2A	Insulation power factor/dissipation factor
11	Stator winding insulation power factor tip-up	NA	NA	NA	2A	2A	Insulation power factor/dissipation factor
12	Stator winding surge comparison	2A	2A	2A	2A	2A	
13	Insulated bearing insulation resistance	2A	2A	2A	2	2	
14	Temperature detection device	2A	2A	2A	2	2	
15	Machine space heater	2	2	2	2	2	
16	Vibration analysis	1A	1A	1A	1A	1A	
17	Current signature analysis	1A	1A	1A	1A	1A	
18	Partial discharge	NA	NA	NA	1A	1A	
19	Surge protection device	2A	2A	NA	2	2	
20	Motor starter	2	2	2	2	2	
21	Current transformers	2A	2A	NA	2	2	
22	Potential transformers	2A	2A	NA	2	2	

NA: Not applicable.
*Types specified in accordance with Section 8.3, as follows: Type 1 = online standard test; Type 1A = online enhanced test; Type 2 = offline standard test; Type 2A = offline enhanced test.

Shaded text = Revisions. ∆ = Text deletions and figure/table revisions. • = Section deletions. N = New material

Chapter 28 Motor Control Equipment

28.1 Scope.

28.1.1 This chapter identifies electrical maintenance requirements for low-voltage single- and three-phase ac and dc motor control equipment and medium-voltage single- and three-phase motor control equipment.

28.2 Frequency of Maintenance. The periodic maintenance procedures in Section 28.3 shall be performed in accordance with the frequencies in Chapter 9, unless otherwise specified in this chapter.

28.3 Periodic Maintenance Procedures.

28.3.1 Visual Inspections. Motor control equipment shall be visually inspected in accordance with Table 28.3.1.

N **28.3.2 Cleaning.** Bus, cables, terminals or terminations, electrical equipment surfaces, enclosures, and insulating materials shall be cleaned to prevent a buildup of contaminants that negatively affect performance, reduce life expectancy, or create a hazard.

N **28.3.3 Lubrication.** Moving and sliding surfaces shall be lubricated in accordance with Table 28.3.3.

N **28.3.4 Mechanical Servicing.** Motor control equipment shall be mechanically serviced in accordance with Table 28.3.4.

N **28.3.5 Electrical Testing.** Motor control equipment shall be electrically tested in accordance with Table 28.3.5.

N **28.3.6 Special. (Reserved)**

Table 28.3.1 Motor Control Equipment Visual Inspections

No.	Task	Low-Voltage Test Type*	Medium-Voltage Test Type*	Notes
1	Inspect physical and mechanical condition	1 or 2	1 or 2	
2	Inspect anchorage and grounding	1 or 2	1 or 2	
3	Physical integrity of contactors	1	1	
4	Verify circuit breakers, fuses, and overload elements are the correct sizes and types and correspond to the drawings	2	2	EMP determines when these inspections can be done energized.
5	Verify instrument transformer ratios are correct	2	2	
6	Inspect insulators for damage, tracking, or contaminated surfaces	2	2	
7	Verify filters are clean and in place	2	2	
8	Ensure maintenance devices are available for servicing	NA	1	
9	Verify switch phase barriers are in place	2	2	
10	Verify fuse expulsion-limiting devices are in place	NA	2	
11	For individual components and exposed conductors, refer to the appropriate chapter(s) of this standard	NA	NA	

NA: Not applicable.
*Types specified in accordance with Section 8.3, as follows: Type 1 = online standard test; Type 1A = online enhanced test; Type 2 = offline standard test; Type 2A = offline enhanced test.

N **Table 28.3.3 Moving and Sliding Surfaces Lubrication**

No.	Task	Test Type*		Notes
		1000 Volts or Less	Greater than 1000 Volts	
1	Apply a thin coating of conductive lubricant to exposed contacts as specified by the manufacturer	2	2	
2	Apply nonconductive lubricant as needed to mechanism parts as specified by the manufacturer	2	2	
3	Apply conductive lubricant to pivot points, as well as moving and sliding surfaces, as specified by the manufacturer	2	2	

NA: Not applicable.
*Types specified in accordance with Section 8.3, as follows: Type 1 = online standard test; Type 1A = online enhanced test; Type 2 = offline standard test; Type 2A = offline enhanced test.

N **Table 28.3.4 Motor Control Equipment Mechanical Servicing**

No.	Task	Test Type*					Notes
		Low-Voltage Machines			Medium-Voltage Machines		
		≤200 hp	>200 hp	dc Machines	Induction	Synchronous	
1	Integrity of accessible bolted connections	2	2	2	2	2	
2	Cooling system operation, as applicable	2	2	2	2	2	
3	Mechanical operation	2	2	2	2	2	
4	Machine guards and assemblies	2	2	2	2	2	

NA: Not applicable.
*Types specified in accordance with Section 8.3, as follows: Type 1 = online standard test; Type 1A = online enhanced test; Type 2 = offline standard test; Type 2A = offline enhanced test.

N **Table 28.3.5 Motor Control Equipment Electrical Tests**

No.	Task	Low-Voltage Test Type*	Medium-Voltage Test Type*	Notes
1	Inspect electrical connections for high resistance	1 or 2	1 or 2	See Section 7.2.
2	Measure insulation resistance of electrical power circuits	2	2	
3	Measure insulation resistance across each open starter pole	2	2	
4	Measure insulation resistance of control wiring with respect to ground	2A	2A	
5	Test motor protection devices	2	2	
6	Perform control system operational tests	1A	1A	Include automatic throw-overs, paralleling controls, interlock and safety systems, or any other operational or maintenance-related control.
7	Perform vacuum bottle integrity test or a magnetron atmospheric condition (MAC) test on vacuum bottles	NA	2	
8	Perform dielectric withstand test	2A	2A	
9	Measure contact resistance	2		
10	For individual components, refer to the appropriate chapter(s) of this standard	NA	NA	

NA: Not applicable.
*Types specified in accordance with Section 8.3, as follows: Type 1 = online standard test; Type 1A = online enhanced test; Type 2 = offline standard test; Type 2A = offline enhanced test.

N **Chapter 29   Portable Electrical Tools and Equipment**

N **29.1 Scope.**

N **29.1.1*** This chapter identifies electrical maintenance requirements for portable electrical tools and equipment, both cord and plug connected and temporarily hard-wired.

N **29.1.2** This chapter does not apply to mobile equipment.

N **29.2 Frequency of Maintenance.** The periodic maintenance procedures in Section 29.3 shall be performed in accordance with the frequencies in Chapter 9, unless otherwise specified in this chapter.

N **29.3 Periodic Maintenance Procedures.**

N **29.3.1 Visual Inspection.**

N **29.3.1.1*** Portable electrical tools and equipment shall be visually inspected before each use for the following conditions:

(1) Pinched, crushed, nicked, or frayed cord jacket
(2) Damaged plug or missing pins
(3) Damage to grounding means, such as terminals, straps, or pins
(4) Signs of loosening, fraying, or overheating of the plug, cord, or tool
(5) External casing defects, such as cracks, damaged or loose components, or missing screws
(6) Damaged or missing guards
(7) Damaged wheels or blades
(8) Signs of leaking fluids
(9) Missing cover plates
(10) Loose or frayed conductors at termination points
(11) Damaged strain relief cord connectors

N **29.3.1.2** Portable equipment and flexible cord sets (extension cords) that remain connected once they are put in place and are not exposed to damage shall not be required to be visually inspected until they are relocated.

N **29.3.2 Cleaning.** Portable electrical tools and equipment shall be kept free of debris or other substances that could damage components or prevent heat dissipation.

N **29.3.3 Lubrication.**

N **29.3.3.1** Manufacturer's instructions shall be followed when lubricating components of portable electrical tools and equipment, except as permitted in 29.3.3.2.

N **29.3.3.2** If manufacturer's instructions are not available, lubrication of portable electrical equipment shall be conducted in accordance with one of the following:

(1) A procedure specified by the EMP
(2) Applicable industry standards

N **29.3.4 Mechanical Servicing.** Mechanical servicing of portable electrical tools and equipment shall be carried out according to the manufacturer's instructions.

Shaded text = Revisions.   Δ = Text deletions and figure/table revisions.   • = Section deletions.   N = New material.

2023 Edition

N **29.3.5* Electrical Testing.** When a GFCI or an assured equipment grounding conductor program is not implemented, electrical testing of portable electrical tools and equipment shall be conducted to verify the following, at a minimum:

(1) Equipment grounding from the tool or equipment to the plug ground pin
(2) Insulation resistance
(3) Correct polarity

N **29.3.6 Special. (Reserved)**

N   **Chapter 30   Photovoltaic Systems**

N **30.1* Scope.** This chapter identifies electrical maintenance requirements for solar photovoltaic (PV) systems and its associated equipment.

N **30.2 Frequency of Maintenance.**

N **30.2.1*** The periodic maintenance procedures in Section 30.4 shall be performed in accordance with the frequencies in Chapter 9, unless otherwise specified in this chapter.

N **30.2.2*** The EMP shall identify events that trigger more frequent inspections or maintenance activities.

N **30.3 Documentation and Labeling.**

N **30.3.1*** The equipment owner shall ensure that supporting documentation, including the following, is available:

(1) System designer/installer, with installation and commissioning dates
(2) Emergency contacts for system owner
(3) Specifications

(4) Electrical schematics and as-built drawings
(5) Signage, markings, and labels
(6) Mechanical drawings
(7) Commissioning manual, test plan, and appropriate test results
(8) Operations and maintenance manuals
(9) Materials list of expendable maintenance items, such as filters and fuses

N **30.3.2*** A label that identifies the highest internal dc voltage shall be affixed to combiners, disconnects, and other enclosures with dc voltage.

N **30.4 Periodic Maintenance Procedures.**

N **30.4.1* Visual Inspections.** PV systems and their associated equipment shall be visually inspected in accordance with Table 30.4.1.

N **30.4.2* Cleaning.** The EMP shall determine when and if the installed system requires cleaning.

N **30.4.3 Lubrication. (Reserved)**

N **30.4.4 Mechanical Servicing.** PV systems and their associated equipment shall be mechanically serviced in accordance with Table 30.4.4.

N **30.4.5* Electrical Testing.** PV systems and their associated equipment shall be electrically tested in accordance with Table 30.4.5.

N **30.4.6 Special. (Reserved)**

N **Table 30.4.1 PV System Visual Inspections**

No.	Task	Test Type*	Notes
1	Front of PV modules	1 or 2	Damage, debris, soiling, discoloration, cracks, and broken glass.
2	Backs of PV modules	1 or 2	Damage, debris, discoloration, cracks, and tears.
3	No unintentional shading of the array	1 or 2	Foliage, weeds, trees, or structures.
4	Conductors, connectors, and wiring harnesses are secured	1 or 2	Damaged insulation, melted plastic, broken or missing wiring and raceway supports.
5	Signage, markings, and labels	1 or 2	Arc flash, shock, mechanical hazards, means of isolation location.
6	String fuses are sized in accordance with system design	1A or 2A	Array fires can be caused by improperly sized string fuses. Replacement fuses should be matched to the design criteria.
7	Ensure all electrical equipment enclosures, raceways, structures, and mechanical apparatus are secured	1 or 2	Loose connections or connectors, broken raceways, and supports, missing hardware.
8	Electrical terminations, module interconnections	1	Damage, corrosion, discoloration.
9	Tracking and mechanical systems (e.g., gearbox, drivetrain)	1 or 2	Leaking fluids, bent, broken or damaged drivetrains, array alignment.
10	Grounding and bonding	1 or 2	Secure attachment, missing, damaged or broken connections, protection from physical damage.
11	Battery cells and jumpers	1 or 2	Leaking, bulging, corrosion, fluid levels, damage, melted plastic, discoloration.
12	Roof or wall penetrations	1 or 2	Moisture, dust, and dirt ingress.
13	Site	1 or 2	Storm water runoff channels clear of debris, erosion around piers and pads, vegetation management, animal infestation/nesting/burrowing.

*Types specified in accordance with Section 8.3, as follows: Type 1 = online standard test; Type 1A = online enhanced test; Type 2 = offline standard test; Type 2A = offline enhanced test.

N **Table 30.4.4 PV System Mechanical Servicing**

No.	Task	Test Type*	Notes
1	Tracking and mechanical systems (e.g., gearbox, drivetrain)	1 or 2	Torque of bolted mechanical systems, mechanical alignment.

*Types specified in accordance with Section 8.3, as follows: Type 1 = online standard test; Type 1A = online enhanced test; Type 2 = offline standard test; Type 2A = offline enhanced test.

Shaded text = Revisions.   Δ = Text deletions and figure/table revisions.   • = Section deletions.   *N* = New material.

2023 Edition

N Table 30.4.5 PV System Electrical Tests

No.	Task	Test Type*	Notes
1	Electrical terminations	1 or 2	Any or all the following could be utilized: infrared thermography, contact resistance, millivolt drop, calibrated torque device.
2	Grounding and bonding	1 or 2	Any or all the following could be utilized: infrared thermography, contact resistance, fall of potential, point to point, current reading, calibrated torque device.
3	PV strings and modules	1 or 2	IV curve trace, insulation resistance, operating voltage, and current readings, electroluminescence imaging, infrared thermography.
4	Module interconnections	1	Infrared thermography.

*Types specified in accordance with Section 8.3, as follows: Type 1 = online standard test; Type 1A = online enhanced test; Type 2 = offline standard test; Type 2A = offline enhanced test.

N   **Chapter 31   Wind Power Electric Systems and Associated Equipment**

N 31.1 Scope. This chapter identifies electrical maintenance requirements for wind power electric systems and associated equipment.

N 31.2 Frequency of Maintenance. The periodic maintenance procedures in Section 31.3 shall be performed in accordance with the frequencies in Chapter 9, unless otherwise specified in this chapter.

N 31.3 Periodic Maintenance Procedures.

N 31.3.1* Visual Inspection and Mechanical Testing. Wind power electric systems and associated equipment shall be visu-ally inspected and mechanically tested in accordance with Table 31.3.1.

N 31.3.2 Cleaning. (Reserved)

N 31.3.3 Lubrication. (Reserved)

N 31.3.4 Mechanical Servicing. (Reserved)

N 31.3.5 Electrical Testing. Wind power electric systems and associated equipment shall be electrically tested in accordance with Table 31.3.5.

N 31.3.6 Special. (Reserved)

N Table 31.3.1 Wind Power Electric Systems and Associated Equipment Visual Inspections and Mechanical Tests

No.	Task	Test Type*	Notes
1	Check towers and foundations for:		
	Grounding and bonding	1 or 2	
	Functional navigational warning lights	1 or 2	
	Weather measurement devices	1 or 2	
	Lightning protection	1 or 2	
2	Check yaw systems for damage, wear, and signs of overheating	1 or 2	
3	Check pitch systems for damage, wear, and signs of overheating	1 or 2	
4	Check cables, terminations, and cable support systems for:		
	Structural integrity	1 or 2	
	Signs of vibration damage or abrasion	1 or 2	
	Overheating	1 or 2	
5	In-tower emergency lighting is functioning	1	
6	For other individual components, refer to the appropriate chapter(s) of this standard or manufacturer's instructions	NA	

NA: Not applicable.

*Types specified in accordance with Section 8.3, as follows: Type 1 = online standard test; Type 1A = online enhanced test; Type 2 = offline standard test; Type 2A = offline enhanced test.

Shaded text = Revisions.   **Δ** = Text deletions and figure/table revisions.   • = Section deletions.   **N** = New material.

Table 31.3.5 Wind Power Electric Systems and Associated Equipment Electrical Tests

No.	Task	Test Type*	Notes
1	Check grounding electrode system resistance	1 or 2	
2	Check emergency stops, safety shutdowns, controls, and warning indicators are functional	1 or 2	
3	Verify supervisory control and data acquisition (SCADA) systems are functional	1 or 2	
4	Check functionality of blade heat trace systems, if installed	1 or 2	
5	For other individual components, refer to the appropriate chapter(s) of this standard or manufacturer's instructions	NA	

NA: Not applicable.
*Types specified in accordance with Section 8.3, as follows: Type 1 = online standard test; Type 1A = online enhanced test; Type 2 = offline standard test; Type 2A = offline enhanced test.

Chapter 32   Battery Energy Storage Systems

32.1 Scope.

32.1.1 This chapter identifies electrical maintenance requirements and applies to all battery energy storage systems (ESS) having a capacity greater than 3.6 MJ (1 kWh) that could be stand-alone or interactive with other electric power production sources. These systems are primarily intended to store and provide energy during normal operating conditions.

32.1.2* This chapter does not apply to the following:

(1) Stationary standby batteries that meet the requirements of Chapter 36 and are comprised of lead-acid or nickel-cadmium (NiCd) cells
(2) Uninterruptible power supplies (UPS)
(3) Standby battery systems for substation or switchgear control power
(4) Batteries for telecommunications backup power

32.2 Frequency of Maintenance. The periodic maintenance procedures in Section 32.4 shall be performed in accordance with the frequencies in Chapter 9, unless otherwise specified in Table 32.2.

32.3 Documentation. An installed ESS shall include supporting documentation to include the following:

(1) System designer and installer with installation and commissioning dates

(2) Emergency contacts for system owner
(3) Specifications
(4) Electrical schematics and as-built drawings
(5) Signage, markings, and labels
(6) Mechanical drawings
(7) Commissioning manual, test plan, and appropriate test results
(8) Operations and maintenance manuals
(9) Materials list of expendable maintenance items, such as filters and fuses

N 32.4 Periodic Maintenance Procedures.

N 32.4.1 Visual Inspections. ESS shall be visually inspected in accordance with Table 32.4.1.

N 32.4.2 Cleaning. Electrical equipment surfaces, enclosures, insulating materials, terminals, or terminations shall be kept in a clean and contaminant-free state.

N 32.4.3 Lubrication. (Reserved)

N 32.4.4 Mechanical Servicing. The ventilation system shall be serviced to ensure that airflow is maintained in accordance with the design requirements.

N 32.4.5 Electrical Testing. Energy storage systems shall be electrically tested in accordance with Table 32.4.5.

N 32.4.6 Special. (Reserved)

Table 32.2 Maintenance Intervals

Test to be Performed	Equipment Condition Assessment			Notes
	Condition 1	Condition 2	Condition 3	
Visual	12 months	12 months	1 month	When batteries are accessible, see Section 36.2 for specific battery technology and maintenance test intervals.
Connection resistances	12 months	12 months	1 month	
Battery management system data and associated alarms	12 months	12 months	1 month	
Battery performance testing	36 months	36 months	12 months	

N **Table 32.4.1 Battery ESS Visual Inspections**

No.	Task	Test Type*	Notes
1	Physical condition, including operating environment	1 or 2	Damage or deterioration, supports or restraints, bending radius, excessive tension, signs of overheating.
2	Correct labeling or identification	1 or 2	Phasing, cable ID, multiple sources, hazard, or other warning labels.
3	Grounding/bonding	1 or 2	Damage, missing or loose terminations, clearance from energized parts, protection from physical damage.
4	Batteries	1 or 2	Damage, leaking, swelling, discolored or melted plastic, terminal corrosion, electrolyte level, restraint systems. See Chapter 36 for stationary standby batteries.
5	Cables	1 or 2	Damage, deterioration, supports, bending radius, excessive tension, discoloration, or evidence of overheating.
6	Fire alarm notification, detection, and suppression systems	1 or 2	Damaged heads, physical obstruction to spray, leaking, corrosion, suppression agent is charged.
7	Raceway/cable tray	1 or 2	Damage or deterioration, cable jacket abrasion or wear when exposed, continuity, tight joints, missing or loose bonding jumpers, corrosion.
8	Barriers, guards, and assemblies	1 or 2	Damage or signs of deterioration, arcing, tracking, supports, and mounting hardware.

*Types specified in accordance with Section 8.3, as follows: Type 1 = online standard test; Type 1A = online enhanced test; Type 2 = offline standard test; Type 2A = offline enhanced test.

N **Table 32.4.5 Battery ESS Electrical Tests**

No.	Task	Test Type*	Notes
1	Infrared thermography or equivalent thermal inspection	1 or 2	Overall battery case(s) and terminations; should be performed under load.
2	Airborne ultrasonic acoustic emissions	1A	
3	Insulation resistance	2	Cables/conductors.
4	Bolted connection resistance	1 or 2	Includes intercell resistance, when accessible.
5	Battery performance test	2	
6	Review of battery management system data and associated alarms	1 or 2	

*Types specified in accordance with Section 8.3, as follows: Type 1 = online standard test; Type 1A = online enhanced test; Type 2 = offline standard test; Type 2A = offline enhanced test.

Shaded text = Revisions.　　△ = Text deletions and figure/table revisions.　　• = Section deletions.　　N = New material.

Chapter 33 Electric Vehicle Power Transfer Systems and Associated Equipment

33.1 Scope. This chapter identifies electrical maintenance requirements for electric vehicle power transfer systems and associated equipment.

33.2 Frequency of Maintenance. The periodic maintenance procedures in Section 33.4 shall be performed in accordance with the frequencies in Chapter 9, unless otherwise specified in this chapter.

33.3 Documentation.

33.3.1 The following electric vehicle transfer power system markings shall be maintained:

(1) Emergency contacts for system owner
(2) Signage, markings, and labels
(3) Rating or adjusted rating
(4) Identification that load management is used, if applicable

33.3.2 The following supporting documentation shall be available for maintenance:

(1) Mechanical drawings (mounting and structural)
(2) Operations and maintenance manuals

(3) Electrical schematics and drawings

***N* 33.4 Periodic Maintenance Procedures.**

***N* 33.4.1 Visual Inspection.**

***N* 33.4.1.1** Electric vehicle power transfer system equipment shall be visually inspected in accordance with Table 33.4.1.1.

***N* 33.4.1.2** The following inspections shall be performed annually:

(1) The cord and cord connector shall be inspected to verify that the strain relief is intact, stress is not placed on the cord terminations, and the pins are not damaged.
(2) The equipment mounting shall be inspected to ensure the integrity of the mounting means.
(3) The physical protection for the equipment shall be inspected to ensure its integrity.

***N* 33.4.2 Cleaning. (Reserved)**

***N* 33.4.3 Mechanical Servicing. (Reserved)**

***N* 33.4.4 Electrical Testing. (Reserved)**

Table 33.4.1.1 Electric Vehicle Power Transfer System Equipment Visual Inspections

No.	Task	Test Type*	Notes
1	Inspect doors and latches for fit, dents, corrosion, and missing hardware	1 or 2	Damage or deterioration, supports or restraints.
2	Inspect wiring, bus, and connections for damaged insulation, broken leads, tightness of connections, crimping, and overall general condition including corrosion	1 or 2	Excessive tension, signs of overheating, multiple sources, hazard, or other warning labels.
3	Inspect grounding/bonding	1 or 2	Damage, missing or loose terminations, clearance from energized parts, protection from physical damage.
4	Inspect cables	1 or 2	Damage, deterioration, supports, bending radius, excessive tension, cable ID, discoloration, cable jacket abrasion or wear when exposed, or evidence of overheating.
5	Inspect raceway/cable tray	1 or 2	Damage or deterioration, cable jacket abrasion or wear when exposed, continuity, tight joints, missing or loose bonding jumpers, corrosion.
6	Inspect barriers, guards, and assemblies	1 or 2	Damage or signs of deterioration, arcing, tracking, supports and mounting hardware.

*Types specified in accordance with Section 8.3, as follows: Type 1 = online standard test; Type 1A = online enhanced test; Type 2 = offline standard test; Type 2A = offline enhanced test.

Shaded text = Revisions. Δ = Text deletions and figure/table revisions. • = Section deletions. *N* = New material.

2023 Edition

N Chapter 34 Public Pools, Fountains, and Similar Installations

N 34.1 Scope.

N 34.1.1 This chapter identifies electrical maintenance requirements for the electrical maintenance and inspection of permanently installed public pools, fountains, and similar installations.

N 34.1.2 This chapter does not apply to pools, fountains, and similar installations located at one- and two-family dwellings, storable pools, storable spas, storable hot tubs, pools and tubs for therapeutic use, and hydromassage bathtubs.

N 34.2 Frequency of Maintenance. The periodic maintenance procedures in Section 34.3 shall be performed in accordance with the frequencies in Chapter 9, unless otherwise specified in this chapter.

N 34.3 Periodic Maintenance Procedures.

N 34.3.1* Visual Inspections. Public pools, fountains, and similar installations shall be visually inspected in accordance with Table 34.3.1.

N 34.3.2 Mechanical Inspections. Public pools, fountains, and similar installations shall be mechanically inspected in accordance with Table 34.3.2.

N 34.3.2.1 Luminaires with a discolored lens or evidencing water intrusion shall be replaced.

N 34.3.2.2* Luminaires with cords exhibiting physical damage, repair, or splices or that are an inconsistent type for the luminaire shall be replaced.

N 34.3.2.3* Luminaires or niches with incorrect, missing, or damaged attachment screws or sockets shall be repaired or replaced.

N 34.3.2.4 Insulating (nonconducting) wedges or similar appliances shall be replaced with conducting wedges or similar appliances.

N 34.3.3 Electrical Testing. Public pools, fountains, and similar installations shall be electrically tested in accordance with Table 34.3.3.

N Table 34.3.1 Public Pools, Fountains, and Similar Installation Visual Inspections

No.	Task	Test Type*	Notes
1	Correct labeling or identification	1 or 2	Controls, emergency controls, shutoff indications, schematics, or other information that requires public or operating personnel access.
2	Physical condition of equipment, including corrosion and deterioration	1 or 2	Metal enclosures and other metal parts, including panel connections and busbars.
3	Physical condition of connections	1 or 2	Readily accessible bonding and grounding connections, for corrosion, electrical equipment associated with the pool.
4	Corrosive environment inspection	1 or 2	Investigate areas that exhibit excessive corrosion for corrosive gas, liquid leaks, and ventilation.
5	Electric motor labeling	1 or 2	
6	Overhead conductor clearance	2	

*Types specified in accordance with Section 8.3, as follows: Type 1 = online standard test; Type 1A = online enhanced test; Type 2 = offline standard test; Type 2A = offline enhanced test.

N Table 34.3.2 Public Pools, Fountains, and Similar Installation Mechanical Inspections

No.	Task	Test Type*	Notes
1	Verify operation	1 or 2	Verify accessible means for shutting off the suction and discharge piping for electrically operated pumps.
2	Wet niche pool luminaires	2	Inspect for water intrusion, damaged attachment screws or sockets, insulating wedges or similar appliances, and visible cord damage and/or modification.
3	Operating pressures	1	Verify operating pressures after operating for minimum of 15 minutes.

*Types specified in accordance with Section 8.3, as follows: Type 1 = online standard test; Type 1A = online enhanced test; Type 2 = offline standard test; Type 2A = offline enhanced test.

Shaded text = Revisions.　Δ = Text deletions and figure/table revisions.　• = Section deletions.　*N* = New material.

Table 34.3.3 Public Pools, Fountains, and Similar Installation Electrical Tests

No.	Task	GFCI Components Test Type*	Electric Motors and Valves Test Type*	System Grounding and Bonding Test Type*	Notes
1	Test electrically operated valves	NA	1	NA	Test for correct operation.
2	For individual components, refer to the appropriate chapter(s) of this standard.	NA	NA	NA	

NA: Not applicable.

Types specified in accordance with Section 8.3, as follows: Type 1 = online standard test; Type 1A = online enhanced test; Type 2 = offline standard test; Type 2A = offline enhanced test.

Chapter 35 Protective Relays

35.1 Scope. This chapter identifies electrical maintenance requirements for electromechanical, solid-state, and microprocessor-based relays used to protect and control power system apparatus.

35.2 Frequency of Maintenance. The periodic maintenance procedures specified in Section 35.3 shall be performed in accordance with the frequencies specified in Chapter 9, unless otherwise specified in this chapter.

35.3 Periodic Maintenance Procedures.

35.3.1 Visual Inspections. Protective relays shall be visually inspected in accordance with Table 35.3.1.

N 35.3.2 Cleaning. If contamination is present, protective relays shall be cleaned in accordance with Table 35.3.2.

N 35.3.3 Lubrication. (Reserved)

N 35.3.4 Mechanical Servicing. Protective relays shall be mechanically serviced in accordance with Table 35.3.4.

N 35.3.5 Electrical Testing. Protective relays shall be electrically tested in accordance with Table 35.3.5.

N 35.3.6 Special. (Reserved)

Table 35.3.1 Protective Relay Visual Inspections

No.	Task	Electromechanical Test Type*	Solid-State Test Type*	Microprocessor Test Type*	Notes
1	Inspect case and windows for cracks and proper seal	2	2	2	
2	Inspect current transformer shorting blocks and voltage disconnects	2	2	2	
3	Check for proper operation of LEDs, targets, and visual displays	2	2	2	
4	Inspect wiring and connections for damaged insulation, broken leads, tightness of connections, proper crimping, and overall general condition including corrosion	2	2	2	
5	Inspect clearances, mechanical freedom, and condition of contacts and control springs	2	NA	NA	
6	Inspect contact bearing clearances and freedom of movement	2	NA	NA	
7	Check that settings are in accordance with coordination study	2	2	2	
8	Download or document events, oscillographs, and maintenance and statistical data	NA	NA	2A	

NA: Not applicable.

Types specified in accordance with Section 8.3, as follows: Type 1 = online standard test; Type 1A = online enhanced test; Type 2 = offline standard test; Type 2A = offline enhanced test.

N Table 35.3.2 Protective Relay Cleaning

No.	Task	Electromechanical Test Type*	Solid-State Test Type*	Microprocessor Test Type*	Notes
1	Clean the relay case and cover	2	2	2	
2	Clean relay contacts, disks, and magnets	2	NA	NA	
3	Burnish burned or pitted contacts	2	NA	NA	

NA: Not applicable.

*Types specified in accordance with Section 8.3, as follows: Type 1 = online standard test; Type 1A = online enhanced test; Type 2 = offline standard test; Type 2A = offline enhanced test.

N Table 35.3.4 Protective Relay Mechanical Servicing

No.	Task	Electromechanical Test Type*	Solid-State Test Type*	Microprocessor Test Type*	Notes
1	Check relay disks for friction, freedom of movement, correct travel, and clearance.	2	NA	NA	
2	Operate targets and reset mechanisms.	2	2	NA	
3	Update to most current firmware.	NA	NA	2A	
4	Check trip and close coil monitoring functions.	NA	NA	2	
5	Check circuit breaker monitoring.	NA	NA	2	

NA: Not applicable.

*Types specified in accordance with Section 8.3, as follows: 1 = online standard test, 1A = online enhanced test, 2 = offline standard test, 2A = offline enhanced test.

Shaded text = Revisions.   Δ = Text deletions and figure/table revisions.   • = Section deletions.   *N* = New materia

Table 35.3.5 Protective Relay Electrical Tests

No.	Task	Test Type* Electromechanical	Solid-State	Microprocessor	Notes
1	Perform an insulation resistance test on each branch circuit to frame	2	NA	NA	
2	Perform a pickup test to determine the minimum or maximum current, voltage, power, or frequency that causes closure of relay contacts for all active functions	2	2	2A	
3	Perform a timing at three points on the time dial curve to verify the timing characteristics of the relay	2	2	2A	
4	Perform tests as required to check operation of restraint, directional, and other protective elements	2	2	2A	
5	Perform a zero check test to determine proper time dial position when the relay is fixed and moving contacts are closed by the manual rotation of the time dial towards zero	2	NA	NA	
6	Perform relay checks to verify relay status, meter readings (if applicable), and contact inputs/outputs	NA	NA	2	
7	Test arc energy reduction technology in accordance with the manufacturer's instructions	NA	NA	2	
8	Verify each input and output performs the intended function in accordance with control drawings	2A	2A	2A	
9	After testing is complete, clear trip counters, targets, events, and oscillographs from testing	2	2	2A	
10	Review maintenance and statistical data	NA	2	2	
11	Download or document settings, logic, and other parameters when changes are made	NA	2	2	

NA: Not applicable.
*Types specified in accordance with Section 8.3, as follows: Type 1 = online standard test; Type 1A = online enhanced test; Type 2 = offline standard test; Type 2A = offline enhanced test.

Shaded text = Revisions.   Δ = Text deletions and figure/table revisions.   • = Section deletions.   *N* = New material.

2023 Edition

N **Chapter 36 Stationary Standby Batteries**

N **36.1* Scope.** This chapter identifies electrical maintenance requirements for all stationary installations of storage stationary standby batteries comprised of lead-acid or nickel-cadmium (NiCd) cells.

N **36.2 Frequency of Maintenance.** The periodic maintenance procedures in Section 36.4 shall be performed in accordance with the frequencies in Chapter 9, unless otherwise specified in Table 36.2.

N **36.3 Documentation.**

N **36.3.1*** Measurements shall be recorded for future reference along with log notations of the visual inspection and corrective action.

N **36.3.2** A stationary standby battery installation shall include supporting documentation to include the following:

(1) Electrical schematics and as-built drawings
(2) Signage, markings, and labels
(3) Commissioning manual, test plan, and test results

(4) Operations and maintenance manuals
(5) Materials list of expendable maintenance items, such as filters and fuses

N **36.4* Periodic Maintenance Procedures.**

N **36.4.1* Visual Inspections.** Stationary standby batteries and their associated equipment shall be visually inspected in accordance with Table 36.4.1.

N **36.4.2* Cleaning.** Terminal connectors, battery posts, and cable ends shall be checked and be cleaned to remove all corrosion and dirt.

N **36.4.3 Lubrication. (Reserved)**

N **36.4.4 Mechanical Servicing. (Reserved)**

N **36.4.5* Electrical Testing.** Stationary standby batteries and their associated equipment shall be electrically tested in accordance with Table 36.4.5.

N **36.5 Special. (Reserved)**

N **Table 36.2 Maintenance Intervals**

Battery Technology	Test to be Performed	Equipment Condition Assessment			Notes
		Condition 1	Condition 2	Condition 3	
Vented lead-acid	Overall float voltage	3 months	3 months	1 month	
	Visual inspections	12 months	12 months	1 month	
	Electrolyte levels	3 months	3 months	1 month	
	Ambient temperature	3 months	3 months	1 month	
	Float current	3 months	3 months	1 month	
	Individual cell/unit float voltages	12 months	12 months	1 month	
	Representative cell temperatures	3 months	3 months	1 month	
	Inspect electrical connection for high resistance	12 months	12 months	1 month	
	Performance testing	60 months	60 months	12 months	
Valve-regulated lead-acid	Overall float voltage	1 month	1 month	1 month	
	Visual inspections	12 months	12 months	1 month	
	Ambient temperature	3 months	3 months	1 month	
	Float current	1 month	1 month	1 month	
	Ohmic testing	3 months	3 months	1 month	
	Individual cell/unit float voltages	3 months	3 months	1 month	
	Representative cell temperatures	3 months	3 months	1 month	
	Inspect electrical connection for high resistance	12 months	12 months	1 month	
	Performance testing	24 months	24 months	12 months	
Ni-Cad	Overall float voltage	3 months	3 months	1 month	
	Visual inspections	12 months	12 months	1 month	
	Electrolyte levels	3 months	3 months	1 month	
	Ambient temperature	3 months	3 months	1 month	
	Float current	3 months	3 months	1 month	
	Individual cell/unit float voltages	12 months	12 months	1 month	
	Representative cell temperatures	3 months	3 months	1 month	
	Inspect electrical connection for high resistance	12 months	12 months	1 month	
	Performance testing	60 months	60 months	12 months	

Table 36.4.1 Stationary Standby Batteries Visual Inspections

No.	Task	Test Type*	Notes
1	Inspect containers, covers, and vent caps for cracks and structural damage	1	
2	Inspect plates and internal parts when visible	1	Document excessive positive plate growth, sulfate crystal formation, buckling, warping, scaling, swelling, cracking, hydration rings, excessive sedimentation, mossing, copper contamination, internal post seal cracks, and changes in color.
3	Inspect interconnection cables, cell connectors, and other conductors for wear, contamination, corrosion, and discoloration	1	
4	Inspect battery racks for corrosion, cleanliness, proper grounding, and structural integrity, seismic protection	1	
5	Inspect electrolyte for containment, leaking, spills, and levels	1	
6	Inspect ventilation equipment operation, dampers, filters, alarms, and other items that might restrict air movement	1	
7	Inspect heating and air conditioning equipment including filters that control ambient room temperature for restricted air movement	1	
8	Verify the functionality of lights, strobes, horns, and related alarm notifications	1	

*Types specified in accordance with Section 8.3, as follows: Type 1 = online standard test; Type 1A = online enhanced test; Type 2 = offline standard test; Type 2A = offline enhanced test.

N **Table 36.4.5 Stationary Standby Battery Electrical Tests**

No.	Task	Test Type*	Notes
1	Overall float voltage	1	Measured at the battery and verified annually to be in accordance with the battery manufacturer's instructions.
2	Measure cell temperature	1	
3	Specific gravity	1A	No less than 10% of the units in the string(s).
4	Ohmic testing	1A	Resistance, impedance, or conductance.
5	Inspect electrical connection for high resistance	1 or 1A	See Section 7.2.
6	Performance testing	1	
7	Thermal imaging	1	Under full load of performance testing.
8	Float current	1	
9	Individual cell/unit float voltage	1	Record voltage measurements on individual cells or units to two decimal places.

*Types specified in accordance with Section 8.3, as follows: Type 1 = online standard test; Type 1A = online enhanced test; Type 2 = offline standard test; Type 2A = offline enhanced test.

N   **Chapter 37   Instrument Transformers (Reserved)**

N   **Chapter 38   Control Power Transformers (Reserved)**

Annex A   Explanatory Material

Annex A is not a part of the requirements of this NFPA document but is included for informational purposes only. This annex contains explanatory material, numbered to correspond with the applicable text paragraphs.

N **A.1.5.3.2** Users of this standard should apply one system of units consistently and not alternate between units.

Δ **A.3.2.1 Approved.** The National Fire Protection Association does not approve, inspect, or certify any installations, procedures, equipment, or materials nor does it approve or evaluate testing laboratories. In determining the acceptability of installations or procedures, equipment, or materials, the "authority having jurisdiction" may base acceptance on compliance with NFPA or other appropriate standards. In the absence of such standards, said authority may require evidence of proper installation, procedure, or use. The "authority having jurisdiction" may also refer to the listings or labeling practices of an organization that is concerned with product evaluations and is thus in a position to determine compliance with appropriate standards for the current production of listed items.

A.3.2.2 Authority Having Jurisdiction (AHJ). The phrase "authority having jurisdiction," or its acronym AHJ, is used in NFPA standards in a broad manner because jurisdictions and approval agencies vary, as do their responsibilities. Where public safety is primary, the authority having jurisdiction may be a federal, state, local, or other regional department or individual such as a fire chief; fire marshal; chief of a fire prevention bureau, labor department, or health department; building official; electrical inspector; or others having statutory authority. For insurance purposes, an insurance inspection department, rating bureau, or other insurance company representative may be the authority having jurisdiction. In many circumstances, the property owner or his or her designated agent assumes the role of the authority having jurisdiction; at government installations, the commanding officer or departmental official may be the authority having jurisdiction.

A.3.2.4 Listed. The means for identifying listed equipment may vary for each organization concerned with product evaluation; some organizations do not recognize equipment as listed unless it is also labeled. The authority having jurisdiction should utilize the system employed by the listing organization to identify a listed product.

N **A.3.3.1 Adjustable Speed Drive.** A variable frequency drive is one type of electronic adjustable speed drive that controls the rotational speed of an ac electric motor by controlling the frequency and voltage of the electrical power supplied to the motor. [**70**, 2023]

N **A.3.3.9 Circuit Breaker.** One example of a listing standard for circuit breakers is UL 489, *Molded-Case Circuit Breakers, Molded-Case Switches and Circuit Breaker Enclosures.*

Molded-Case Circuit Breaker (MCCB). MCCBs are most often available in one-, two-, three-, or four-pole versions and are available in 120 V to 1000 V ratings. All MCCBs, including ICCBs, will include some sort of instantaneous protection, which might be adjustable but cannot be completely disabled.

Insulated-Case Circuit Breaker (ICCB). There is no specific definition or mention of ICCB within the MCCB standard.

However, their stated ratings will be those of MCCBs but they can operate like LVPCBs. ICCBs can either include a two-step stored energy operating mechanism that will require manual charging of closing and opening springs when the circuit breaker is manually operated or include internal charging motors for closing and opening springs. ICCBs are normally housed in a case of dielectric materials providing a layer of insulation between its exterior and internal mechanisms. The characteristics of ICCBs vary widely between models and manufacturers.

Low-Voltage Power Circuit Breaker (LVPCB). LVPCBs are mechanical switching devices consisting of a frame that contains some number of field replaceable component parts or subassemblies capable of making, carrying, interrupting, and breaking currents. Modern LVPCBs are rated 1000 V ac or less, or 1500 V dc or less, and do not include MCCBs. They are typically larger circuit breakers with frames rated at 600 A or more that have a significant degree of maintainability, such as the ability to replace contact structures, arc chutes, and other parts subject to wear. Modern versions are listed to UL 1066, *Low-Voltage AC and DC Power Circuit Breakers Used in Enclosures,* and are commonly installed in switchgear as draw-out devices. More rarely, they might be installed as fixed mounted devices in older equipment. LVPCBs manufactured prior to 2000 generally had metal frames; those manufactured after 2000 tend to use frames made from nonconductive materials. LVPCBs are sometimes also referred to as metal frame or air frame breakers.

A.3.3.14 Corona. High electrical gradients exceeding the breakdown level of air lead to corona discharges. Mild corona has a low sizzling sound and might not be audible above ambient noise in the substation. As the corona increases in activity, the sizzling sound becomes louder and is accompanied by popping, spitting, or crackling as flashover level nears. Corona ionizes the air, converting the oxygen to ozone, which has a distinctive, penetrating odor.

A.3.3.16 Electrical Maintenance Program (EMP). Electrical maintenance relies on knowing the electrical systems and equipment being maintained and on knowing the operating experience, loss exposures, potential for injury, and maintenance resources.

A.3.3.19 Energy Storage System (ESS). An ESS(s) can include but is not limited to batteries, capacitors, and kinetic energy devices (e.g., flywheels and compressed air). An ESS(s) can include inverters or converters to change voltage levels or to make a change between an ac or a dc system. [**70,** 2023]

These systems differ from a stationary standby battery installation where a battery spends the majority of the time on continuous float charge or in a high state of charge, in readiness for a discharge event. [**70,** 2023]

A.3.3.21 Fault Current, Available (Available Fault Current). A short-circuit can occur during abnormal conditions such as a fault between circuit conductors or a ground fault. Available fault current can be different values at different points in the same circuit. See Figure A.3.3.21.

A.3.3.26 Ground-Fault Circuit Interrupter (GFCI). See UL 943, *Standard for Ground-Fault Circuit Interrupters,* for further information. Class A ground-fault circuit interrupters trip when the ground-fault current is 6 mA or higher and do not trip when the ground-fault current is less than 4 mA. [**70,** 2023]

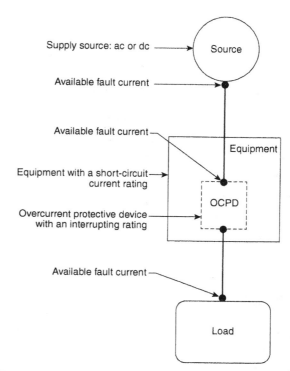

N FIGURE A.3.3.21 Available Fault Current. [70:Informational Note Figure 100.1]

A GFCI does not eliminate the electric shock sensation since normal perception level is approximately 0.5 mA; nor does it protect from electric shock hazard from line-to-line contact.

△ A.3.3.27 Ground-Fault Protection of Equipment. There are two applications where ground-fault protection of equipment is intended to be used: where there could be excessive ground-fault leakage current from equipment and where equipment and conductors are to be protected from damage in the event of a higher-level ground fault (either solid or arcing). These types of protective equipment are for use only on ac, grounded circuits; they cause the circuit to be disconnected when a current equal to or higher than its pickup setting or rating flows to ground. They are not designed to protect personnel from electrocution. Equipment ground-fault protective devices are intended to operate on a condition of excessive ground-fault leakage current from equipment. The ground current pickup level of these devices is from above 6 mA to 50 mA. Circuit breakers with equipment ground-fault protection are combination circuit breaker and equipment ground-fault protective devices designed to serve the dual function of providing overcurrent protection and ground-fault protection for equipment. The ground current pickup level of these breakers is typically 30 mA. They are intended to be used in accordance with *NFPA 70*, Articles 426 and 427. Ground-fault sensing and relaying equipment is intended to provide ground-fault protection of equipment at services and feeders. They are rated for ground current pickup levels from 4 amperes to 1200 amperes.

N A.3.3.33 Ground Loop. Current will flow in the ground loop if there is voltage difference between the connection nodes. Regrounding of the grounded circuit conductor (neutral) beyond the service point will result in ground loops. This might or might not be harmful depending on the application.

N A.3.3.35 Interharmonics. Not all frequencies that occur on an electrical power system are integer multiples of the fundamental frequency (usually 60 Hz), as are harmonics. Some loads draw currents that result in voltages that are between harmonic frequencies or less than the fundamental frequency. These frequencies are referred to as interharmonics and can be made of discrete frequencies or as a wide-band spectrum. A special category of these interharmonics is called subharmonics, in which the frequencies involved are less than the fundamental power line frequency.

N A.3.3.36 Long-Duration Undervoltage. See IEEE 1159, *Recommended Practice for Monitoring Electric Power Quality*, Table 4-2.

N A.3.3.48 Reconditioned. The term *reconditioned* is frequently referred to as *rebuilt, refurbished,* or *remanufactured.* [70, 2023]

N A.3.3.50 Sag. If the voltage drops below 10 percent of the normal voltage, then this is classified as an interruption.

N A.3.3.51 Service Point. The service point can be described as the point of demarcation between where the serving utility ends and the premises wiring begins. The serving utility generally specifies the location of the service point based on the conditions of service.

N A.3.3.52 Servicing. Servicing often encompasses maintenance and repair activities. [70, 2023]

N A.3.3.54 Ground-Fault Circuit Interrupter, Special Purpose (SPGFCI). (Special-Purpose Ground-Fault Circuit Interrupter) See UL 943C, *Outline of Investigation for Special Purpose Ground-Fault Circuit Interrupters,* for information on Classes C, D, or E special purpose ground-fault circuit interrupters. [70, 2023]

N A.3.3.55 Stationary Standby Battery. Uninterruptible power supply (UPS) batteries fall under this definition.

N A.3.3.56 Survey. The systems and equipment covered in specific parts of the survey should be based on logical divisions of the electrical system.

N A.3.3.59 Switchboard. These assemblies can be accessible from the rear or side as well as from the front and are not intended to be installed in cabinets. [70, 2023]

N A.3.3.60 Switchgear. All switchgear subject to *NEC* requirements is metal enclosed. Switchgear rated below 1000 V or less may be identified as "low-voltage power circuit breaker switchgear." Switchgear rated over 1000 V may be identified as "metal-enclosed switchgear" or "metal-clad switchgear." Switchgear is available in non–arc-resistant or arc-resistant constructions. [70, 2023]

N A.3.3.61.1 Acceptance Tests. Acceptance tests can be used to establish test benchmarks that can be used as reference during future tests, performed either at the factory, on-site, or after installation.

N A.3.3.61.4 Enhanced Tests. Examples of enhanced tests are cable fault-locating tests or tests performed on a circuit breaker that has interrupted a high level of fault current. Tests can be performed at the discretion of the EMP and provide additional diagnostic information about equipment.

N A.3.3.63 Transients. Transients were formerly referred to as surges, spikes, or impulses. Waveshapes of the excursions are usually unidirectional pulses or decaying amplitude, high-frequency oscillations. Durations range from fractions of a microsecond to milliseconds, and the maximum duration is in the order of one half-cycle of the power frequency. Instantaneous amplitudes of voltage transients can reach thousands of volts.

N A.4.2.4.2 The person developing the EMP should verify if the local codes or ordinances include an electrical maintenance requirement. If an electrical maintenance requirement has been adopted into the local codes or ordinances, the person should verify that all requirements for this standard and the local codes or ordinances are satisfied in the EMP.

N A.4.7.1 Rework, remanufacturing, or retrofitting of equipment typically involves replacement or refurbishing of major components of equipment or systems. Repairs or modifications not authorized by the original equipment manufacturer might void the equipment warranties and third-party certifications. Equipment can be reconditioned under rebuild programs provided the reconditioning follows established guidelines. The AHJ can assess the acceptability of reconditioned equipment to determine if a re-evaluation of the modified product by the organization that listed the equipment is necessary.

N A.4.7.2 See also NFPA 791 and OSHA Safety & Health Information Bulletin (SHIB), "Certification of Workplace Products by Nationally Recognized Testing Laboratories."

N A.4.8 When cleaning equipment, the method used should be determined by the type of contamination to be removed and whether the apparatus is to be returned to service immediately. Drying is necessary after using a solvent or water. Insulation should be tested to determine if it has been properly cleaned. Enclosure and substation room filters should be cleaned at regular intervals and replaced if they are damaged or clogged. Loose hardware, dust, and debris should be removed from equipment enclosures. When properly cleaned, new or unusual wear or loss of parts can be detected during subsequent maintenance operations.

Wiping off dirt with a clean, dry, lint-free cloth or soft brush is usually satisfactory if the apparatus is small, the surfaces to be cleaned are accessible, and only dry dirt is to be removed. Lint-free rags should be used so lint will not adhere to the insulation and act as a further dirt-collecting agent. Care should be used to avoid damage to delicate parts.

To remove loose dust, dirt, and particles, suction cleaning methods should be used.

Where dirt cannot be removed by wiping or vacuuming, compressed-air blowing might be necessary.

If compressed air is used, protection should be provided against injury to workers' faces and eyes from flying debris and to their lungs from dust inhalation. The use of compressed air should comply with OSHA regulations in 29 CFR 1910.242(b), "Hand and Portable Powered Tools and Equipment, General — Compressed Air Used for Cleaning," including limiting air pressure for such cleaning to less than a gauge pressure of 208.85 kPa (30 psi) and the provision of effective chip guarding and appropriate PPE.

Care should be exercised because compressed air can cause contaminants to become airborne, which can compromise the integrity of insulation surfaces or affect the mechanical operation of nearby equipment. Protection might also be needed against contamination of other equipment if the insulation is cleaned in place with compressed air. Either equipment should be removed to a suitable location for cleaning or other equipment should be covered and guarded from cross contamination. Air should be dry and directed in a manner to avoid further blockage of ventilation ducts and recesses in insulation surfaces.

Accumulated dirt, oil, or grease might require a solvent to remove it. A lint-free cloth barely moistened (not wet) with a nonflammable solvent can be used for wiping. Solvents used for cleaning of electrical equipment should be selected carefully to ensure compatibility with the materials being cleaned. Liquid cleaners, including spray cleaners, are not recommended unless solvent compatibility is verified with the equipment manufacturer because residues could cause damage, interfere with electrical or mechanical functions, or compromise the integrity of insulation surfaces.

Some equipment could require cleaning by nonconductive abrasive blasting.

Shot blasting should not be used.

CAUTION: Cleaning with abrasives or abrasive blasting methods can create a hazard to personnel and equipment.

Abrasive blasting operations should comply with OSHA regulations in 29 CFR 1910.94(a), "Ventilation — Abrasive Blasting." Protection should be provided against injury to workers' faces and eyes from abrasives and flying debris and to their lungs from dust inhalation.

Airborne asbestos fibers can endanger health and are subject to government regulations. Knowledge of government regulations related to the handling of asbestos is required before handling asbestos and other such materials. (Copies of the Toxic Substances Control Act as defined in the US Code of Federal Regulations can be obtained from the US Environmental Protection Agency.)

If sweeping of an electrical equipment room is required, a sweeping compound should be used to limit the amount of dirt and dust becoming airborne. During mopping, the mop bucket should be kept as far as practical from the electrical equipment.

A.1.2 In addition to *NFPA 70E*, IEEE C2, *National Electrical Safety Code*, applicable legal requirements (e.g., 29 CFR 1926, "Occupational Safety and Health Standards," and 29 CFR 1910, "Safety and Health Regulations for Construction"); and NFPA 70 are among the references that should be utilized for the development of programs and procedures associated with electrical maintenance activities and are necessary to be used in conjunction with this document.

Equipment should be placed in an electrically safe work condition for inspections, tests, repairs, and other servicing. Where electrical maintenance tasks must be performed when equipment is energized, provisions are to be made to allow electrical maintenance to be performed safely.

A.1.1 Engineering studies generally cover the following areas:

Short-circuit studies
Coordination studies
Load-flow studies
Reliability studies

(5) Incident energy analysis (arc-flash hazard calculations)
(6) Maintenance-related design studies

In order to conduct short-circuit, coordination, and arc flash studies, specific data should be collected. Data that should be included on a single-line diagram are utility company points of contact and data records for equipment such as transformers, cables, overhead lines, fuses, medium-voltage breakers, reclosers, capacitor banks, low-voltage breakers, disconnects, generators, and motors. This information should be developed for each type of operating condition. Examples of data collection forms are included in Annex E.

Utility information should at least include the minimum and maximum short circuit megavolt-amperes (MVA) and the X/R ratio at the service point; point of contact name, address, and telephone number; and facility point of contact, address, and telephone number.

Transformer data records should include location, rated kilovolt-amperes (kVA), maximum kVA, primary voltage, secondary voltage, impedance in percent, type of primary and secondary connection, ground impedance, and, if appropriate, the voltage tap.

Cable data should include "to" and "from," rated volts, nominal volts, single-conductor or three-conductor cable, the number of conductors per phase, the neutral size, copper or aluminum, and length in feet.

Raceway material (i.e., magnetic or nonmagnetic) should be noted.

Overhead line information should include "to" and "from," connection configuration, nominal volts, number of lines, lines per phase, ground size, type of cable (material), and length in feet.

Medium-voltage breaker information should include location, manufacturer, type, rated volts, interrupting current, interrupting time (cycles), close/latch amps and for the associated relays the manufacturer/type, time delay range and existing tap, time dial, instantaneous range and existing tap, and CT ratio.

Recloser information should include location, CT ratio, nominal volts, manufacturer, type, BIL, continuous current rating, interrupting rating, minimum trip, operational sequence, reclosing times (if available), and tripping curves (if available).

Low-voltage information for the breaker should include location, manufacturer, type, rated volts, frame rating, and interrupting rating and for the trip device should include manufacturer, type, long time delay range and bands available, short time delay range and bands available, instantaneous range, and ground range and bands available.

Generator information should include location, type, kVA rating, generated volts, rated current, rpm, wiring connection (e.g., delta or wye), system ground, subtransient impedance, ground impedance, and power factor.

Motor information should include location, type, horsepower, rated volts, full load amps, rpm, code letter, locked rotor amps, power factor, and starter type.

Capacitor bank information should include location, kVAR rating, rated volts, and wiring connection (e.g., delta or wye).

Fuse information should include location, voltage rating, interruption rating, fuse type or class, manufacturer, and manufacturer's part number.

N A.6.3 Protecting electrical systems against damage during short-circuit faults is required in 110.9 and 110.10 of *NFPA 70*. Additional information on short-circuit currents can be found in ANSI/IEEE 242, *Recommended Practice for Protection and Coordination of Industrial and Commercial Power Systems (IEEE Buff Book)*; ANSI/IEEE 141, *Recommended Practice for Electric Power Distribution for Industrial Plants (IEEE Red Book)*; ANSI/IEEE 241, *Recommended Practice for Electric Power Systems in Commercial Buildings (IEEE Gray Book)*; and ANSI/IEEE 399, *Recommended Practice for Industrial and Commercial Power Systems Analysis (IEEE Brown Book)*.

IEEE is incorporating the information in the color book series into the IEEE 3000 Standards. The content will be organized into approximately 70 IEEE "dot" standards as follows:

(1) IEEE 3000 Standards: *Fundamentals*
(2) IEEE 3001 Standards: *Power Systems Design*
(3) IEEE 3002 Standards: *Power Systems Analysis*
(4) IEEE 3003 Standards: *Power Systems Grounding*
(5) IEEE 3004 Standards: *Protection & Coordination*
(6) IEEE 3005 Standards: *Energy & Standby Power Systems*
(7) IEEE 3006 Standards: *Power Systems Reliability*
(8) IEEE 3007 Standards: *Maintenance, Operations & Safety*

The user should refer to the IEEE website (www.ieee.org) for updated information regarding available standards.

Short circuits or fault currents represent a significant amount of destructive energy that can be released into electrical systems under abnormal conditions. During normal system operation, electrical energy is controlled and does useful work. However, under fault conditions, short-circuit currents can cause serious damage to electrical systems and equipment and create the potential for serious injury to personnel. Short-circuit currents can approach values as large as several hundred thousand amperes.

During short-circuit conditions, thermal energy and magnetic forces are released into the electrical system. The thermal energy can cause insulation and conductor melting as well as explosions contributing to major equipment burndowns. Magnetic forces can bend busbars and cause violent conductor whipping and distortion. These conditions have grim consequences on electrical systems, equipment, and personnel.

The following are some of the conditions that might require an update of the baseline short-circuit study:

(1) A change by the utility
(2) A change in the primary or secondary system configuration within the facility
(3) A change in the transformer size (kVA) or impedance (percent Z)
(4) A change in conductor lengths or sizes
(5) A change in the motors connected to the system

A comprehensive treatment of short-circuit currents is beyond the scope of this document. However, there is a simple method to determine the maximum available short-circuit current at the transformer secondary terminals. This value can be calculated by multiplying the transformer full load amperes by 100 and dividing the product by the percent impedance of the transformer.

Figure A.6.3 shows an example calculation: 500 kVA transformer, 3-phase, 480 volt primary, 208 Y/120 volt secondary, 2 percent Z.

There are several computer programs commercially available to conduct thorough short-circuit calculation studies.

N A.6.4 *NFPA 70* and various IEEE standards contain the requirements and suggested practices to coordinate electrical systems. The IEEE standards include ANSI/IEEE 242, *Recommended Practice for Protection and Coordination of Industrial and Commercial Power Systems (IEEE Buff Book)*; ANSI/IEEE 141, *Recommended Practice for Electric Power Distribution for Industrial Plants (IEEE Red Book)*; ANSI/IEEE 241, *Recommended Practice for Electric Power Systems in Commercial Buildings (IEEE Gray Book)*; and ANSI/IEEE 399, *Recommended Practice for Industrial and Commercial Power Systems Analysis (IEEE Brown Book)*. (See A.6.3.)

Improper coordination can cause unnecessary power outages. For example, branch-circuit faults can open multiple upstream overcurrent devices. This process can escalate and cause major blackouts, resulting in the loss of production. Blackouts also affect personnel safety.

Changes affecting the coordination of overcurrent devices in the electrical system include the following:

(1) A change in the available short-circuit current
(2) Replacing overcurrent devices with devices having different ratings or operating characteristics
(3) Adjusting the settings on circuit breakers or relays
(4) Changes in the electrical system configuration
(5) Inadequate maintenance, testing, and calibration

N A.6.5 Load-flow studies show the direction and amount of power flowing from available sources to every load. By means of such a study, the voltage, current, power, reactive power, and power factor at each point in the system can be determined.

This information is necessary before changes to the system can be planned and will assist in determining the operating configuration. This study also helps determine losses in the system. ANSI/IEEE 399, *Recommended Practice for Industrial and Commercial Power Systems Analysis (IEEE Brown Book)*, provides more detailed information.

Some of the events that result in load-flow changes include changing motors, motor horsepower, transformer size, or impedance; operating configurations not planned for in the existing study; adding or removing power-factor correction capacitors; and adding or removing loads.

It is important that the system single-line diagrams and operating configurations (both normal and emergency) be kept current along with the load-flow study.

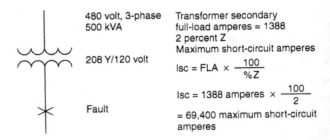

480 volt, 3-phase
500 kVA

208 Y/120 volt

Fault

Transformer secondary
full-load amperes = 1388
2 percent Z
Maximum short-circuit amperes

$$I_{sc} = FLA \times \frac{100}{\%Z}$$

$$I_{sc} = 1388 \text{ amperes} \times \frac{100}{2}$$

$$= 69,400 \text{ maximum short-circuit amperes}$$

N   **FIGURE A.6.3**   **Example Calculation of Maximum Available Short-Circuit Current at the Transformer Secondary Terminals.**

FIGURE A.9.1.1 Maintenance Interval Adjustments.

N A.9.1.1.1 Maintenance intervals are used to plan inspections, testing, monitoring, analysis and service of equipment on a predetermined frequency. The interval frequency is commonly calendar-based but other possibilities, such as a frequency based on the number of switch operations, cycle count, or hours of operation can be used. The intervals can be modified based on the type, criticality, and perceived condition of the equipment.

N A.9.1.1.2 Continuous monitoring of specific equipment conditions can be performed using an uninterrupted method of data collection. Examples include the use of permanently mounted counters, sensors, or controllers to measure a condition or state inside the equipment. Multiple types of data can be continuously monitored, including voltage, current, temperature, humidity, cycle count, open/closed state, and others. The monitored data can be used to actively alert personnel to the existence of a condition that is either above or below a predetermined control limit. In many cases this data can obtained without removing covers or opening doors and without exposing workers to electrical hazards. The use of real-time data and actual performance of the equipment can be used to modify (shorten or lengthen) a predetermined maintenance interval.

Predictive techniques monitor multiple conditions in equipment using various sensors and analyze and interpret the data using analytical methods and algorithms. These proactive techniques identify trends or issues and notify personnel of recommended actions before the condition reaches an alarm point or alert them to urgent issues that are at or over a predetermined level. These technologies and methods often can detect minor items before they propagate into major issues or equipment failure.

N A.9.1.2.1.2 Statistics show that loss of production due to an emergency shutdown is almost always more expensive than loss of production due to a planned shutdown. Accordingly, the interval between inspections should be planned to avoid the diminishing returns of either too long or too short an interval.

N A.9.2.1 Manufacturer's service manuals and industry standards should have a recommended frequency of inspection. The frequency given is based on standard or usual operating conditions and environments.

N A.9.2.2 For more information on risk management, see ISO 31000, *Risk Management — Principles and Guidelines*, and Annex F of NFPA *70E*.

N A.9.3.2 A criticality assessment team should be comprised of personnel who are familiar with the electrical equipment, safety requirements, operational capabilities, potential impact of downtime, required maintenance activities, and business priorities. The team can include external expertise when needed. Some examples of the type of personnel to include in a criticality assessment include the following:

(1) The electrical foreman or superintendent
(2) Production personnel thoroughly familiar with the operation capabilities of the equipment and the effect its loss will have on quality and productivity
(3) The senior maintenance individual who is generally familiar with the maintenance and repair history of the equipment or process
(4) A technical individual knowledgeable in the theoretical fundamentals of the process and its hazards (e.g., in a chemical plant, a chemist; in a mine, a geologist)
(5) A safety engineer or the individual responsible for the overall security of the plant and its personnel against fire and accidents of all kinds

The team should review the entire plant or each of its operating segments in detail, considering each unit of equipment as related to the entire operation and the effect of its loss on safety and production. The purpose of the review is to identify failure modes and their cause and effect.

There should be objective criteria consistently used to evaluate all equipment to make a clear determination in establishing whether a system is critical and in having the proper amount of emphasis placed on its maintenance. The determination of critical parts should be the responsibility of the electrical foreman or superintendent on the team.

The entire team should consider each alarm in the system with the same thoroughness with which they have considered

Shaded text = Revisions.   Δ = Text deletions and figure/table revisions.   • = Section deletions.   N = New material.

2023 Edition

the shutdown circuits. A critical alarm should be characterized by its separate sensing device, a separate readout device, and separate circuitry and power source. The maintenance department should thoroughly understand the critical level of each alarm. The critical alarms and their significance should be distinctly marked on drawings, in records, and on the operating unit. For an alarm to be critical does not necessarily mean that it is complex or related to complex action. A simple valve position indicator can be one of the most critical alarms in an operating unit.

N A.9.3.2.1 The owner can also choose to assign criticality based on the threat to operational continuity. The criticality assessment should consider personnel exposure to electrical hazards. Electrical system criticality should be evaluated with consideration of the possible widespread effect of a fault in electrical equipment.

N A.10.1 Hazardous location electrical equipment is used in areas that are recognized to commonly or infrequently contain ignitible vapors or dusts. Designs of hazardous location electrical equipment include, but are not limited to, explosionproof, dust-ignitionproof, dusttight, purged pressurized, intrinsically safe, nonincendive, oil immersion, and hermetically sealed. Maintenance of each type of equipment requires attention to specific items.

Explosionproof enclosures, dust-ignitionproof enclosures, dusttight enclosures, raceway seals, vents, barriers, and other protective features are required for electrical equipment in certain occupancies.

Intrinsically safe equipment and wiring is permitted in locations for which specific systems are approved. Such wiring is to be separate from the wiring of other circuits. Article 504 of *NFPA 70* describes control drawings, grounding, and other features involved in maintenance programs.

Purged and pressurized enclosures can be used in hazardous (classified) areas. NFPA 496 provides guidance useful to maintenance personnel.

N A.10.1.2 In addition to any electrical safety assessments, classified locations require an additional analysis to determine the risk of igniting an explosive atmosphere.

To ensure that there are no ignition-capable sparks when performing maintenance, no equipment should be repaired or maintained in a hazardous location unless the equipment has been electrically isolated. If specific maintenance requires that the equipment be energized during maintenance, the work should be performed in a manner that verifies both initially and periodically that an explosive atmosphere is not present while the work is in progress or until the equipment has been reenergized and tested.

Where work is to be performed inside the classified space, the documented risk assessment should consider the safety of the tools and equipment being used to perform the maintenance activity.

N A.10.2.2 Ignition sources can include high surface temperatures, stored electrical energy, and the buildup of static charges.

N A.10.4.1 Other ignition sources can include static charges generated by clothing, cell phones and other electronic devices.

N A.10.5.2.1 Special attention should be given to joints and other sealed openings in the enclosure that are intended to prevent propagation of flame. Foreign objects can prevent the proper closure of mating joints. Examples of foreign objects include the following:

(1) Caulking
(2) Sealants
(3) Unapproved gaskets
(4) Burrs
(5) Pinched gaskets
(6) Pieces of insulation
(7) Wiring

N A.10.6.2 Damage to factory-installed seals within equipment can necessitate replacing the equipment.

N A.10.8 Rough handling and the use of tools that pry, impact, or abrade components can dent, scratch, nick, or otherwise mar close-tolerance, precision-machined joints and make them unsafe.

N A.10.9 When a product bearing a listing mark is modified or rebuilt after it leaves the factory where the listing mark was applied, it is unknown if the product continues to meet the applicable safety requirements unless the modification or rebuilding has been specifically investigated by the certification body. The only exception is when a listed product has specific markings for field-installed equipment or replacement components.

N A.11.3.5 See Table A.11.3.5.

N A.12.1.2 Some examples of related components that are not covered in this chapter include switches, circuit breakers, transformers, protective relays, batteries, and UPS.

N A.12.3.1 *Insulators and Insulating Supports.* Insulators, insulating stand-offs, and insulating supports should be inspected for evidence of contaminated surfaces or physical damage, such as cracked or broken segments. Contaminated surfaces should be cleaned, and damaged components should be replaced. Where insulators and insulating stands-offs are not accessible, dielectric integrity tests should be used to determine the condition of dielectric properties.

Evidence of corona should be documented, and investigation of the root cause and potential for failure should be planned.

N Table A.11.3.5 Reference Standards for the Electrical Tests Identified in Table 11.3.5

Electrical Test	Reference Standard
Applied voltage test	IEEE C57.12.91
Sample insulating fluid and test for:	ASTM D923
Dielectric breakdown	ASTM D1816
Acid neutralization number	ASTM D974
Specific gravity	ASTM D1298
Interfacial tension	ASTM D971
Color	ASTM D1500
Visual condition	ASTM D1524
Water content	ASTM D1533
Power factor	ASTM D924
Dissolved gas analysis	IEEE C57.104
Furan analysis	ASTM D5837

All exposed conductors should be visually inspected for evidence of overheating at bolted joints and other connections, as well as for corrosion and evidence of any galvanic or chemical action that could deteriorate a connection. All bolts associated with connections that show evidence of overheating should be examined for integrity and tightness. Torque should be verified in accordance with Chapter 7. Manufacturer's instructions should be followed with respect to torque, method of termination, lubrication, and coatings.

Extreme overheating can discolor copper conductors, deteriorate the insulation, and could require additional maintenance. When the substation is de-energized, these bolted connections should be checked. There are infrared detectors that can be used on energized systems to check for overheating by scanning from a distance. Where aluminum-to-copper joints exist, they should be inspected carefully for evidence of corrosion, overheating, or looseness. In all cases, manufacturer's specifications should be followed.

Enclosures and Rooms. The security of fences and other enclosures and rooms should be checked to ensure against entry of animals or unauthorized personnel.

The gates and doors, especially where equipped with panic hardware, should be checked for security and proper operation.

The enclosed area should not be used for storage of anything other than spare parts or other assemblies needed for operations directly associated with the enclosed equipment. Such parts and assemblies should not be stored within the required working space, except where the room is large and an area has been designated for other equipment without negatively impacting working space or egress or impinging within the arc flash boundary.

Spare parts and operating assemblies stored within the area should be identified. Where applicable, the date of acquisition should be marked, any need for periodic evaluation or maintenance should be appropriately noted and planned, and the equipment should be stored per the manufacturer's recommendations.

Equipment Enclosures and Housings. All enclosures, especially arc-resistant enclosures, provide a degree of protection for nearby personnel. However, that protection is compromised if panel bolts, door latches, or any other type of fastening and cover system is not fully utilized and fully secure. This is especially true for arc-resistant equipment ratings that are used to determine the arc flash PPE requirements and the acceptable operating and maintenance practices.

Equipment enclosures should be inspected for any signs of deterioration, oxidation, impact from environmental factors, looseness or lack of fasteners, lack of proper grounding, or worn surfaces or coatings. Where noted, the as-found condition should be recorded, and proper corrective action should be taken or planned.

All equipment doors and access panels should be inspected to ensure that all hardware is in place and in good condition. Hinges, locks, and latches should be lubricated, if recommended by the manufacturer or as needed.

Screens covering ventilation openings should be determined to be in place to prevent entry of rodents or small animals.

On outdoor assemblies, roof or wall seams should be checked for evidence of leakage, and any leaking seams should be repaired. The base should be checked for openings that could permit water to drain into the interior, and any such openings should be repaired in an appropriate manner.

Moisture accumulation might occur on internal surfaces of enclosures even if they are weathertight. The source of this moisture could be condensation. Condensation is prevented by heat and air circulation.

All internal surfaces should be examined for signs of previous moisture such as the following:

(1) Droplet depressions or craters on dust-laden surfaces
(2) Excessive oxidation anywhere on the metal housing
(3) Deposits of salts from water or other liquid evaporation

Where ventilators are supplied on enclosures, including metal-enclosed bus enclosures, they should be checked to ensure that they are clear of obstructions and that the air filters are clean and in good condition. Base foundations should be examined to ensure that structural members have not blocked floor ventilation.

All enclosures and housings for circuit breakers (switchgear, switchboards, or other) should be inspected and checked for integrity of all fasteners annually or as indicated in the maintenance plan.

All ventilation openings should be checked for obstructions and proper operation of any flap or automatic cover intended to assist in arc-resistant ratings. (See ANSI/IEEE C37.20.7, *Guide for Testing Switchgear Rated Up to 52 kV for Internal Arcing Faults.*)

Barriers, Insulation, and Insulators. Evidence of corona when the substation is energized should be documented, the root cause investigated, and the potential for failure planned.

Insulating or isolating barriers between compartments should be examined for signs of wear or looseness.

Grounded metal barriers around compartments and conductors should be examined for integrity and looseness. When barriers surround a power conductor, the barrier should be examined to ensure that the metal around the conductor is not continuous, creating eddy currents that can lead to losses and potential fire hazards.

The following specific areas in which insulation failure is more likely to occur should be inspected where they exist:

(1) Boundaries between two adjoining insulators
(2) Boundaries between an insulating member and the grounded metal structure
(3) Taped or compounded splices or junctions
(4) Bridging paths across insulating surfaces, either phase-to-phase or phase-to-ground
(5) Hidden surfaces such as the adjacent edges between the upper and lower members of split-type bus supports or the edges of a slot through which a busbar protrudes
(6) Edges of insulation surrounding mounting hardware either grounded to the metal structure or floating within the insulating member

Corona. Damage caused by dielectric stress could be evident on the surface of insulating members in the form of corona erosion or markings or tracking paths.

If corona occurs in switchgear assemblies, it is usually localized in thin air gaps that exist between a high-voltage busbar and its adjacent insulation or between two adjacent insulating members. It might form around bolt heads or other sharp projections that are not properly insulated or shielded.

Organic insulating materials, when exposed to corona discharge, initially develop white powdery deposits on their surface. These deposits can be wiped off with solvent. If the surface has not eroded, further maintenance is not required. Prolonged exposure to corona discharge will result in erosion of the surface of the insulating material. In some materials, corona deterioration has the appearance of worm-eaten wood. If the corrosion paths have not progressed to significant depths, surface repair probably can be accomplished. Manufacturer's recommendations should be followed for such repair.

Tracking. Tracking is an electrical discharge phenomenon caused by electrical stress on insulation. This stress can occur phase-to-phase or phase-to-ground. Tracking, when it occurs in switchgear assemblies, typically is found on insulation surfaces.

Tracking develops in the form of streamers or sputter arcs on the surface of insulation, usually adjacent to electrodes. One or more irregular carbon lines in the shape of tree branches are the most common sign of tracking.

Surface tracking can occur on the surfaces of organic insulation or on contaminated surfaces of inorganic insulation. The signs of tracking on organic materials are eroded surfaces with carbon lines. On track-resistant organic materials, these erosion patterns are essentially free of carbon.

Tracking can propagate from either the voltage terminals or the ground terminal. It does not necessarily progress in a regular pattern or by the shortest possible path.

Tracking conditions on surfaces of inorganic material can be completely removed by cleaning the surfaces, because no actual damage to the material occurs. In the case of organic material, the surface is damaged in varying degrees, depending on the intensity of the electric discharge and the duration of exposure. If the damage is not too severe, it can be repaired by sanding and application of track-resistant varnish in accordance with the manufacturer's instructions. Organic material that has been damaged should be replaced or repaired in accordance with manufacturer's instructions.

N A.12.3.4 Temperatures over design levels for prolonged periods can reduce the electrical life of organic insulating materials. Prolonged exposure to higher than rated temperatures can also cause physical deterioration of the materials, resulting in lowered mechanical strength.

Localized heating (hot spots) can sometimes occur and can be masked because the overall temperature of the surroundings is not raised appreciably. Loosely bolted connections in a busbar splice or void spaces (dead air) in a taped assembly are examples of this problem.

Infrared thermography inspections can be used to detect potentially damaging heat. However, infrared inspection should not be utilized as the only method of inspection. External conditions that provide evidence of heat damage include the following:

(1) Discoloration, usually a darkening, of materials or finishes
(2) Crazing, cracking, and flaking of varnish coatings

(3) Embrittlement of tapes and cable insulation
(4) Delamination of materials or finishes
(5) Generalized carbonization of materials or finishes
(6) Melting, oozing, or exuding of substances from within an insulating assembly

Insulating materials that have been physically damaged should be replaced. Mild discoloration is permissible if the cause of overheating is corrected.

N A.12.3.5 Online partial discharge (PD) surveys can be performed by permanently installed sensors and PD detection systems or with portable equipment. Refer to the manufacturer's instructions.

Verifying control power transformers, instrument transformers, and metering are operating correctly could require direct testing or could, in some cases, be accomplished by review of metering and other derived data.

N A.12.3.6.1.1 Examples of dedicated maintenance or operational tools are rack-out devices, hoisting or handling apparatus, and ground and test devices.

N A.13.1.1 Panelboards or switchboards are either fuse or circuit breaker type. Where critical circuits are involved, panelboards or switchboards should be appropriately identified by tags, labels, or color coding.

Seldom are panelboards or switchboards de-energized, and then only for circuit changes; it is for those times that electrical maintenance can be scheduled. There is always the possibility of an error or accidental tripping of a main circuit breaker causing an unscheduled shutdown. During operating periods, the panels can be checked only for hot spots or excessive heat. This electrical maintenance should be done at reasonable intervals in accordance with the importance of the circuit. A record should be made of areas that have given trouble; memory should not be relied on.

N A.13.1.2 Examples of related components that are not covered in this chapter include switches and circuit breakers.

N A.14.1 Additional resources and industry consensus standards that apply to busway include:

(1) UL 857, *Busways,* is a product standard that applies to busways and associated fittings rated at 600 volts or less.
(2) IEEE C37.23, *Standard for Metal-Enclosed Bus,* applies to metal-enclosed (ME) bus assemblies including nonsegregated-phase bus, segregated-phase bus, and isolated-phase bus. Rated maximum voltages of ac ME bus assemblies range from 0.635 kV through 38 kV with continuous current ratings above 600 amperes.
(3) NEMA BU1.1, *General Instructions for Handling, Installation, Operation, and Maintenance of Busway Rated 600 Volts or Less,* contains general instructions for handling, installation, operation, and maintenance of busway systems.
(4) ANSI/NETA MTS, *Standard for Maintenance Testing Specifications for Electrical Power Distribution Equipment and Systems,* Sections 7.4 and 7.21, contains inspection and test procedures that could be applicable to busway systems.

N A.14.3.1 Inspect for moisture or signs of previous wetness or dripping onto the busway or onto connection boxes from leaky roofs, pipes, sprinklers, or other sources of moisture.

Seal off any cracks or openings that have allowed moisture to enter the busway or its connection boxes. Eliminate source of

Shaded text = Revisions. **Δ = Text deletions and figure/table revisions.** **• = Section deletions.** **N = New material.**

any dripping onto the busway and any other source of moisture.

Where busways penetrate floors, a minimum 4-inch-high curb should be installed around the floor openings to prevent liquids from contacting the busway.

N **A.14.3.2** Hydrocarbon spray propellants and hydrocarbon-based sprays or compounds can cause degradation of certain plastics and elastomers. Contact the busway manufacturer before using these products to clean, dry, or lubricate during installation or maintenance.

N **A.14.3.2.1** Where combustible dust is involved, caution should be exercised to ensure that an ignition hazard is not created.

N **A.14.3.3** Hydrocarbon spray propellants and hydrocarbon-based sprays or compounds can cause degradation of certain plastics and elastomers. Contact the busway manufacturer before using these products to clean, dry, or lubricate during installation or maintenance.

N **A.14.3.5** *Insulation Resistance Testing for Busway Rated 600 Volts and Below.* Insulation resistance testing should be performed to ensure that the system is free from short circuits and grounds (phase-to-ground, phase-to-neutral, and phase-to-phase). Record and maintain records of the testing results.

Insulation resistance test readings vary inversely with the length of run and width or number of bars per phase. Readings will vary with humidity.

Dielectric Withstand (High-Potential) Testing for Metal-Enclosed Busway Rated over 600 Volts. Dielectric withstand (high-potential) tests in accordance with IEEE C37.23, *Standard for Metal-Enclosed Bus,* should be conducted at 75 percent of the rated insulation withstand levels shown in Table A.14.3.5. Because this might be above the corona starting voltage of some busways, frequent testing is undesirable.

N **A.15.3.5** For additional information and guidance on testing molded case circuit breakers reference NEMA AB-4, *Guidelines for Inspection and Preventive Maintenance of Molded-Case Circuit Breakers Used in Commercial and Industrial Applications.*

N **A.16.3.1** Evidence of corrosion and wear can include excessive erosion of the inside of the fuse tube; physical damage to the outside of the fuse tube including cracks and cuts; discharge (tracking); dirt on the outside of the fuse tube; or improper assembly and could prevent proper fuse operation.

Fuses Rated 1000 V or Less. Early detection of overheating is possible using infrared examination. If evidence of overheating exists, the cause should be determined. Fuses showing signs of

Table A.14.3.5 Metal-Enclosed Bus Dielectric Withstand Test Voltages

Metal-Enclosed Bus Nominal Voltage (kV, rms)	Insulation Withstand Level (kV, rms)*	High-Potential Field Test (kV, rms)†
4.16	19	14
13.8	36	27
23.0	60	45
34.5	80	60

*Test duration is 1 minute.
†Field test voltage is 75 percent of insulation withstand level.

deterioration, such as discolored or damaged casings or loose terminals, should be replaced.

Fuseholders should be deenergized before installing or removing fuses. Where it is not feasible or would result in a greater hazard to deenergize the fuseholder, installation or removal of fuses should be performed only with the load removed and in accordance with appropriate safety-related work practices for the task.

Many different types of fuses are used in power distribution systems and utilization equipment. Fuses differ by performance, characteristics, and physical size. Fuses, whether new or replacement, should be verified as the proper type and rating. When fuses are replaced, fuseholders should never be altered or forced to accept fuses that do not readily fit. An adequate supply of spare fuses with proper ratings, especially those that are uncommon, minimizes replacement problems.

The most common fuse classes for 0 ampere through 600 ampere applications on power systems are Class H, Class K, Class R, Class J, Class T, Class G, Class CC, and Class L. Class H, Class K, and Class R are the same physical size and are interchangeable in standard nonrejection-style fuseholders. Class H and Class K fuses are not current limiting whereas Class R fuses are current limiting. Special rejection-style fuseholders accept only Class R fuses. Note that Class R fuses are manufactured in two types: Class RK1 and Class RK5. Class RK1 fuses are more current limiting than Class RK5 and are generally recommended to upgrade older distribution systems. Class L fuses are available in the range of 601 amperes through 6000 amperes. Class J, Class T, Class G, Class CC, and Class L are size rejection fuses. One type of fuse should never arbitrarily be replaced with a different type simply because it fits into the fuseholder.

N **A.16.3.5** Fuses can be tested with a continuity tester to verify that the fuse is not open. Resistance readings can be taken using a sensitive 4-wire instrument such as a Kelvin bridge or micro-ohmmeter. Fuse resistance values should be compared against values recommended by the manufacturer. Where the manufacturer's data is not readily available, resistance deviations of more than 15 percent for identical fuses in the same circuit should be investigated.

N **A.17.3** For additional information and guidance on inspection and preventive maintenance of switches, reference NEMA KS-3, *Guidelines for Inspection and Preventive Maintenance of Switches Used in Commercial and Industrial Applications.*

N **A.17.3.3** Where manufacturer's instructions are not available, electrically conductive lubrication should be of a synthetic oil-based solution and should not contain fillers or thickeners that are detrimental to contact action or resistance.

Where manufacturer's instructions are not available, electrical non-conductive lubrication should be a light viscosity, high-grade petroleum oil with formulated solvents to soften and remove contaminants and additives to displace moisture and prevent rust and corrosion.

N **A.17.3.5** See NFPA 110 and NFPA 111 for further information on Line 11 of Table 17.3.5, performing functional tests for automatic transfer switches, bypass switches, and other transfer switch equipment.

N **A.18.1** Electrical maintenance is the one of best ways to ensure continued reliable service from electrical cable installations. Visual inspection and electrical testing of the cable insu-

---

Shaded text = Revisions.   Δ = Text deletions and figure/table revisions.   • = Section deletions.   *N* = New material.

lation are the major maintenance procedures. However, it should be stressed that no amount of maintenance can correct improper application or physical damage done during installation.

N A.18.3.1 If, in addition to the visual inspection, cables are to be touched or moved, they should be in an electrically safe work condition.

Cables in vaults should be inspected for sharp bends, physical damage, excessive tension, oil leaks, pits, cable movement, insulation swelling, soft spots, cracked jackets in nonlead cables, damaged fireproofing, poor ground connections, deterioration of metallic sheath bonding, as well as corroded and weakened cable supports and the continuity of any main grounding system. Terminations and splices of nonlead cables should be inspected for tracking or signs of corona. The ground braid should be inspected for corrosion and tight connections. The bottom surface of the cable should be inspected for wear or scraping, due to movement, at the point of entrance into the vault and where it rests on the cable supports.

The vault should be inspected for deterioration of the concrete, both internal and above ground. In some instances, the vault can be equipped with drains that might require cleaning. In some instances, it might be necessary to pump water from the vault prior to entrance. A vault should not be entered unless a test for dangerous gas has been made and adequate ventilation is provided. The inspection crew should always consist of two or more persons with at least one remaining outside the vault, and the rules and regulations for confined space entry should be followed. [See OSHA requirements in 29 CFR 1910.146, "Permit-Required Confined Spaces," for practices and procedures to protect employees from the hazards of entry into permit-required confined spaces, and 29 CFR 1910.269(e), "Electric Power Generation, Transmission, and Distribution, Enclosed Spaces," for enclosed space entry.]

Potheads, a type of insulator with a bell or pot-like shape typically used to connect underground electrical cables to overhead lines, should be inspected for oil or compound leaks and cracked or chipped porcelain. The porcelain surfaces should be cleaned, and if the connections are exposed, their tightness should be checked.

Cable identification tags or markings should be checked.

Aerial Installations. Aerial cable installations should be inspected for mechanical damage due to vibration, deteriorating supports, or suspension systems. Special attention should be given to the dead-end supports to ensure that the cable insulation is not abraded, pinched, or bent too sharply. Aerial cable installations should be inspected for animal and bird infestation. Terminations should be inspected as covered in Chapter 7.

Raceway Installations. Because the raceway is the primary mechanical support for the cable, it should be inspected for signs of deterioration or mechanical damage or if the cable jacket is being abraded or mechanically damaged. In many installations, the raceway serves as a part of the ground-fault current circuit. Joints should be inspected for signs of looseness or corrosion that could result in a high resistance. Splices and terminations should be verified as covered in Chapter 7.

N A.18.3.5 A preferred testing method should be selected only after all circuit parameters have been analyzed.

Electrical Testing. When performing electrical testing of cables, there are many factors that need to be considered before applying a specific test methodology. The two most commonly used tests for cable insulation are insulation resistance testing and dc over-potential testing. Other tests are listed in ANSI/IEEE 400, *Guide for Field Testing and Evaluation of the Insulation of Shielded Power Cable Systems Rated 5 kV and Above.* In many instances it can be desired to achieve a more comprehensive analysis of cable condition, doing so with techniques and methods other than insulation resistance.

Inspection and Testing Records. Because inspection intervals normally are 1 year or more, comprehensive records are an important part of any maintenance program. Comprehensive records should be arranged to facilitate comparison from year to year.

N A.20.3.1 Common mode noise voltages can develop when the equipment-grounding conductor and the grounded conductor are not effectively bonded. Common mode noise can be produced in wiring without an equipment-grounding conductor and without electrically continuous raceway. Ground loops can be undesirable because they create a path for noise currents to flow. Undesirable touch potentials can result from contacting metallic surfaces that are improperly grounded. Equipment misoperation due to unequal ground potentials results in improper data communication or improper readings of transducers. Shutdown or damage of electronic equipment can be due to electrostatic discharge (ESD). Nonoperation or malfunction of protective circuit devices or voltage sag can be due to high-impedance ground-fault paths. Damage, nonoperation, or misoperation of electronic components can be caused by poor connections in the grounding path. Damage or destruction of the neutral conductor or cable shields can result from improper sizing of a high-impedance neutral grounding device. Voltage can be present on de-energized circuits during testing of these conductors. Destruction of equipment and surge protection devices can follow a voltage transient, such as a lightning strike.

Grounding of surface-mounted equipment can be accomplished by securing the equipment to a properly grounded metal outlet box. Metal outlet boxes have a location to place a grounding screw. The bare copper equipment grounding conductor in the nonmetallic sheathed cable is usually terminated under this screw.

If the outlet box is nonmetallic, the equipment grounding conductor from the equipment is connected to the equipment grounding conductor in the outlet box. For example, with suspended ceiling luminaires, grounding of the luminaire can be accomplished by using metallic wire whips or nonmetallic sheathed cable with ground between the outlet box and the luminaire.

If the wiring method utilizes a metallic armored cable wiring method or nonmetallic-sheathed cable with ground, proper connection of the wiring provides an acceptable equipment ground.

For a more complete list of possible wiring methods or if there is no equipment grounding means found, refer to *NFPA 70* for proper grounding.

N A.20.3.5 An isolation transformer has separate primary and secondary windings. The bonding jumper between the equipment-grounding conductor and the secondary grounded

ductor provides protection from common mode electrical
e.

is recommended that a shielded isolation transformer be
d where grounding is inadequate for sensitive electronic
pment. It contains an electrostatic shield between the
ary and secondary windings that is connected to the
pment-grounding terminal.

e J.7.4.1. See ANSI/IEEE 1100, *Recommended Practice for
ering and Grounding Electronic Equipment (IEEE Emerald Book)*.

Table 20.3.5, tests 4, 5, and 6 are diagnostic tests. These
performed when there is reason to suspect the ground
m might have been compromised. Also consider the use of
wer monitor that can be installed during a maintenance
rval in lieu of discrete measurements.

ne example of an industry practice for conducting Test
4 is the ground grid integrity test found in IEEE 80, *Guide
afety in AC Substation Grounding*.

.1 The term *ground-fault circuit interrupter (GFCI)* is applied
escribe a family of devices intended for shock protection of
onnel.

round-Fault Circuit Interrupter (GFCI). A Class A GFCI is listed
JL 943, *Ground-Fault Circuit-Interrupters*, and is designed to
ect a person from electrocution when contact between a
part of the protected circuit and ground causes current
ugh a person's body. A GFCI disconnects the circuit when a
ent equal to or higher than the calibration point (4 mA to
A) flows through the protected circuit to ground. It does
eliminate the shock sensation since normal perception
is approximately 0.5 mA. Additional GFCI classes are avail-
that offer protection under other conditions.

ecial-Purpose GFCI (SPGFCI). A Class C, Class D, or Class E
I is listed to UL 943C, *Outline of Investigation for Special
ose Ground-Fault Circuit-Interrupters*, and is designed to
ect a person from electrocution when contact between a
part of the protected circuit and ground causes current
ugh a person's body.

round-Fault Protection of Equipment. A system listed to
053, *Ground-Fault Sensing and Relaying Equipment*, is inten-
to provide protection of equipment from damaging line-to-
nd fault currents by causing a disconnecting means to
all ungrounded conductors of the faulted circuit. This
ction is provided at current levels less than those required
otect conductors from damage through the operation of a
ly circuit overcurrent device.

rcuit breakers with equipment ground-fault protection are
nbination of a circuit breaker and ground-fault protective
es designed to serve the dual function of providing over-
nt protection and ground-fault protection for equipment.
are intended to be used in accordance with Articles 426
427 of *NFPA 70*.

ound-fault sensing and relaying equipment is intended to
de ground-fault protection of equipment at services and
rs. They are rated for ground current pickup levels as
as 1200 amperes.

3.1 *Circuit-Breaker with an Integrated GFCI*. A circuit-
ker-type GFCI is designed in the form of a small circuit
ker and is completely self-contained within the unit hous-
The circuit-breaker-type GFCI provides overload and short-

circuit protection for the circuit conductors in addition to
ground-fault protection for personnel. It is intended to be
mounted in a panelboard or other enclosure.

Receptacles with an Integrated GFCI. A receptacle-type GFCI is
designed in the form of a standard receptacle, is completely
self-contained within the unit housing, and does not provide
overload or short-circuit protection. It is intended for permanent installation in conventional-device outlet boxes or other
suitable enclosures.

Portable Receptacles and Cords with Integrated GFCI. A portable-
type GFCI is a unit intended to be easily transported and plugged into a receptacle outlet. Cords, tools, or other devices to be
provided with ground-fault protection for personnel are then
plugged into receptacles mounted in the unit.

Permanently Integrated, In-Equipment GFCI. A permanently
mounted-type GFCI is a self-contained, enclosed unit designed
to be wall- or pole-mounted and permanently wired into the
circuit to be protected.

N A.21.3.2 *Ground-Fault Sensing and Relaying Equipment*. Ground-
fault sensing and relaying equipment is used to prevent
damage to conductors and equipment. The protective equipment consists of three main components: (1) sensors, (2) relay
or control unit, and (3) a tripping means for the disconnect
device controlling the protected circuit.

Sensing Methods. Detection of ground-fault current is done by
either of two basic methods. With one method, ground-fault
current flow is detected by sensing current in the grounded
conductor. With the other method, all phase conductor
currents are monitored by either a single large sensor or
several smaller ones.

Sensors. Sensors are generally a type of current transformer
and are installed on the circuit conductors. The relay or
control unit can be mounted remote from the sensors or can
be integral with the sensor assembly.

N A.22.3.3 OSHA 29 CFR 1926.56, "Illumination," and *The Lighting Library* (Illuminating Engineering Society of North America) provide guidance on acceptable illumination levels.

N A.24.1 The use of wiring devices for the connection of equipment provides for rapid removal and replacement and facili-
tates relocation of electrical equipment.

Devices used in hazardous (classified) locations require
some additional inspections. Flame paths should be inspected
to ensure that safe gaps are not exceeded and that no scratches
are on the ground joints. All screws holding the receptacle to
the body should be installed and tight. Covers and threaded
openings should be properly tightened. These devices should
be checked to make sure that the plug and receptacle marking
agree with the present classification of the area regarding class,
group, and division.

The connection of equipment to supplies of incorrect electrical ratings of current, voltage, phase, or frequency can be
dangerous or can cause damage to equipment. Therefore,
attachment plugs, cord connectors, and equipment are provided with appropriate ratings and configurations to prevent
interconnection that could create hazards. See ANSI/NEMA
WD 6, *Wiring Devices — Dimensional Specifications*, for configurations.

Use of some of these devices to disconnect some equipment under load conditions, such as welders, and running or stalled motors can be hazardous. Other load-interrupting means intended for this purpose should be used prior to disconnecting the wiring device.

If there is abnormal heating of the receptacle, plug, or connector insulation, the device should be checked for loose terminations or insufficient pressure between contacts and terminations should be corrected or the device replaced. If there is arc tracking or evidence of burning of the insulation or other damage, the insulation should be replaced.

Plugs should fit firmly when inserted into the mating connector or receptacle. Insufficient mating force can result in contact erosion caused by arcing of the contacts or accidental disengagement. The connector or receptacle should be checked to ensure that adequate contact pressure is present. The complete interior should be replaced if there is discoloration of the housing or severe erosion of the contact.

Receptacle contacts should retain inserted plugs firmly. Corroded, deformed, or mechanically damaged contacts should be replaced.

All mounting and assembly screws must be present and checked to ensure that they are tight to ensure proper grounding, prevent the entrance of adverse environmental products, and provide cable retention.

Proper wire connections on receptacles and proper polarity of power connection, including the integrity of the equipment grounding conductor, should be confirmed.

The equipment grounding conductor (green insulation) of the cord must be attached to the grounding terminal of the device, thereby ensuring grounding continuity.

N A.25.1.1 There are two basic types of UPS systems: static and rotary. Some systems are hybrid versions that incorporate some features of both.

A static unit rectifies incoming ac power to dc and then inverts the dc into ac of the proper voltage and frequency as input power to the load. A battery bank connected between the rectifier and inverter sections ensures an uninterrupted supply of dc power to the inverter section.

A basic rotary system is essentially a motor-generator set that provides isolation between the incoming power supply and the load and stabilizes power supply aberrations by flywheel mechanical inertia effect.

In the UPS industry, the term *module* refers to a single self-contained enclosure containing the power and control elements needed to achieve uninterrupted operation. These components include transformers, rectifier, inverter, and protective devices.

UPS systems can comprise one or more UPS modules connected in parallel either to increase the capacity of the system power rating or to provide redundancy in the event of a module malfunction or failure. Figure A.25.1.1(a) illustrates a typical single-module static 3-phase UPS configuration. Note that in this configuration the solid-state switch (SSS) is internal to the UPS module.

Figure A.25.1.1(b) illustrates a typical multimodule static 3-phase UPS configuration. Note that in this configuration the SSS is in the stand-alone static transfer switch (STC) control cabinet.

Almost all UPS systems comprise these common elements: disconnecting means, bypass and transfer switches, protective devices and power switchgear, molded-case circuit breakers, and fuses. Depending on the type of UPS (static, rotary, or hybrid), the system might also include transformers, batteries, a battery charger, a rectifier/inverter unit (static system), and a motor-generator set (rotary system). The system might also be supported by a standby generating unit to permit operations to continue during sustained power outages.

N A.25.4.2.2.1 Recommended load steps for determining UPS output stability are expressed as a percentage of the UPS system rating, as follows:

(1)   0 percent to 100 percent to 0 percent
(2)   25 percent to 75 percent to 25 percent
(3)   50 percent to 100 percent to 50 percent
(4)   0 percent to 100 percent to 0 percent

N A.27.1 Information on generator sets can be found in NFPA 110.

N A.27.3.1 In general, the machine should be observed while in operation, if safely possible, and any evidence of maloperation should be noted as an aid to future repairs.

If applicable, bearing oil level should be observed by means such as a sight glass or constant level oiler and oil added as needed (see A.27.3.3). If oil rings are used, free turning of the rings should be checked on starting a new machine, at each inspection period, and after maintenance work. The oil level should be such that a 90-degree segment of the oil ring on the inside diameter is immersed while the machine shaft is at rest,

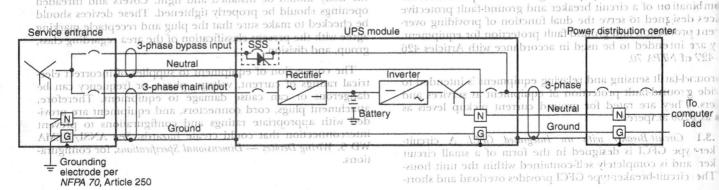

N FIGURE A.25.1.1(a)   Typical Single-Module Static 3-Phase UPS Configuration.

Shaded text = Revisions.   △ = Text deletions and figure/table revisions.   • = Section deletions.   *N* = New material.

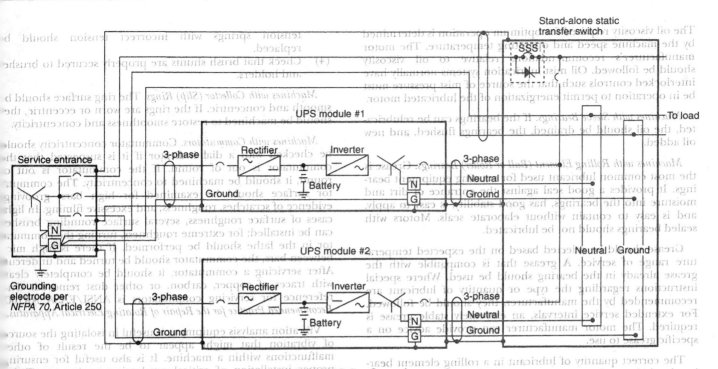

FIGURE A.25.1.1(b)   Typical Multimodule Static 3-Phase UPS Configuration.

as shown in Figure A.27.3.1. A sight glass, constant level oiler, or some other unit should be provided to mark and observe the oil level. Levels should be marked for the at-rest condition and the operating condition.

Large, vertical motors frequently have a surrounding oil bath for lubrication of either rolling-element bearings or plate-thrust bearings. Horizontal units equipped with ball and roller bearings might also have an oil bath. The proper oil level is determined by the manufacturer and depends on the bearing system. A sight glass or some other unit should be provided to mark and observe the oil level. This level can change depending on whether the motor is operating or at rest, and it should be marked for both situations.

For oil-mist lubrication systems the drain/discharge openings at each bearing should be checked to see that pressure can be discharged freely to the atmosphere and that the mist pressure-regulation equipment is functioning properly.

A.27.3.2 Where rotating equipment is exposed to dirt, regular inspections should detect when cleaning is needed. The external surface of motors should be kept clean because a pileup of dirt restricts heat dissipation.

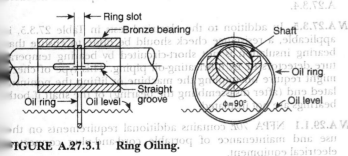

FIGURE A.27.3.1   Ring Oiling.

Machines that have been clogged with mud from dust storms, floods, or other unusual conditions should be given a thorough water washing, usually with a hose with pressure not exceeding 1.72 kPa (25 psi). Initial cleaning should be made with hot nonsaline water plus detergent, followed by a rinse with hot nonsaline water (no detergent). The machine should be completely dismantled, terminal boxes opened, and all corroded parts identified for repair or replacement. All components that are to be reused should be washed in a tank of hot, fresh, nonsaline water for at least four hours. The winding insulation resistance should be measured with a megohmmeter every 2 hours until the insulation resistance has stabilized. Allow the insulation to cool in a dry environment to avoid moisture absorption. Sleeve bearings and housings should be cleaned and rolling element bearings should be replaced with the same type as originally supplied with the machine.

Drying Methods. The commonly used methods are external heat or internal heat. External heat is preferred because it is the safer application. Forced hot air can be heated electrically, by steam, or by a controlled gas burner. Electric space heaters or infrared lamps can also be used. They should be distributed so as not to overheat any machine components.

Coil insulation can be dried by circulating current through the winding. There is some hazard involved with this method because the heat generated in the inner parts is not readily dissipated. This method should be followed only under competent supervision.

N A.27.3.2.2 One reference for minimum insulation resistance levels is ANSI/IEEE 43, *Recommended Practice for Testing Insulation Resistance of Rotating Machinery.*

N A.27.3.3 Oils for lubricating rotating equipment should be high-quality circulating oils with rust and oxidation inhibitors.

The oil viscosity required for optimum operation is determined by the machine speed and operating temperature. The motor manufacturer's recommendations relative to oil viscosity should be followed. Oil mist lubrication systems normally have interlocked controls such that the source of mist pressure must be in operation to permit energization of the lubricated motor.

Machines with Sleeve Bearings. If the bearings can be relubricated, the oil should be drained, the bearings flushed, and new oil added.

Machines with Rolling Element (Ball or Roller) Bearings. Grease is the most common lubricant used for rotating equipment bearings. It provides a good seal against the entrance of dirt and moisture into the bearings, has good stability, is easy to apply, and is easy to contain without elaborate seals. Motors with sealed bearings should not be lubricated.

Grease should be selected based on the expected temperature range of service. A grease that is compatible with the grease already in the bearing should be used. Where special instructions regarding the type or quantity of lubricant are recommended by the manufacturer, they should be followed. For extended service intervals, an extremely stable grease is required. The motor manufacturer can provide advice on a specific grease to use.

The correct quantity of lubricant in a rolling element bearing should be used to assure proper operation.

Machines equipped with grease fittings and relief plugs should be lubricated by a low-pressure grease gun using the following procedure:

(1) The pressure-gun fitting and the regions around the motor grease fittings should be wiped clean.
(2) The relief plug should be removed, and the relief hole should be freed of any hardened grease.
(3) Grease should be added with the machine at standstill until new grease is expelled through the relief hole.
(4) The machine should be run for about 10 minutes with the relief plug removed to expel excess grease.
(5) The relief plug should be cleaned and replaced.

Observation at the time of greasing should determine whether the bearings are operating quietly and without undue heating.

N **A.27.3.4** Where possible, bearings, gears, and couplings should be uniformly preheated before installation to minimize damage. All rotating elements should be dynamically balanced to within standard tolerance.

All rotating equipment should be properly aligned at operating temperature when installed. Rim and face or reverse indicator methodology should be used. Dial indicators or laser alignment equipment should be used for alignment.

Machines with Brushes. If safely possible, the following should be performed offline:

(1) Check brushes in holders for fit and free play, and those that are worn down almost to the brush rivet should be replaced.
(2) Inspect brush faces for chipped toes or heels and for heat cracks; replace damaged brushes.
(3) Check the brush spring pressure and readjust in accordance with the manufacturer's instructions; constant

tension springs with incorrect tension should be replaced.
(4) Check that brush shunts are properly secured to brushes and holders.

Machines with Collector (Slip) Rings. The ring surface should be smooth and concentric. If the rings are worn or eccentric, they should be machined to restore smoothness and concentricity.

Machines with Commutators. Commutator concentricity should be checked with a dial indicator if it is suspected that the commutator is out of round. If the commutator is out of round, it should be machined to concentricity. The commutator surface should be examined for high bars, grooving, evidence of scratches, roughness, and excessive filming. In light cases of surface roughness, several surface rounding brushes can be installed; for extreme roughness, turning the commutator in the lathe should be performed. If there is high mica between bars, the commutator should be turned and undercut. After servicing a commutator, it should be completely clean with traces of copper, carbon, or other dust removed. One reference for servicing commutators is ANSI/EASA AR100, *Recommended Practice for the Repair of Rotating Electrical Apparatus.*

Vibration analysis equipment is useful in isolating the source of vibration that might appear to be the result of other malfunctions within a machine. It is also useful for ensuring proper installation of critical production equipment. Today there are computerized data collecting analyzers that store vibration spectrums, using fast fourier transform (FFT) methodology. In addition to detecting vibration due to unbalance, FFT analysis of the instruments can identify faults in stator windings, rotor bars and end rings, and bearings.

A formal vibration analysis program can reduce costly machine failures. The program can range from the use of simple handheld analyzers to sophisticated multichannel recorders with permanently mounted sensors to provide data for comparison. Such a program makes it possible to keep track of the condition of rotating equipment, particularly high speed types. Trend charts assist in establishing maintenance needs.

The most common methods of measuring vibration are in units of velocity. Velocity measurements are in millimeters per second or inches per second. Vibration is usually measured at the bearing housing.

Displacement is generally used as an indicator of vibration severity for both low-speed equipment operating at less than 1200 rpm and low-frequency vibration. When measured as displacement, the units are microns peak-to-peak or mils peak-to-peak. Velocity is independent of machine speed and therefore a better general indicator of overall vibration severity. Suggested vibration limits for machines are specified in Table A.27.3.4.

N **A.27.3.5** In addition to the electrical tests in Table 27.3.5, if applicable, a resistance check should be done to ensure that bearing insulation is not short-circuited by bearing temperature detectors or by lubricating-oil piping. This type of check might require uncoupling the machine or lifting the noninsulated end (after disassembling the bearing) of the shaft if both bearings are not insulated.

N **A.29.1.1** NFPA *70E* contains additional requirements on the use and maintenance of portable cord-and-plug connected electrical equipment.

N Table A.27.3.4 Vibration Severity Chart

Velocity rms		Class 1	Class 2	Class 3	Class 4
mm/sec	in./sec				
0.71	0.028	A	A	A	A
1.12	0.044	B	A	A	A
1.8	0.071	B	B	A	A
2.8	0.110	C	B	B	A
4.5	0.177	C	C	B	B
7.1	0.279	D	C	C	B
11.2	0.440	D	D	C	C
18.0	0.708	D	D	D	C
28.0	1.10	D	D	D	D

Notes:

(1) Class 1: up to 20 hp on fabricated steel foundation; Class 2: 25 hp–100 hp on fabricated steel foundation, 100 hp–400 hp on heavy solid foundation; Class 3: above 400 hp on heavy solid foundation; Class 4: above 100 hp on fabricated steel foundation.

(2) Grade A: good; Grade B: usable; Grade C: just acceptable; Grade D: not acceptable.

N A.29.3.1.1 Visual inspections are aimed at detecting signs of damage. This could also include the mechanical adjusting and tune-up of equipment and the detection and correction of small problems before they become major problems. Items requiring attention should be reported, removed from use, and tagged "Do Not Use."

N A.29.3.5 Tool and appliance testers are available to perform these tests quickly and easily.

N A.30.1 A solar photovoltaic (PV) electrical energy system is a renewable source of energy. The major electrical system components include the array circuit(s), inverter(s), and controller(s). The arrays are generally found mounted either on a building roof or on supports in a ground mounted array. Photovoltaic systems can be interactive with other electrical power production sources or standalone, with or without electrical energy storage such as batteries.

Photovoltaic systems typically generate voltages in the 48 Vdc to 1500 Vdc range. Only properly trained and qualified persons should perform maintenance on PV systems due to the unique hazards associated with the arrays. The array can produce hazardous electrical energy when exposed to sunlight and even artificial light.

Energy monitoring is a primary means of determining the "health" of the array performance. Short- or long-term reductions in output power can be associated with individual module failure, dirt accumulation, or deposits of debris on the array. Obtaining performance data and monitoring the array from the time of commissioning provides a baseline performance for ongoing system analysis.

N A.30.2.1 A maintenance program helps to ensure the greatest level of safety to the maintenance worker and that the highest level of efficiency and reliability can be obtained from the operation of the system. The system owner or maintenance personnel should consider performing maintenance during the nighttime, during periods of low moonlight and with minimal artificial light illuminating the array. This helps to reduce electrical hazards and lost production.

N A.30.2.2 Significant weather, such as hail, heavy snow, high winds, driving rain, or lightning, can adversely impact PV systems and their associated equipment. The priority is to render the site physically and electrically safe by tying down loose items and disconnecting exposed circuits and ground faults.

N A.30.3.1 Proper signage should be installed to identify the location of rooftop panels on the building prior to completion of installation. Marking on conduits and enclosures is needed to provide guidance for maintenance and emergency personnel to isolate the PV electrical system. This can facilitate identifying energized electrical lines that connect the solar modules to the inverter, which can be energized even when the inverter is offline. See also *NFPA 70*, Article 690.

N A.30.3.2 See *NFPA 70*, Article 690.

N A.30.4.1 See IEC 62446-2, *Photovoltaic (PV) systems — Requirements for testing, documentation and maintenance — Part 2: grid connected systems — Maintenance of PV systems.*

N A.30.4.2 PV systems and their associated equipment can be damaged when cleaned improperly. The following precautions should be considered:

(1) Cold water should never be applied to a hot PV array as thermal shock can damage the modules.
(2) Cleaning robots and systems should be validated with the system owner and designer as acceptable for the climate, environment, and module types.
(3) Water or cleaning solutions should not be applied to damaged or cracked modules.

N A.30.4.5 *Infrared thermography (IR):* This noncontact electrical test can be performed on photovoltaic modules, strings, systems, and/or associated wiring connections. The modules or systems must have current flowing to acquire useful data. These images can identify potential issues, including failed modules, high-resistance connections, cell hot spots, and interconnection issues.

IV curve trace — current and voltage (IV) tracing: This electrical testing is used to determine output and electrical parameters of photovoltaic modules, strings, and systems. Tests are conducted on electrically isolated photovoltaic devices. Electrical parameters are evaluated, including open circuit voltage, short-circuit current, maximum power, maximum power voltage, and maximum power current. This test can give an accurate snapshot of the health of the module, string, or system.

Electroluminescence imaging (EL): This noncontact electrical test is a useful tool to find and identify cracked cells in deployed crystalline or wafer-based photovoltaic modules. Depending on the equipment used, the modules or strings might need to be isolated to acquire useful images. Cracks in cells can contribute to power loss.

N A.31.3.1 See additional lightning protection requirements in NFPA 780 and applicable FAA requirements.

N A.32.1.2 All other chemistries and lead-acid and NiCd stored energy systems that do not fall under 36 are covered by Chapter 32.

N A.34.3.1 Any components found to be excessively corroded should be repaired or replaced. Leaks should be mitigated, or ventilation should be added or corrected as needed. Missing motor nameplates should be replaced. Electrically operated pool pumps should be listed and labeled. Overhead conductor clearances should be in accordance with 680.9(A) of *NFPA 70*. Any components found to be excessively corroded should be repaired or replaced. Leaks should be mitigated, or ventilation shall be added or corrected as needed. Missing motor nameplates should be replaced. Electrically operated pool pumps should be listed and labeled. Overhead conductor clearances should be in accordance with 680.9(A) of *NFPA 70*.

N A.34.3.2.2 Simple cord surface discoloration from pool chemicals is not considered physical damage.

N A.34.3.2.3 The maximum resistance value permitted between the luminaire and niche is 0.0003 ohms.

N A.36.1 See Chapter 32 for installations that do not meet the definition of stationary standby batteries or are comprised of cells other than lead-acid or NiCd. See Chapter 32 for installations that do not meet the definition of stationary standby batteries or are comprised of cells other than lead-acid or NiCd.

Battery Hazard Awareness. Personnel should be aware of the types of hazards associated with stationary batteries, such as flammable/explosive gas hazards, chemical hazards, electric shock hazards, and arc flash/thermal hazards. Not all stationary batteries have the same types or degrees of hazards. Personnel must understand the potential hazards and do a risk assessment prior to any work. Personnel should also follow the manufacturer's instructions. IEEE 1657, *Recommended Practice for Personnel Qualifications for Installation and Maintenance of Stationary Batteries,* provides recommended curriculum for various skill levels.

Flammable Gas Hazard. Lead-acid and NiCd batteries will emit hydrogen gas, and if not vented the hydrogen concentration will reach a flammable level. Where lead-acid and NiCd batteries are charging, the following steps should be taken:

(1) Verify that the ventilation system in the room or compartment where the batteries are located is operating as required, including both the intake and exhaust systems.
(2) Prevent the use of open flames, sparks, and other ignition sources in the vicinity of storage batteries, gas ventilation paths, and places where flammable gas can accumulate.

AC and DC Voltage Hazard. Voltage is always present on battery systems, so the safety procedures in *NFPA 70E* and IEEE 3007.3, *Recommended Practice for Electrical Safety in Industrial and Commercial Power Systems,* for energized equipment should be followed. Voltages present on large systems, including chargers, can cause injury or death. Personnel should determine the voltages that are present, use insulated tools, and use PPE as appropriate. Conductive objects should not be used near battery cells.

Chemical Hazard. Electrolyte can cause severe injury to the eyes and mucus linings and can cause rash or burns to skin if not treated promptly. Not all battery maintenance activities expose personnel to electrolyte, so the service person must understand the potential exposure as part of the risk assessment prior to doing any work on a battery system.

Arc Flash and Thermal Hazard. Prior to performing the task, personnel should perform a risk assessment and note the potential arc flash and thermal hazards, which should be already posted, and wear the appropriate level of PPE. Measures to avoid arc flash can include separating the battery into

low-voltage segments and ensuring that positive and negative conductive paths are not exposed at the same time.

N A.36.3.1 Measurements and inspections will vary from one type of battery to another. Two examples of battery records for one type of battery, VRLA, are shown in Figure E.21(a) and Figure E.21(b). The records should be modified to correspond to the user's maintenance program.

N A.36.4 Applicable industry maintenance standards include the following:

(1) ANSI/NETA ATS, *Standard for Acceptance Testing Specifications for Electrical Power Distribution Equipment and Systems*
(2) ANSI/NETA MTS, *Standard for Maintenance Testing Specifications for Electrical Power Distribution Equipment and Systems*
(3) ANSI/IEEE 450, *Recommended Practice for Maintenance, Testing, and Replacement of Vented Lead-Acid Batteries for Stationary Applications*
(4) IEEE 1106, *Recommended Practice for Installation, Maintenance, Testing, and Replacement of Vented Nickel-Cadmium Batteries for Stationary Application*
(5) IEEE 1188, *Recommended Practice for Maintenance, Testing, and Replacement of Valve-Regulated Lead-Acid (VRLA) Batteries for Stationary Applications*
(6) IEEE 1578, *Recommended Practice for Stationary Battery Electrolyte Spill Control and Management*
(7) IEEE 1657, *Recommended Practice for Personnel Qualifications for Installation and Maintenance of Stationary Batteries*

N A.36.4.1 Battery chargers play a critical role in maintaining batteries because they supply normal dc requirements and maintain batteries at appropriate levels of charge.

A solution of water and bicarbonate of soda (baking soda) can be used to neutralize lead-acid battery spills, and a solution of boric acid and water can be used for Ni-Cad spills. The battery manufacturer's instructions should be consulted for proper proportions. Information on prevention of and response to electrolyte spills can be found in IEEE 1578, *Recommended Practice for Stationary Battery Electrolyte Spill Containment and Management.*

Excessive water consumption can be a sign of overcharging or cell damage. For lead-antimony batteries, including low-antimony designs such as lead-selenium, water consumption increases gradually with age. Distilled or deionized water needs to be used unless otherwise recommended by the battery manufacturer.

CAUTION: Never add anything but water to a battery unless recommended to do so by the manufacturer.

Local sources of heating and cooling can create cell temperature differentials that cause battery damage.

If deionized water is used, it is important to check for proper operation of the deionizer (or if deionizing filters need replacement).

Excess sedimentation and plate damage can be caused by any of the following:

(1) *Vibration caused by an external source.* Vibration reduces battery life. Excessive vibration can be detected by observing vibration of plates and sediment in the jar. If vibration is observed, then steps should be taken to reduce the vibration source, isolate the batteries from the vibration,

and/or plan for an earlier-than-normal scheduled battery replacement.

(2) *Incorrect charging regimes.* The charger settings should be set to the battery manufacturer's recommended voltage range. If not, they should be adjusted as appropriate.

(3) *Excessive cycling.* The cause of excessive discharge/recharge cycles should be determined and corrected, if possible. Otherwise, it might be necessary to plan for an earlier-than-normal battery replacement.

(4) *Aging.* The battery date codes should be noted, and it should be determined if the observed condition is within the predicted condition for a battery of that age.

(5) *Manufacturing defect.* If the battery is relatively new, or if the condition is only observed in one or a few cells within the same manufacturing "batch number," the manufacturer should be contacted for possible warranty replacement.

(6) *AC ripple current from charger or connected load.* Readings should be taken to determine if the amount of ripple current exceeds the manufacturer's recommended limit.

N A.36.4.2 Lead-acid battery surfaces should be cleaned with a solution of water and sodium bicarbonate to avoid leakage currents caused by electrolyte on the battery. NiCd battery surfaces should be cleaned with a solution of boric acid and water. Cleaners, soaps, or solvents should not be used to clean battery containers and covers since damage can result. Consult the battery manufacturer for the proper solution and dilution.

N A.36.4.5 Inspection results should be recorded to establish trends that can be used in predicting state of health for a battery or batteries.

For VRLA batteries, cell temperature should be obtained by measuring at the negative post of the unit.

For vented batteries in which electrolyte samples are being collected, electrolyte temperature could be determined at the same time.

Use of ohmic measurements should be in accordance with the manufacturer's instructions and with an EMP to set baselines, identify trends, and identify anomalies.

Connections should only be tightened when the need is indicated by resistance readings or infrared scan.

Where a connection resistance persists high, the connection should be cleaned and torqued in accordance with the manufacturer's procedures.

Where test sets to read intercell connection resistance are not available or cannot be used due to inaccessible posts, an infrared scan should be performed while under load to indicate which connections need to be corrected to the battery manufacturer's specified values and repaired.

For batteries that require periodic water additions, the electrolyte levels should be checked on a periodic basis. If the level is approaching the low-level line, distilled or other approved-quality water should be added.

Float current can be measured with a calibrated amp clamp at any point in a series connected battery string. The amp clamp needs to be accurate to currents below one amp. An alternate method could be using a calibrated voltmeter with a calibrated shunt installed in-line with the battery strings, which would be accurate for currents below one amp.

Annex B Suggestions for Inclusion in a Walk-Through Inspection Checklist

This annex is not a part of the requirements of this NFPA document but is included for informational purposes only.

B.1 General. The items suggested in this annex are directed toward minimizing day-to-day electrical hazards. The list is not complete, nor do the items necessarily appear in order of importance. It is presented as a guide for the preparation of a checklist that should be developed for each facility.

△ B.1.1 Flexible Cords (Including Those on Appliances). An inspection should be made for badly worn or frayed spots, splices (not permitted), improper type, or current-carrying capacity that is too small.

△ B.1.2 Plugs and Connectors. Plugs and connectors should be grounding type where required for specific appliances.

B.1.3 Extension Cords. Are extension cords used in place of permanent wiring, and are they of excessive length and of proper type? They should not pass through walls, partitions, or doors.

B.1.4 Multiple Current Taps. Are multiple current taps used because of too few receptacles? In particular, are they used in areas such as canteens, lunchrooms, and offices?

△ B.1.5 Appliances. Grills, toasters, and similar equipment should be spaced from combustible material.

B.1.6 Office Equipment. The condition of flexible cords, plugs, and connectors should be checked, and excessive use of extension cords and multiple current taps should be noted.

△ B.1.7 Receptacle Outlets. Grounding-type receptacles are generally required. Are special receptacle configurations used for those supplying unusual voltages, frequencies, and so on? Are they well marked or identified? In particular, missing faceplates, receptacles showing signs of severe arcing, loose mounting, and so on should be noted.

△ B.1.8 Portable Equipment (Tools, Extension Lamps, and Extension Cords). The condition of cords and plugs should be inspected, and any defective equipment should be removed from service. The condition of guards and shields on lamps should be checked.

△ B.1.9 Luminaires. No luminaire should be located close to highly combustible material. The location of luminaires with burned out bulbs or tubes; luminaires that are heavily coated with dust, dirt, or other material; and reflectors that need cleaning should be noted.

B.1.10 Equipment Grounding. Broken or loose connections at boxes and fittings, flexible connections, and exposed ground straps should be identified. Multiple bonding of conduit and other metallic enclosures to interior water piping systems, including sprinkler systems, is sometimes used as a precaution where building vibration is severe, even though a separate equipment grounding conductor is run with the circuit conductors inside the raceway.

△ B.1.11 Yard Transformer Stations. The condition of transformers, fence, gates, and locks should be noted. Yard and equipment should be free of storage of combustible material, weeds, grass, vines, nests, and so on. Localized overheating, indicated by conductor discoloration, should be watched for.

Shaded text = Revisions. △ = Text deletions and figure/table revisions. • = Section deletions. *N* = New material.

Indication of excessive transformer temperature, pressure, or oil leakage should be noted.

B.1.12 Services. The condition of weatherheads and weatherhoods should be visually checked to determine that they remain in good condition. Nests, such as rodent, insect, and bird nests, should be documented. At the same time, the apparent condition of lightning arresters, surge capacitors, grounding conductors, and grounds should be determined. Are switches safely and readily accessible?

B.1.13 Electrical Equipment Rooms and Motor Control Centers. Electrical equipment rooms and motor control centers should be clean, used for no other purpose, and free of storage of any kind, especially combustible material. Ventilation equipment should be in working condition and unobstructed. Any unusual noises or odors should be noticed and reported promptly. Metering equipment should be checked for high or low voltage and current and any indication of accidental grounding (ungrounded systems). Are switches, disconnects, and motor controllers properly identified as to function? Are fire extinguishers in place, of suitable type, and charged?

B.1.14 Grouped Electrical Control Equipment (Such as Might Be Mounted on Walls). Is grouped electrical control equipment protected from physical damage and readily accessible? Are any equipment enclosures damaged, or do any have missing or open covers? Are any live parts exposed? Any condition that prevents quick or ready access should be reported.

Δ **B.1.15 Enclosures of Electrical Parts (e.g., Motor Control Equipment, Junction Boxes, Switches).** All loose or missing covers and unused openings in enclosures should be documented.

B.1.16 Hazardous (Classified) Location Equipment. All cover bolts should be in place and tight. Permanent markings should not be obstructed by paint. Joints between cover and case should be examined for signs of having been pried open in the removal of the cover. This might have damaged the mating surfaces of the joints. Excessive accumulations of dust and dirt should be noted for removal from all enclosures, including motors, which also should be examined for obstructed ventilation. The use of nonexplosionproof electric equipment, including lighting that might have been installed in the hazardous (classified) location area, should be noted and reported.

B.1.17 Emergency Equipment.

B.1.17.1 All exit lights should be functioning properly.

B.1.17.2 Emergency lights should all be in working condition. Periodic tests are recommended to ensure that emergency lights function when normal lighting is lost.

B.1.17.3 Emergency power supplies, such as batteries and engine-driven generators, normally receive scheduled tests. Records of periodic tests should be checked. Are fuel and cooling supplies for engine drives adequate? Are fire extinguishers in place, of proper type, and charged?

B.1.17.4 Alarm systems, such as for fire, intrusion, smoke detection, sprinkler water flow, and fire pumps, also receive periodic tests. Records of these tests should be checked to ensure that all signals are properly transmitted and that equipment is in good working condition.

Annex C Symbols

This annex is not a part of the requirements of this NFPA document but is included for informational purposes only.

C.1 Figure C.1 contains some typical electrical symbols that are used on electrical power and control schematic drawings.

C.2 Figure C.2 contains some typical electrical symbols that are used on electrical control schematic drawings.

C.3 Figure C.3 contains some typical miscellaneous electrical symbols and tables that are used on electrical control schematics.

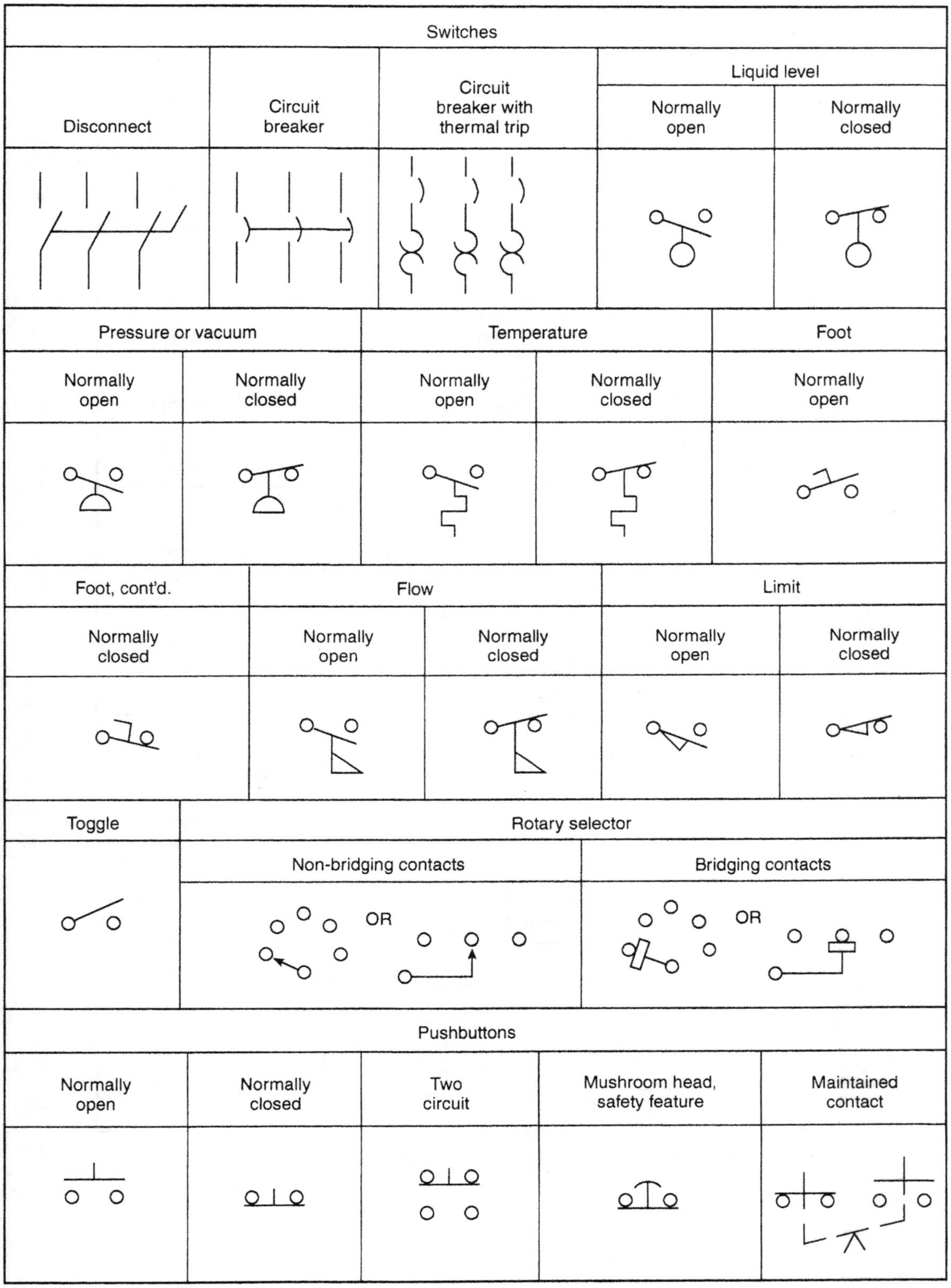

FIGURE C.1 Some Typical Electrical Symbols for Power and Control Schematics. (Courtesy of ANSI/IEEE 315, *Graphic Symbols for Electrical and Electronics Diagrams.*)

Contacts					
Normally open-timed closed	Normally closed-timed open	Normally closed-timed open	Normally open-timed closed	Normally open	Normally closed

Coils				Connections	
Relay, timer, contactor, etc.	Solenoid	Thermally operated relay	Magnetic core transformer	Wires connected	

Connections, cont'd.				Motors	
Wires not connected	Plug and receptacle	Ground to earth	Connection to chassis, not necessarily to earth	3-phase induction motor	

Motors, cont'd.	Resistors, capacitors, etc.		
Direct current shunt motor	Resistor	Capacitor	Fuse

Resistors, capacitors, etc., cont'd.					
Ammeter	Voltmeter	Pilot light (red lens)	Horn	Bell	Multicell battery

FIGURE C.2   Some Typical Electrical Symbols for Electrical Control Schematic Drawings.

Shaded text = Revisions.   Δ = Text deletions and figure/table revisions.   • = Section deletions.   *N* = New material.

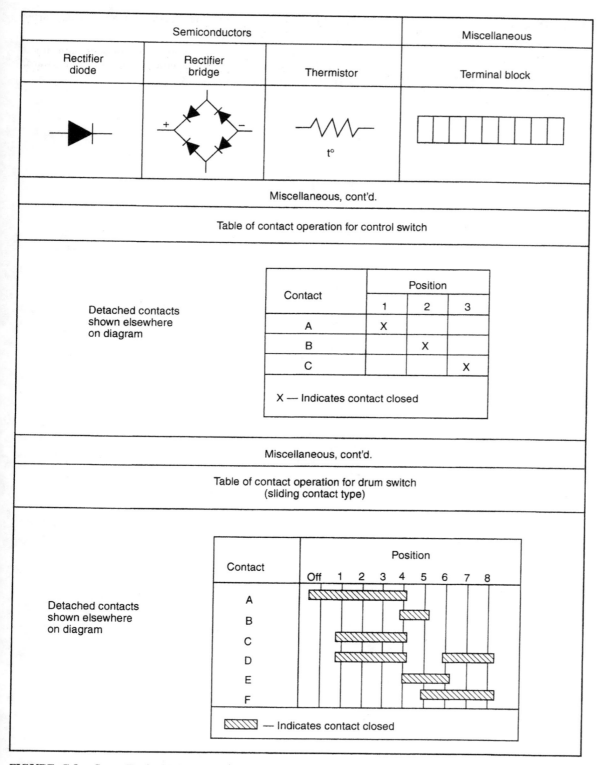

FIGURE C.3   Some Typical Miscellaneous Electrical Symbols.

Shaded text = Revisions.   △ = Text deletions and figure/table revisions.   • = Section deletions.   *N* = New material.

2023 Edition

Annex D Diagrams

This annex is not a part of the requirements of this NFPA document but is included for informational purposes only.

D.1 Note that Annex D is presented to show use of symbols and should not be construed to indicate recommendations. Figure D.1 shows the use of some typical symbols in a single-line power distribution program.

D.2 Figure D.2 shows a wiring diagram for a reversing starter with control transformer.

D.3 Figure D.3 shows a power and control schematic for a reversing starter with low-voltage remote pushbuttons. Forward, reverse, and stop connections are shown.

Shaded text = Revisions. Δ = Text deletions and figure/table revisions. • = Section deletions. *N* = New material.

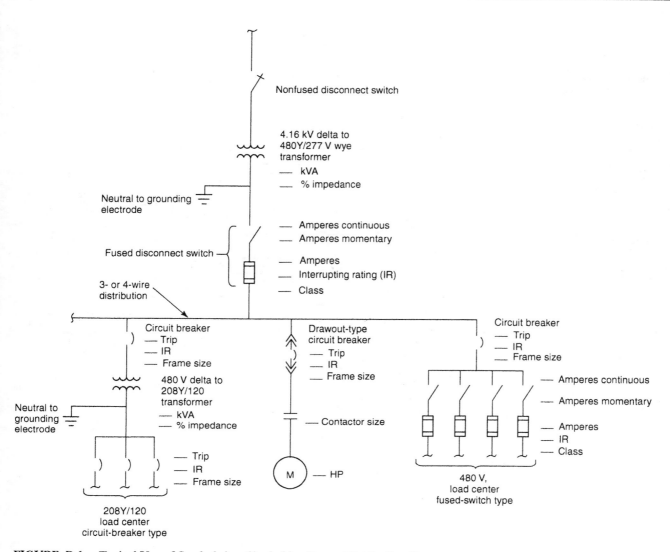

FIGURE D.1   Typical Use of Symbols in a Single-Line Power Distribution Program.

Shaded text = Revisions.   △ = Text deletions and figure/table revisions.   • = Section deletions.   *N* = New material.

2023 Edition

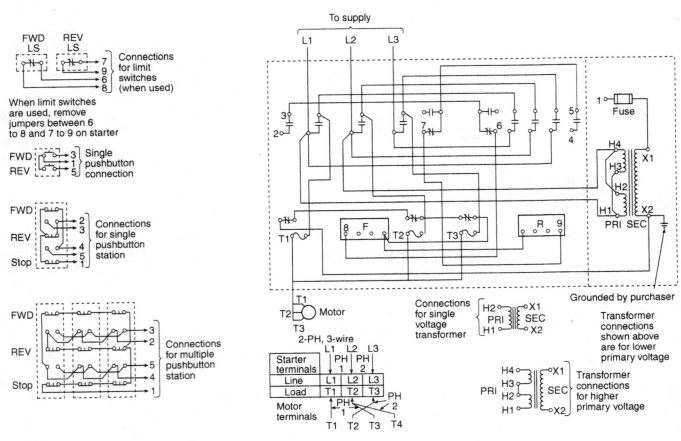

FIGURE D.2 Wiring Diagram for a Reversing Starter with Control Transformer.

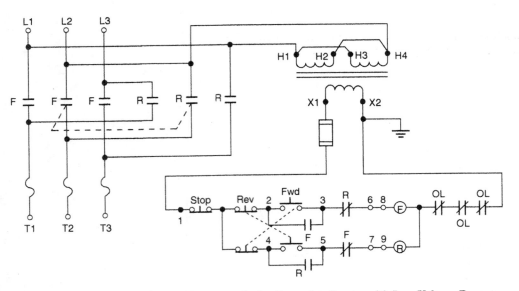

△ **FIGURE D.3** Power and Control Schematic for Reversing Starter with Low-Voltage Remote Pushbuttons.

Shaded text = Revisions.   △ = Text deletions and figure/table revisions.   • = Section deletions.   ***N*** = New material.

Annex E   Forms

This annex is not a part of the requirements of this NFPA document but is included for informational purposes only.

E.1   Figure E.1 shows a typical work order request form.

E.2   Figure E.2 shows a typical air circuit breaker inspection record.

E.3   Figure E.3 shows a typical air circuit breaker test and inspection report.

E.4   Figure E.4 shows a typical medium-voltage vacuum breaker form.

E.5   Figure E.5 shows a typical oil circuit breaker test report.

E.6   Figure E.6 shows a typical disconnect switch test report.

E.7   Figure E.7 shows a typical low-voltage circuit breaker 5-year tests form.

E.8   Figure E.8 shows a typical electrical switchgear–associated equipment inspection record.

E.9   Figure E.9 shows a typical current or potential transformer ratio test report.

E.10   Figure E.10 shows a typical overload relay test report.

E.11   Figure E.11 shows a typical ground-fault system test report.

E.12   Figure E.12 shows a typical instrument/meter calibration and test report.

E.13   Figure E.13 shows a typical watt-hour meter test sheet.

E.14   Figure E.14 shows a typical panelboard/circuit breaker test report.

E.15   Figure E.15 shows a typical transformer test and inspection report.

E.16   Figure E.16 shows a typical transformer (dry type) inspection record.

E.17   Figure E.17 shows a typical transformer (liquid filled) inspection record.

E.18   Figure E.18 shows a typical transformer oil sample report.

E.19   Figure E.19 shows a typical transformer oil trending report.

E.20   Figure E.20 shows a typical transformer insulation resistance record.

E.21   Figure E.21(a) shows an example of a VRLA battery inspection report. Figure E.21(b) shows an example of a VRLA maintenance work sheet.

E.22   Figure E.22 shows a typical engine generator set inspection checklist.

E.23   Figure E.23 shows a typical automatic transfer switch form.

E.24   Figure E.24 shows a typical uninterruptible power supply system inspection checklist.

E.25   Figure E.25 shows a typical back-up power system inspection checklist.

E.26   Figure E.26 shows a typical insulation resistance–dielectric absorption test sheet for power cable.

E.27   Figure E.27 shows a typical cable test sheet.

E.28   Figure E.28 shows a typical insulation resistance test record.

E.29   Figure E.29 shows a typical insulation resistance test record for rotating machinery.

E.30   Figure E.30 shows a typical motor test information form.

E.31   Figure E.31 shows a typical ground system resistance test report.

E.32   Figure E.32 shows a typical ground test inspection report for health care facilities.

E.33   Figure E.33 shows a typical line isolation monitor test data report for health care facilities.

E.34   Figure E.34 shows a typical torque value record.

E.35   Figure E.35 shows a typical main power energization checklist.

E.36   Figure E.36 shows instructions to contractor.

E.37   Figure E.37 shows project scope of work template.

E.38   Figure E.38 shows project scope of work form.

E.39   Figure E.39 shows project scope of work modification form.

E.40   Figure E.40 shows cover and contents.

E.41   Figure E.41 shows point of contact.

E.42   Figure E.42 shows power distribution unit (PDU) survey.

E.43   Figure E.43 shows generator set survey.

E.44   Figure E.44 shows electrical panel survey.

E.45   Figure E.45 shows inverter survey.

E.46   Figure E.46 shows building lightning protection survey.

E.47   Figure E.47 shows rectifier survey.

E.48   Figure E.48 shows electrical panel survey.

E.49   Figure E.49 shows transfer switches survey.

E.50   Figure E.50 shows power transformers survey.

E.51   Figure E.51 shows uninterruptible power system survey.

E.52   Figure E.52 shows low-voltage breaker data record.

E.53   Figure E.53 shows recloser data record.

E.54   Figure E.54 shows generator data record.

Shaded text = Revisions.   Δ = Text deletions and figure/table revisions.   • = Section deletions.   *N* = New material.

2023 Edition

WORK ORDER REQUEST

| Work Order No. | | | | Craft |

Plant Department

Directions to Requester: Complete Section I ONLY. Submit four copies to the Plant Department. Maintain last copy for your files. Prepare a separate request for each job. This request will be returned to you and becomes a work order only when approved and assigned a work order number by the Plant Department. Allow sufficient time for completion. Please TYPE your request.

I. To be completed by requester: Date _____ / _____ / _____

Summary of work request _____

Location of work: Room(s) _____ Building _____

Details of work request _____

Typical work order request form consists of five parts — includes copies for plant department (or plant engineer), data processing, receiving stores, requester, and requester's department. Work to be done is spelled out in detail.

Special time requirement: Date needed _____ / _____ / _____   Indicate reason _____

Department _____ Tel. ext. _____   ❑ Plan attached   ❑ Info. attached

Authorized signature _____ Title _____   Approval if required _____

II. For plant department use only: Date Received _____ / _____ / _____
  A. Your request has been ❑ Approved   ❑ Disapproved   ❑ Forwarded to _____

    for action. Use the assigned work order number when referring to this request.

  B. Instructions: _____

Job Estimates	Craft	Total Hours	Total Labor	Material	Grand Total
	Hours		$	$	$

Assigned to _____ Craft _____   ❑ Day   ❑ Night

Foreman —
  C. Completed per plant instructions? ❑ Yes ❑ No   Requester —
    Can recurrence be prevented? ❑ Yes ❑ No   Completed per your request? ❑ Yes ❑ No
    If yes, indicate _____

    Plant and requester note variations _____

Actual hours used	Tot. reg.	Tot. O/T	Tot. equiv. hrs.

Date _____ Foreman's signature _____   Requester's signature _____

III. For data processing use only:

Dept.	Bldg.	Class	Category	Cause	Pay	O/T $

Total Labor $	+	Total Material $	=	Total $

Work description (alphabetic)

Plant Department

Work Order No.   Craft

© 2023 National Fire Protection Association

NFPA 70B

△ **FIGURE E.1   Typical Work Order Request Form.**

AIR CIRCUIT BREAKER INSPECTION RECORD

Plant ——————————— Date ———————————

Location ——————————— Serial No. ———————————

Mfr. ——————————— Type or Model ———————————

Drawout ❏   Non-drawout ❏   Switchboard ❏   Metal clad ❏

Rating: Volts ———— Amperes ———— Interrupting Amperes ————

Operation: Manual ❏   Electrical ❏   Remote Control ❏

Volts close ———— ac ❏ dc ❏   Volts trip ———— ac ❏ dc ❏

Protective Devices: Induction Relays ❏   Direct Trips ❏   Direct Trips ❏

CL Fuses ❏   TD Setting ————   Inst. Setting ————

Annual Inspection

Date	Aux.	Main	Aux.	Main	Aux.	Main	Aux.	Main	Aux.	Main
Inspector's Initials										
Contact Condition										
Good — Surface Smooth										
Fair — Minor Burns										
Poor — Burned and Pitted										
Contact Check										
Pressure (Good, Weak, Bad)										
Drawout Contacts										
Pressure (Good, Weak, Bad)										
Alignment (Good, Bad)										
Lubricate (Must Do — Use a No-Oxide Lubricant by Mfr.)										
Arcing Assemblies										
Clean and Check the Arc-Splitting Plates Surface Conditions										
Bushings										
Clean and Check Surface Condition										

Date					
Inspector's Initials					
Operating Mechanisms					
Checks					
Positive Close and Trip					
Bushing and Pin Wear					
Set Screws and Keepers					
Protective Devices					
Lubricate Wear Points					
Clean Pots and Replace Oil with Equipment Mfrs. Recommended Oil					
Insulation Condition					
Loose Connections					
Discolored Areas					
Corona Tracking					
Clean Surfaces					
Insulation Tests					
Phase to Phase (Megohm)					
Phase to Ground (Megohm)					
Test Operation					
Close and Trip					
Counter Reading					
(No. of Ops.)					
Electrical Load					
Peak Indicated Amperes					

Remarks (record action taken when indicated by inspection or tests):

———————————————————————————
———————————————————————————

Other repairs recommended:

———————————————————————————
———————————————————————————

© 2023 National Fire Protection Association

NFPA 70B

FIGURE E.2   Typical Air Circuit Breaker Inspection Record.

AIR CIRCUIT BREAKER TEST AND INSPECTION REPORT

Customer _____ Date _____ Work Order No. _____

Address _____ Air Temp. _____ Rel. Humidity _____

Breaker Owner/User _____ Date Last Inspection _____

Address _____ Last Inspection Report No. _____

Equipment Location _____

Owner Identification _____

Breaker Data:

Manufacturer _____ Voltage _____ Type _____ Amperes _____ Int. Rating _____

Serial No. _____ Type Oper. Mech. _____ Age _____ Other N.P. Data _____

Test Data:	Tank 1	Tank 2	Tank 3	Inspection and Maintenance:	Insp.	Dirty	Cleaned/ Lubed	See Remarks
Ins. Res. _____ kV, Megohms ___								
Contact Resistance, Microhms ___				Overall Cleanliness ____				
Closing Speed/Opening Speed ___				Insulating Members ____				
Reference, P.F. Test Sheet No. ___				Mech. Connections ____				
	Mfr's. Rec.	As Found	As Left	Structural Members ____				
Adjustments:				Cubicle ____				
Arcing Contact Wipe ____				Pri. Contact Fingers ____				
Main Contact Gap ____				Shutter Mech. ____				
Main Contact Wipe ____				Relays ____				
Latch Wipe ____				Auxiliary Devices ____				
Latch Clearance ____				Racking Device ____				
Contact Travel ____				Arc Chutes ____				
Prop Clearance ____				Blow Out Coil ____				
Stop Clearance ____				Puffers ____				
				Liner ____				
				Arc Runners ____				
				Main Contacts ____				
				Cubicle Wiring ____				
				Breaker Wiring ____				
				Heaters ____				
				Panel Lights ____				
				Bearings ____				
				Contact Sequence ____				
				Ground Connection ____				
				Counter Reading ____				

Remarks: _____
_____
_____
_____
_____

Inspections and Test by: _____ Equipment Used: _____ Sheet No.: _____

© 2023 National Fire Protection Association   NFPA 70B

△ **FIGURE E.3** **Typical Air Circuit Breaker Test and Inspection Report.**

MEDIUM VOLTAGE VACUUM BREAKER

SHEET NO. _____ OF _____

CUSTOMER _____
ADDRESS _____
OWNER/USER _____
ADDRESS _____
EQUIPMENT LOCATION _____
OWNER IDENTIFICATION _____

DATE _____
AIR TEMP. _____
DATE LAST INSPECTION _____
LAST INSPECTION REPORT NO. _____

PROJECT NO. _____
REL. HUMIDITY _____

BREAKER DATA:

Manufacturer _____   Voltage _____   Type _____   Amps _____   Age _____

Serial No. _____   Type Oper Mech _____   Int. Rating _____   Other _____

TEST DATA:

Ins Res @ _____ kV

	A to G	B to G	C to G
	A to B	B to C	C to A
	A-L to L	B-L to L	C-L to L

Results In

Gigaohms _____

Megohms _____

Contact Resistance
Microhms - As Found
Microhms - As Left

	A-L to L	B-L to L	C-L to L

HiPot Test @ _____

ADJUSTMENTS:

	MFR'S. REC.	AS FOUND	AS LEFT
Erosion Indicator			
Main Contact Gap			

INSPECTION AND MAINTENANCE:

	INSP	NA	CLEAN LUBE	SEE REMARKS
Overall Cleanliness				
Insulating Members				
Mech. Connections				
Structural Members				
Cubicle				
Pri. Contact Fingers				
Shutter Mech.				
Relays				
Auxiliary Devices				
Racking Device				
Main Contacts				
Cubicle Wiring				
Breaker Wiring				
Heaters				
Panel Lights				
Bearings				
Contact Sequence				
Ground Connection				
Counter Reading				

Remarks _____

Equipment Used _____
Submitted By _____

Courtesy of Northeast Electrical Testing

NFPA 70B

FIGURE E.4 Typical Medium-Voltage Vacuum Breaker Form.

Shaded text = Revisions.   Δ = Text deletions and figure/table revisions.   • = Section deletions.   N = New material.

OIL CIRCUIT BREAKER TEST

SHEET NO. _____ OF _____

CUSTOMER _____ DATE _____ PROJECT NO. _____
ADDRESS _____ AIR TEMP. _____ REL. HUMIDITY _____
OWNER/USER _____ DATE LAST INSPECTION _____
ADDRESS _____ LAST INSPECTION REPORT _____
EQUIPMENT LOCATION _____
OWNER IDENTIFICATION _____

BREAKER DATA:

Manufacturer _____ Voltage _____ Type _____ Amps _____ Age _____

Serial No. _____ Type Oper Mech _____ Int. Rating _____ Other _____

Bushing Data _____

TEST DATA:

Ins Res @ _____ kV

Results In

	A to G	B to G	C to G
	A to B	B to C	C to A
	A-L to L	B-L to L	C-L to L

Gigaohms _____

Megohms _____

Contact Resistance
Microhms   - As Found
Microhms   - As Left
Reference PF Test Sheet

ADJUSTMENTS:

	MFR'S. REC.	AS FOUND	AS LEFT
Stop Clearance			
Contact Travel			
Overtravel			
Contact Wipe			
Trip Roller			
Latch Wipe			
Latch Clearance			
Prop Wipe			
Prop Clearance			
Cut-off Switch			
AA Switch			

INSPECTION AND MAINTENANCE:

	INSP	NA	CLEAN LUBE	SEE REMARKS
Tank Liners				
Insulating Members				
Oil Gauges				
Opening Spring				
Bushings				
Main Contacts				
Secondary Contacts				
Interrupters				
Linkage				
Dashpots				
Shutter Mechanism				
Elevating Mechanism				
Compressor Air Strainer				
Unload Valve				
Check Valve				
Compressor Belt				
Air Leaks				
Compressor Oil				
Gaskets				
Nuts, Bolts, Pins				
Closing Sequence				
Heater				
Oil Level				
Ground Connection				
Counter Reading As-Found				
Counter Reading As-Left				

Remarks _____
_____
_____
_____

Equipment Used _____
Submitted By _____

Courtesy of Northeast Electrical Testing   NFPA 70B

FIGURE E.5   Typical Oil Circuit Breaker Test Report.

    Shaded text = Revisions.   Δ = Text deletions and figure/table revisions.   • = Section deletions.   *N* = New material

DISCONNECT SWITCH TEST REPORT

SHEET NO. _____ OF _____

CUSTOMER _____ DATE _____ PROJECT NO. _____

ADDRESS _____ AIR TEMP. _____ REL. HUMIDITY _____

OWNER/USER _____ DATE LAST INSPECTION _____

ADDRESS _____ LAST INSPECTION REPORT NO. _____

EQUIPMENT LOCATION _____

OWNER IDENTIFICATION _____

Fused _____ Non-Fused _____

SWITCH DATA:

Manufacturer _____ Voltage _____ Type _____ Amps _____ Age _____

Serial No. _____ Type Oper Mech _____ Int. Rating _____ Other _____

TEST DATA:

Ins Res @ _____ kV

	A to G	B to G	C to G
Results In			
	A to B	B to C	C to A
Gigaohms _____			
Megohms _____			
Contact Resistance			
Microhms-As Found			
Microhms-As Left			

FUSE DATA:

	A	B	C
Manufacturer			
Size			
Catalog No.			
I.C. Rating			
Contact Resistance			
Microhms-As Found			
Microhms-As Left			

INSPECTION AND MAINTENANCE:

	INSP	NA	CLEAN LUBE	SEE REMARKS
Overall Cleanliness				
Insulating Members				
Mech. Connections				
Structural Members				
Cubicle				
Pri. Contact Fingers				
Main Contacts				
Arc Chutes				
Arc Runners				
Manual Operation				
Contact Lube				
Mechanical Lube				
Paint				
Door Interlock				
Ground Connection				

Remarks _____

_____

_____

_____

_____

Equipment Used _____

Test Technician _____

Courtesy of Northeast Electrical Testing

NFPA 70B

FIGURE E.6 Typical Disconnect Switch Test Report.

LOW-VOLTAGE CIRCUIT BREAKER 5-YEAR TESTS FORM

Plant _____ Date _____

Substation _____ Feeder _____ Load Reading _____

Breaker Data

Mfr. _____ Type _____ Serial No. _____

Trip Coil Rating _____ Amperes   Characteristic _____ Mfr's. Time Curve _____

Trip Devices: Long Time Delay ❑   Short Time Delay ❑   Instantaneous Trip ❑

Time Delay Type: Oil Sucker Dashpot ❑   Air Bellows ❑   Air Orifice ❑   Oil Orifice ❑
                 Other ❑

Settings:

LT Delay — Amperes _____ Adjustable Range _____ Time Adjustable?   Yes ❑   No ❑

ST Delay — Amperes _____ Adjustable Range _____ Time Adjustable?   Yes ❑   No ❑

Instantaneous Trip — Amperes _____ Adjustable?   Yes ❑   No ❑

Test Data

Date of Test _____		Left Pole	Center Pole	Right Pole	Time Range from Curve
Inspector's Initials _____					
As Found Test (Trip Time in Seconds)					
% Pickup Amperes					
_____ _____					
Time Delay	(As Found — Amperes)				
Minimum Pickup (Nullify Time Delay)	(Adjusted — Amperes)				
Time Delay Tests (Trip Time in Seconds)					
% Pickup Amperes Long Time					
_____ _____					
Short Time					
_____ _____					
_____ _____					
Resettable Delay	(Satisfactory)				
(___ % for ___ sec)	(Tripped)				
Instantaneous Trip	(As Found — Amperes)				
	(Adjusted — Amperes)				

Remarks (record unusual conditions, corrections, needed repairs, etc.; use separate form to record annual breaker inspection details):

_____

_____

_____

© 2023 National Fire Protection Association   NFPA 70B

△ **FIGURE E.7**   **Typical Low-Voltage Circuit Breaker 5-Year Tests Form.**

ELECTRICAL SWITCHGEAR–ASSOCIATED EQUIPMENT INSPECTION REPORT

Plant ——————————————— Date ———————————————

Location ——————————————— Serial No. ———————————————

Mfr. ——————————————— Year Installed ———————————————

Rating: Volts ——————————————— Bus Capacity Amperes ———————————————

Type: Switchboard ❏   Indoor Metal Clad ❏   Outdoor Metal Clad ❏

Annual Inspection (Disregard items that do not apply.)

Date						Date					
Inspector's Initials						Inspector's Initials					
Switchboards						Disconnect Switches					
Clean						Check Contact Surfaces					
Check Wiring						Check Insulation Condition					
Inspect Panel Insulation						Lubricate per Mfr's. Instructions					
Exposed Bus and Connections						Test Operate					
Clean and Check Porcelain						Fuses and Holders					
Check Insulators for Cracks or Chips						Check Contact Surfaces					
Check and Tighten Connections						Lubricate per Mfr's. Instructions					
Inspect Potheads for Leaks						Meters and Instruments					
Check for Environmental Hazards						Check Operation					
Test Insulation (Megohms)						Test Meters per Eng. Std.					
Metal Clad Enclosures						Test Relays per Mfr's. Instructions					
Clean						Interlocks and Safety					
Check for Openings That Permit Dirt, Moisture and Rodent Entrance — Repair						Check for Proper Operations					
Check Hardware for Rust or Corrosion						Check Lightning Arresters					
Paint Condition						Check Ground Detectors					
Check Heaters and Ventilators						Check Equipment Grounds					
Metal Clad Bus and Connections						Station Battery					
Clean Insulators and Supports						Periodic Routine					
Check and Tighten Connections						Maintenance is performed					
Check for Corona Tracking											
Inspect Potheads for Leaks											
Test Insulation (Megohms)											

Remarks (record action taken when indicated by inspection or tests):

——————————————————————————————

——————————————————————————————

Recommendations:

——————————————————————————————

——————————————————————————————

——————————————————————————————

© 2023 National Fire Protection Association   NFPA 70B

FIGURE E.8 Typical Electrical Switchgear–Associated Equipment Inspection Record.

CURRENT OR POTENTIAL TRANSFORMER RATIO TEST REPORT

SHEET NO. _____ OF _____

CUSTOMER _____   DATE _____   PROJECT NO. _____

ADDRESS _____   AIR TEMP. _____   REL. HUMIDITY (%) _____

OWNER/USER _____   DATE LAST INSPECTION _____

ADDRESS _____   LAST INSPECTION REPORT NO. _____

EQUIPMENT LOCATION _____

CIRCUIT IDENTIFICATION _____

LOCATION OF C.T. OR P.T. _____

C.T. OR P.T. IDENTIFICATION	C.T. OR P.T. SECONDARY TAPS	NAMEPLATE RATIO	APPLIED VOLTAGE OR CURRENT	MEASURED VOLTAGE OR CURRENT	PERCENT (%) ACCURACY	POLARITY PRIMARY	POLARITY SECONDARY
POLE #1 (A)	X1-X2						
BURDEN TEST							AMPS / VOLTS
SATURATION TEST							VOLTS / MA
MEGGER TEST							MEGOHMS
POLE #2 (B)	X1-X2						
BURDEN TEST							AMPS / VOLTS
SATURATION TEST							VOLTS / MA
MEGGER TEST							MEGOHMS
POLE #3 (C)	X1-X2						
BURDEN TEST							AMPS / VOLTS
SATURATION TEST							VOLTS / MA
MEGGER TEST							MEGOHMS

REMARKS _____
_____
_____
_____
_____

SUBMITTED BY _____

Courtesy of Northeast Electrical Testing

NFPA 70B

△ **FIGURE E.9**   **Typical Current or Potential Transformer Ratio Test Report.**

OVERLOAD RELAY TEST REPORT

SHEET NO. _____ OF _____

TEST REPORT NO. _____

CUSTOMER _____ DATE _____ PROJECT NO. _____

ADDRESS _____ AIR TEMP. _____ REL. HUMIDITY _____

OWNER/USER _____ DATE LAST INSPECTION _____

ADDRESS _____ LAST INSPECTION REPORT _____

EQUIPMENT LOCATION _____

OWNER IDENTIFICATION _____

MOTOR PROTECTED _____

MOTOR FLA _____ MOTOR VOLTAGE _____

OVERLOAD INFORMATION

OVERLOAD MANUFACTURER _____ CATALOG NUMBER _____

OVERLOAD RELAY HEATER COIL _____ HEATER POSITION _____

MANUFACTURERS CURVE NO. _____ AMBIENT TEMP. _____

FULL LOAD CURRENT AMPERES _____ MIN. _____ MAX. _____

TEST RESULTS

| PHASE | HEATER CURRENT | TEST CURRENT | | TEST TIME |
		PERCENTAGE	AMPS	SECONDS
PHASE 1				
PHASE 2				
PHASE 3				

STARTER INFORMATION

STARTER MANUFACTURER _____

STARTER SIZE _____ STARTER CATALOG NO. _____

STARTER _____ OTHER INFORMATION _____

CONDUCTOR _____ CONDUCTOR INSULATION _____

DATE _____

INSULATION RESISTANCE RESULTS:

Aø - GND _____ Aø - Bø _____

Bø - GND _____ Bø - Cø _____

Cø - GND _____ Cø - Aø _____

DATE _____

MEGGER MOTOR ø-GND: (1/2 MIN) _____ (1 MIN) _____

DATE _____

MEGGER MOTOR ø-GND W/CONDUCTOR INCLUDED: _____ (1 MIN) _____

REMARKS: _____

EQUIPMENT USED _____ SERIAL NUMBER _____

QUALITY CONTROL REP. _____ TITLE _____

SUBMITTED BY _____ TEST CREW _____

Courtesy of Northeast Electrical Testing

NFPA 70B

△ FIGURE E.10   Typical Overload Relay Test Report.

Shaded text = Revisions.   △ = Text deletions and figure/table revisions.   • = Section deletions.   *N* = New material.

2023 Edition

GROUND FAULT SYSTEM TEST

SHEET NO. _____ OF _____

CUSTOMER _____   DATE _____   PROJECT NO. _____
ADDRESS _____   AIR TEMP. _____   REL. HUMIDITY _____
OWNER/USER _____   DATE LAST INSPECTION _____
ADDRESS _____   LAST INSPECTION REPORT NO. _____
EQUIPMENT LOCATION _____
CIRCUIT IDENTIFICATION _____

FIELD DATA

MAIN OVERCURRENT DEVICE:

☐ CIRCUIT   ☐ FUSED SWITCH

MANUFACTURER _____

TYPE _____

MODEL/CAT. # _____

CURRENT RATING _____

SYSTEM VOLTAGE _____

VOLTAGE RATING _____

GROUND FAULT SYSTEM:

☐ NEUT-GND STRAP   ☐ ZERO SEQUENCE

MANUFACTURER _____

MODEL _____

CAT. NO. _____

PICK-UP RANGE _____

TIME RANGE _____

SENSOR/ C.T. _____

INSPECTION

CORRECT	INCORRECT	INSPECTION POINT	SIZE - REMARKS
		NEUT.-GRD LOCATION	
		CONTROL POWER	
		MONITOR OR TEST PANEL OPERATION	
		OTHER _____	

ELECTRICAL TESTS

1. BREAKER/SWITCH REACTION TIME (RT) _____   ☐ SEC.   ☐ CYC.

2. PICK UP CURRENT _____ AMPS

3. PICK UP CURRENT MINUS 10% (_____) A.   ☐ TRIP   ☐ NO TRIP

4. SHUNT TRIP COIL PICK-UP VOLTAGE _____ VOLTS

5. SYSTEM NEUTRAL INSULATION RESISTANCE TO GND _____ MEGOHMS

6. TIME-CURRENT CALIBRATION TESTS:

PRIMARY CURRENT AMPERE-TURNS	% PICKUP	TOTAL TIME	RT	RELAY TIME	MFG. TOLERANCE

REMARKS: _____
_____

SUBMITTED BY: _____

Courtesy of Northeast Electrical Testing

NFPA 70B

FIGURE E.11   Typical Ground-Fault System Test Report.

INSTRUMENT/METER CALIBRATION AND TEST REPORT

SHEET NO. _____ OF _____

CUSTOMER _____ DATE _____ PROJECT NO. _____
ADDRESS _____ AIR TEMP. _____
OWNER/USER _____ DATE LAST INSPECTION _____
ADDRESS _____ LAST INSPECTION REPORT NO. _____
EQUIPMENT LOCATION _____
CIRCUIT IDENTIFICATION _____

LOCATION/FUNCTION OF INSTRUMENT/METER _____
TYPE _____ MANUFACTURER _____ MODEL _____
FULL SCALE _____ ACTUAL INPUT _____
P.T. RATIO _____ C.T. RATIO _____ CAL. WATTS _____

FULL SCALE							
CARDINAL POINTS							
BASIC RANGE							
CALCULATED VALUE							
STANDARD "AS FOUND"							
STANDARD "AS LEFT"							
"AS LEFT" ACCURACY (%)							

REMARKS _____
_____
_____
_____
_____

LOCATION/FUNCTION OF INSTRUMENT/METER _____
TYPE _____ MANUFACTURER _____ MODEL _____
FULL SCALE _____ ACTUAL INPUT _____
P.T. RATIO _____ C.T. RATIO _____ CAL. WATTS _____

FULL SCALE							
CARDINAL POINTS							
BASIC RANGE							
CALCULATED VALUE							
STANDARD "AS FOUND"							
STANDARD "AS LEFT"							
"AS LEFT" ACCURACY (%)							

REMARKS _____
_____
_____
_____

SUBMITTED BY: _____ EQPT. USED: _____

Courtesy of Northeast Electrical Testing

NFPA 70B

△ **FIGURE E.12** Typical Instrument/Meter Calibration and Test Report.

Shaded text = Revisions.   △ = Text deletions and figure/table revisions.   • = Section deletions.   N = New material.

2023 Edition

WATT-HOUR METER TEST SHEET

SHEET NO. _____ OF _____
PROJECT NO. _____

CUSTOMER _____   DATE _____
ADDRESS _____   AIR TEMP. _____
OWNER/USER _____   DATE LAST INSPECTION _____
ADDRESS _____   LAST INSPECTION REPORT NO. _____
EQUIPMENT LOCATION _____
CIRCUIT IDENTIFICATION _____

TEST LOCATION _____   CIRCUIT METERED _____
METER MANUFACTURER _____   TYPE _____ SER. NO. _____
VOLTS _____ AMPS _____   PHASE _____ WIRE ____ INTERVAL _____
C.T. RATIO _____ P.T. RATIO _____   TEST K _____ PRI. TEST K _____

	AS FOUND	AS LEFT		AS FOUND	AS LEFT
KWH REGISTER READING			POTENTIAL IND LAMPS		
DEMAND REGISTER READING			CHECK AND VERIFY REGISTER RATIO		
DISC R.P.M.			SYNCHRONOUS MOTOR		
WORM WHEEL MESH			CHECK KW PTR AGAINST KWH PTR		
MAGNET CLEANLINESS			CREEP CHECK		
MAGNET TIGHTNESS			TIME INTERVAL		

	ACCURACY CHECK (% REG.)		COIL BALANCE CHECK					
			COIL NO. 1		COIL NO. 2		COIL NO. 3	
TEST FUNCTION	AS FOUND	AS LEFT	AS FOUND	AS LEFT	AS FOUND	AS LEFT	AS FOUND	AS LEFT
LIGHT LOAD								
FULL LOAD								
POWER FACTOR								

REMARKS: _____
_____
_____
_____
_____
_____
_____
_____
_____
_____
_____
_____
_____
_____
_____
_____

CUSTOMER REPRESENTATIVE _____   TITLE _____
TEST EQUIPMENT USED _____   SERIAL # _____
SUBMITTED BY _____   TEST _____

Courtesy of Northeast Electrical Testing   NFPA 70B

△ **FIGURE E.13**   **Typical Watt-Hour Meter Test Sheet.**

PANELBOARD/CIRCUIT BREAKER TEST REPORT

SHEET NO. _____ OF _____

CUSTOMER _____   DATE _____   PROJECT NO. _____
ADDRESS _____   AIR TEMP. _____   REL. HUMIDITY _____
OWNER/USER _____   DATE LAST INSPECTION _____
ADDRESS _____   LAST INSPECTION REPORT _____
EQUIPMENT LOCATION _____
OWNER IDENTIFICATION _____

PANEL BUS INSULATION RESISTANCE IN MEGOHMS

A-G _____ B-G _____ C-G _____ A-B _____ B-C _____ A-C _____

PANEL BOARD RATINGS: AMPS: _____   VOLTAGE: _____

TEST VOLTAGE: _____   MODEL NO: _____   CATALOG _____

MFG. _____   CURVE NO. _____   CURVE RANGE: _____
MFG. _____   CURVE NO. _____   CURVE RANGE: _____
MFG. _____   CURVE NO. _____   CURVE RANGE: _____
MFG. _____   CURVE NO. _____   CURVE RANGE: _____

CIRCUIT #	CKT. BKR. SIZE	TEST AMPS	TRIP TIME	INST. TRIP	CONTACT RESIS.	CIRCUIT #	CKT. BKR. SIZE	TEST AMPS	TRIP TIME	INST. TRIP	CONTACT RESIS.

REMARKS: _____
_____
_____
_____
_____

CUSTOMER REPRESENTATIVE _____   TITLE _____
TEST EQUIPMENT _____   SERIAL # _____
SUBMITTED BY _____

Courtesy of Northeast Electrical Testing   NFPA 70B

FIGURE E.14   Typical Panelboard/Circuit Breaker Test Report.

TRANSFORMER TEST AND INSPECTION REPORT

SHEET NO. _____ OF _____

CUSTOMER _____	DATE _____ PROJECT NO. _____
ADDRESS _____	AIR TEMP. _____ REL. HUMIDITY (%) _____
OWNER/USER _____	DATE LAST INSPECTION _____
ADDRESS _____	LAST INSPECTION REPORT _____
EQUIPMENT LOCATION _____	
OWNER IDENTIFICATION _____	

NAMEPLATE INFORMATION:

MANUFACTURER _____   KVA _____   PHASE _____   CYCLE _____

SERIAL NO. _____   TYPE _____   CLASS _____

PRI. VOLTAGE _____ △ ☐ OR Y ☐   RATED CURRENT _____ AMPERES

SEC. VOLTAGE _____ △ ☐ OR Y ☐   RATED CURRENT _____ AMPERES

COOLANT ☐ OIL ☐ ASKAREL ☐ AIR ☐ NITROGEN ☐ OTHER _____

COOLANT CAPACITY _____ TEMP. RISE (°C) _____ IMPEDANCE (%) _____

NO LOAD TAP CHANGER VOLTAGES _____

GAUGES AND COUNTERS

TEMP. _____ TEMP. RANGE _____ RESET GAUGE _____

PRESSURE _____ OIL LEVEL _____ TAP SETTING _____

VISUAL INSPECTION

BUSHING _____ CONNECTIONS _____ PAINT _____ OTHER _____

LOAD TAP CHANGER _____ LEAKS _____

FANS & CONTROLS _____ GAS REGULATOR _____ GROUNDS _____

WINDING INSULATION RESISTANCE TEST (MEGOHMS)

	30 SEC.	1 MIN.	10 MIN.	D.A.	P.I.
PRIMARY TO GROUND, SEC. GUARDED _____ KVDC					
SECONDARY TO GROUND, PRI. GUARDED _____ KVDC					
PRIMARY TO SECONDARY, GROUND GUARDED _____ KVDC					

EQUIPMENT USED _____

TURNS RATIO TEST

NAMEPLATE PRIMARY VOLTS	TAP POSITION	CONNECTION H___ H___ X___ X___	CONNECTION H___ H___ X___ X___	CONNECTION H___ H___ X___ X___	CALCULATED RATIO
	A1				
	B2				
	C3				
	D4				
	E5				

REMARKS: _____

EQUIPMENT USED _____   SUBMITTED BY _____

Courtesy of Northeast Electrical Testing   NFPA 70B

△ FIGURE E.15   Typical Transformer Test and Inspection Report.

TRANSFORMER (DRY TYPE) INSPECTION RECORD

Plant _____ Date _____

Location _____ Serial No. _____

Year Purchased _____ Year Installed _____ Mfr. _____

kVA _____ Voltage _____ Impedance _____

Phase _____ Taps _____

Cooling System: Room Vent Fan ❑ Trans. Fan ❑ Gravity ❑

Annual Inspection

Date						Date					
Inspector's Initials						Inspector's Initials					
Electrical Load						Bushings					
						Cracks or Chips					
						Cleanliness					
Secondary Voltage											
No Load Volts						Equipment Ground					
Full Load Volts						Check Connections					
						Measured V					
Dust on Windings						Resistance					
Minor Collection											
Major Collection						Temperature Alarms and Indicators					
Cleaned						Operation					
						Accuracy					
Connections											
Checked						Case Exterior					
Tightened						Covers Intact					
						Paint Condition					
Cooling Systems											
Fan Operation						Lighting Arresters					
Filter Cleanliness						Check Connections					
System Adequate						Check Bushings					

Complete Internal Inspection

Report of Conditions Found:

Cooling System _____

Coil Insulation _____

Other _____

Description of Work Performed:

_____

_____

Other Repairs Recommended: _____

_____

_____

Shop or Contractor: _____ Cost: _____

© 2023 National Fire Protection Association NFPA 70B

FIGURE E.16 Typical Transformer (Dry Type) Inspection Record.

TRANSFORMER (LIQUID FILLED) INSPECTION RECORD

Plant _____ Date _____

Location _____ Serial No. _____

Year Purchased _____ Year Installed _____ Mfr. _____

kVA _____ Voltage _____ Taps _____

Check type: Free Breathing ☐   Conservator ☐   Sealed ☐   Fan Cooled ☐

Phase _____ Weight _____ Impedance _____

Insulating Fluid: Type _____ Gallons _____

Annual Inspection

Date						Date					
Inspector's Initials						Inspector's Initials					
Tank — Liquid Level						Exposed Bushings					
Normal						Cracks or Chips					
Below						Cleanliness					
Added Fluid											
Entrance Compartment Liquid Level						Equipment Ground Connection					
Normal						Good					
Below						Questionable					
Added Fluid						Tested					
Electrical Load						Temperature Indicator					
Peak Amperes						Highest Reading					
						Reset Pointer					
Secondary Voltage						Pressure–Vacuum Indicator					
Full Load						Pressure					
No Load						Vacuum					
Gaskets and Case Exterior						Ventilators, Dryers, Gauges, Filters, and Other Auxiliaries					
Liquid Leaks						Operation OK					
Paint Condition						Maint. Req'd.					

Remarks (record action when inspection data or tests are out of limits, etc.):

_____

_____

Reports of Conditions Found: _____

_____

Description of Work Performed: _____

_____

Other Repairs Recommended: _____

Shop or Contractor: _____ Cost: _____

© 2023 National Fire Protection Association   NFPA 70B

△ **FIGURE E.17**   **Transformer (Liquid Filled) Inspection Record.**

Shaded text = Revisions.   △ = Text deletions and figure/table revisions.   • = Section deletions.   *N* = New material.

TRANSFORMER OIL SAMPLE REPORT

CUSTOMER _____

LOCATION _____

TOTAL NO. OF SAMPLES _____

PROJECT NO. _____

DATE _____

LOCATION _____ ☐ OIL _____ SAMPLE NO. _____

IDENTIFICATION _____ ☐ ASKAREL

MFG. _____ ☐ NO GAUGE PAINT _____ ☐ GOOD

SERIAL NO. _____ KVA _____ ☐ PRESSURE ☐ POOR

CLASS _____ TYPE _____ ☐ VACUUM

INSUL. CLASS _____ PHASE _____ ☐ INDOOR GASKETS _____ ☐ OK

VOLTAGE _____ ☐ OUTDOOR ☐ LEAK

INSTR. BOOK _____ ☐ TEMP. GA.

AVG. DIELECTRIC _____ KV _____ BUSHINGS _____ ☐ OK

ACIDITY NO. _____ KOH _____ ☐ LEAK

ASTM COLOR NO. _____ LIQUID CAPACITY _____

PARTICLES ☐ YES ☐ NO TEMP _____ OIL LEVEL _____ ☐ OK

WEATHER _____ ☐ LOW

RECOMMENDATIONS _____

_____

_____

_____

LOCATION _____ ☐ OIL _____ SAMPLE NO. _____

IDENTIFICATION _____ ☐ ASKAREL

MFG. _____ ☐ NO GAUGE PAINT _____ ☐ GOOD

SERIAL NO. _____ KVA _____ ☐ PRESSURE ☐ POOR

CLASS _____ TYPE _____ ☐ VACUUM

INSUL. CLASS _____ PHASE _____ ☐ INDOOR GASKETS _____ ☐ OK

VOLTAGE _____ ☐ OUTDOOR ☐ LEAK

INSTR. BOOK _____ ☐ TEMP. GA.

AVG. DIELECTRIC _____ KV _____ BUSHINGS _____ ☐ OK

ACIDITY NO. _____ KOH _____ ☐ LEAK

ASTM COLOR NO. _____ LIQUID CAPACITY _____

PARTICLES ☐ YES ☐ NO TEMP _____ OIL LEVEL _____ ☐ OK

WEATHER _____ ☐ LOW

RECOMMENDATIONS _____

_____

_____

_____

LOCATION _____ ☐ OIL _____ SAMPLE NO. _____

IDENTIFICATION _____ ☐ ASKAREL

MFG. _____ ☐ NO GAUGE PAINT _____ ☐ GOOD

SERIAL NO. _____ KVA _____ ☐ PRESSURE ☐ POOR

CLASS _____ TYPE _____ ☐ VACUUM

INSUL. CLASS _____ PHASE _____ ☐ INDOOR GASKETS _____ ☐ OK

VOLTAGE _____ ☐ OUTDOOR ☐ LEAK

INSTR. BOOK _____ ☐ TEMP. GA.

AVG. DIELECTRIC _____ KV _____ BUSHINGS _____ ☐ OK

ACIDITY NO. _____ KOH _____ ☐ LEAK

ASTM COLOR NO. _____ LIQUID CAPACITY _____

PARTICLES ☐ YES ☐ NO TEMP _____ OIL LEVEL _____ ☐ OK

WEATHER _____ ☐ LOW

RECOMMENDATIONS _____

_____

_____

EQUIPMENT USED _____ SUBMITTED BY _____

Courtesy of Northeast Electrical Testing

NFPA 70B

FIGURE E.18 Typical Transformer Oil Sample Report.

Shaded text = Revisions. Δ = Text deletions and figure/table revisions. • = Section deletions. *N* = New material.

2023 Edition

TRANSFORMER OIL TRENDING REPORT

CUSTOMER _____   PROJECT NO. _____

LOCATION _____   DATE _____

LOCATION _____   ☐ OIL _____   SAMPLE NO. _____

IDENTIFICATION _____   ☐ ASKAREL _____

MFG. _____   ☐ GAUGE _____ PAINT _____   ☐ GOOD

SERIAL NO. _____ KVA _____   ☐ PRESSURE _____   ☐ POOR

CLASS _____ TYPE _____   ☐ VACUUM _____

INSUL. CLASS _____ PHASE _____   ☐ INDOOR _____ GASKETS _____   ☐ OK

VOLTAGE _____   ☐ OUTDOOR _____   ☐ LEAK

INSTR. BOOK _____   ☐ TEMP. GA. _____

DIELECTRIC FLUID ANALYSIS

YR - JOB#	DIELE. (KV)	ACIDITY (mgKOH/g)	IFT (dynes/cm2)	COLOR	VISUAL	SPECIFIC GRAVITY	WATER (PPM)	POWER FACTOR (%)	PCB (PPM)

ACCEPTABLE DIELECTRIC TEST VALUES:

DIELECTRIC (ASTM D877) 30KV MIN. NEW OIL / 26KV MIN. USED OIL / 30KV MIN. NEW SILICONE/ 25kV MIN. USED SILICONE

ACID (ASTM D974) 0.03 mgKOH/g MAX. NEW OIL / 0.20mgKOH/g MAX. USED OIL / 0.1mgKOH/g MAX. NEW SILICONE/ 0.2mgKOH USED SILICONE

IFT (ASTM D971) 35 dynes/cm2 MIN. NEW OIL / 24 dynes/cm2 MIN. USED OIL / 31 dynes/cm2 MIN. SILICONE

COLOR (ASTM D1500) 1 MAX. NEW OIL / 4 MAX. USED OIL / CLEAR FOR SILICONE

WATER (ASTM D1533B) 25PPM MAX. NEW OIL / 35PPM MAX. USED OIL / 50PPM MAX. NEW SILICONE/ 100PPM MAX. USED SILICONE

DISSOLVED GAS ANALYSIS

YEAR	HYDROGEN (H2) (<100PPM)	OXYGEN (O2)	NITROGEN (N2)	METHANE (CH4) (<120PPM)	CARBON MONOXIDE (CO) (<350PPM)	CARBON DIOXIDE (CO2) (<2500PPM)	ETHYLENE (C2H4) (<50PPM)	ETHANE (C2H6) (<65PPM)	ACETYLENE (C2H2) (<1PPM)	TOTAL GAS CONTENT (%)	TOTAL COMBUST. GAS

REMARKS: _____
_____
_____

SUBMITTED BY _____

Courtesy of Northeast Electrical Testing   NFPA 70B

FIGURE E.19   Typical Transformer Oil Trending Report.

TRANSFORMER INSULATION RESISTANCE RECORD

Plant _____ Date _____

Scope: Power transformers of 150 kVA and greater capacity with primary voltage of 2300 volts or higher. Direct reading — recorded and plotted.

Transformer Serial No. _____ Phase _____

Location _____ Instrument Used _____

Equipment Included in Test _____

_____

_____

I I*	Date	Primary to Ground	Secondary to Ground	Primary to Secondary	Internal Temp.	Ambient Temp.

*Inspector's Initials

Date ➝ | Primary to Ground | Secondary to Ground | Primary to Secondary

Infinity
10,000
5,000
3,000
2,000
1,000
800
600
400
300
200
150
100
80
60
40
30
20
15
10
6
4
2
1
0.6
0.2
0.1
0.06
0.02
Zero

Remarks: _____

_____

_____

_____

© 2023 National Fire Protection Association

NFPA 70B

FIGURE E.20 Typical Transformer Insulation Resistance Record.

VALVE-REGULATED LEAD-ACID (VRLA) STATIONARY BATTERIES AND CHARGERS INSPECTION REPORT

Inspected by: _____

Inspection date: _____

User's Name:	Authorized Site Contact:
Installation Location:	Phone No.:
	Other:
System OEM:	Installation by:

BATTERY AND CHARGER SYSTEM INFORMATION

VENDOR INSPECTION	USER INSPECTION
	Appearance of Following Battery Items
Order Number	
Ship Date	Positive Posts
Date Installed	Negative Posts
Battery Model	Cell Covers
Cells x Strings	Presence of Lubricant on Cells ☐ Yes ☐ No
Application	
Bus Voltage, Portable Meter	
Bus Voltage, Equipment, Final	
Charger Size, Type, Serial No. & Mfg.	
Ambient Room Temperature	
Last Discharge	
Peak Load Current Amp. or KW	
Typical Load Current/KW	
Cell Arrangement	

COMMENTS AND RECOMMENDATIONS

© 2023 National Fire Protection Association   NFPA 70B

△ **FIGURE E.21(a)   VRLA Inspection Report.**

Shaded text = Revisions.   △ = Text deletions and figure/table revisions.   • = Section deletions.   *N* = New materia

VALVE-REGULATED LEAD-ACID (VRLA) MAINTENANCE WORKSHEET

BATTERY CHARGE STATUS   ❏ OPEN CIRCUIT   ❏ FLOAT   ❏ EQUALIZE
BATTERY BUS VOLTAGE _____ Vdc   _____Vdc   _____Vdc

Location: Model: Date:

Cell No.	Volts +2.000	Serial No.	Connection Resistance	Internal Cell Conductance /Impedance/ Resistance	Cell No.	Volts +2.000	Serial No.	Connection Resistance	Internal Cell Conductance /Impedance/ Resistance

© 2023 National Fire Protection Association   NFPA 70B

Δ **FIGURE E.21(b)**   **Example of a VRLA Maintenance Worksheet.**

ENGINE GENERATOR INSPECTION

SHEET NO. _____ OF _____

CUSTOMER _____ DATE _____ PROJECT NO. _____
ADDRESS _____ AIR TEMP. _____ REL. HUMIDITY _____
OWNER/USER _____ DATE LAST INSPECTION _____
ADDRESS _____ LAST INSPECTION REPORT _____
EQUIPMENT LOCATION _____
CIRCUIT IDENTIFICATION _____

ENGINE TYPE: ☐ GASOLINE ☐ DIESEL ☐ GAS TURBINE

MAKE _____ MODEL _____ SERIAL NO. _____ KS # _____
KVA _____ KW _____ VOLTAGE _____ F.L.A. _____
RPM _____ HZ _____ HP _____ TECH. BULL. # _____

1. ☐ Change oil and lube oil filters.
2. ☐ Remove unused oil from premises.
3. ☐ Change fuel oil elements.
4. ☐ Service crankcase breather.
5. ☐ Inspect air cleaner element, clean if required. If replacement is required, element(s) will be billed separately. Price of element(s) not included in contract price.
6. ☐ Check coolant level and maintain safe degree of protection. Engine mounted radiators only. (Remote radiators, cooling towers & heat exchangers serviced at user's request on a time and material basis.)
7. ☐ Check manifolds, brackets, mountings and flex connections.
8. ☐ Inspect fan belts, adjust if required.
9. ☐ Check pulley hub, bearings, lubricate if required.
10. ☐ Check operation of auxiliary water pump or fan motor.
11. ☐ Check operation of automatic louvers.
12. ☐ Repair minor fuel, coolant and lube oil leaks.
13. ☐ Check operation of jacket water heater(s).
14. ☐ Inspect generator, perform any routine maintenance as required.
    ☐ Megger
15. ☐ Inspect governor/actuator linkage.
16. ☐ Check battery electrolyte level and maintain to include:
    ☐ Temperature   ☐ Specific Gravity   ☐ Voltage
17. ☐ Check operation of charger and/or alternator.
18. ☐ Inspect fuel supply system for leaks or low level, inform owner of any discrepancies.
19. ☐ Drain condensation from day tank and check for any contamination. ONLY if day tank is equipped with a drain valve.
20. ☐ Check operation of transfer pump.
21. ☐ Check for correct generator output voltage & frequency, adjust if required.
22. ☐ Simulate & check operation of each safety shutdown and alarm device, relay type control panels only.
23. ☐ Check operation of generator control instrumentation; volts, amps, etc.
24. ☐ Test fault lamps & replace bulbs as required, panels with lamp test only.
25. ☐ Tank crankcase oil sample, owner to be notified of any discrepancies.
26. ☐ Submit report to owner
27. ☐ Auto start test.

REMARKS _____
_____
_____
_____
_____
_____

SUBMITTED BY _____ EQUIPMENT USED _____

Courtesy of Northeast Electrical Testing   NFPA 70B

FIGURE E.22 **Typical Engine Generator Set Inspection Checklist.**

AUTOMATIC TRANSFER SWITCH

CUSTOMER _____ DATE _____ SHEET NO. _____ OF _____
ADDRESS _____ AIR TEMP. _____ PROJECT NO. _____
OWNER/USER _____ DATE LAST INSPECTION _____ REL. HUMIDITY _____
ADDRESS _____ LAST INSPECTION REPORT NO. _____
EQUIPMENT LOCATION _____
OWNER IDENTIFICATION _____

Mfg. _____ Type: _____ Bul #: _____
Cat. # _____ Serial # _____ Voltage: _____
Amps: _____ Phase: _____ Op. Coil: _____
Inst. Bk: _____ Parts Bk. _____ Wire Diag: _____

Time Range "Transfer to Emergency" From _____ To _____
Time Range "Retransfer to Normal" From _____ To _____

TEST OPERATIONS

Transfer Time to Emergency As Found _____ As Left _____
Retransfer Time to Normal As Found _____ As Left _____

	NORMAL				EMERGENCY		
Contact Resistance in Microhms:	A ____	B ____	C ____	A ____	B ____	C ____	
Voltage Drop in Millivolts:	A ____	B ____	C ____	A ____	B ____	C ____	
Voltage Readings:	A-N ____	B-N ____	C-N ____	A-N ____	B-N ____	C-N ____	
	A-B ____	B-C ____	C-A ____	A-B ____	B-C ____	C-A ____	
Amperage Readings:	A ____	B ____	C ____	A ____	B ____	C ____	

Undervoltage Relay:

	1V	2V	3V
Pickup	_____	_____	_____
Dropout	_____	_____	_____

_____ Relay: Pickup _____ Dropout _____ _____

_____ Relay: Voltage Pickup _____ Dropout _____ _____
 Frequency Pickup _____ Dropout _____

Arc Chutes: _____ Circuit Properly Tagged: _____
Contacts: _____ Bolted Connections: _____
Megger: _____ Mechanical Operation: _____
Cleaned: _____ Unusual Conditions: _____
Lubrication: _____

Remarks: _____
_____
_____
_____
_____

Test Crew: _____

Courtesy of Northeast Electrical Testing

NFPA 70B

FIGURE E.23 Typical Automatic Transfer Switch Report.

Shaded text = Revisions. Δ = Text deletions and figure/table revisions. • = Section deletions. N = New material.

2023 Edition

UNINTERRUPTIBLE POWER SUPPLY (UPS) SYSTEM INSPECTION CHECKLIST

For use of this form see TM 5-694: the proponent agency is COE.

SECTION A – CUSTOMER DATA

1. PLANT/BUILDING	2. LOCATION	3. JOB NUMBER
4. EQUIPMENT	5. CIRCUIT DESIGNATION	6. DATE (YYYYMMDD)
7. TEST EQUIPMENT		8. TESTED BY

SECTION B – VISUAL AND ELECTRICAL/MECHANICAL INSPECTION

9. CHECK POINT	COND*	NOTES	CHECK POINT	COND*	NOTES
COMPONENT INSPECTION/TESTING			ENERGIZE AND TEST SYSTEM		
INSTALLATION INSPECTION/TESTING			UTILITY TRIP TEST		
WIRING VISUAL VERIFICATION			LOADED TRANSFER TEST (NORMAL, EMERGENCY & RETURN)		
GENERATOR CONTROL FUNCTIONS			TIGHTNESS OF BOLTED CONNECTIONS		
LOADING UPS TEST			BATTERY DISCHARGE TEST		
DISCONNECT RECTIFIERS & INVERTERS SEPARATELY. DOES SYSTEM OPERATE CORRECTLY?			TEST ALL UPS DIAGNOSTIC FAULT INDICATORS		

SECTION C – ELECTRICAL TESTS**

10.	A-N	B-N	C-N	A-B	B-C	C-A	A	B	C	N	G
UPS INPUT											
	A-N	B-N	C-N	A-B	B-C	C-A	A	B	C	N	G
UPS OUTPUT											
	A-N	B-N	C-N	A-B	B-C	C-A	A	B	C	N	G
UPS SWITCHBOARD HARMONIC (THD)											

11. NOTES

* CONDITION: A = ACCEPTABLE; R = NEEDS REPAIR, REPLACEMENT OR ADJUSTMENT; C = CORRECTED; NA = NOT APPLICABLE
** NOTE VALUE AND PHASING

NFPA 70B

FIGURE E.24   Typical Uninterruptible Power Supply System Inspection Checklist.

BACK-UP POWER SYSTEM INSPECTION CHECKLIST

For use of this form see TM 5-694: the proponent agency is COE.

SECTION A – CUSTOMER DATA

1. PLANT/BUILDING	2. LOCATION	3. JOB NUMBER
4. EQUIPMENT	5. CIRCUIT DESIGNATION	6. DATE *(YYYYMMDD)*
7. TEST EQUIPMENT AND CALIBRATION DATE		8. TESTED BY

SECTION B – EQUIPMENT DATA

9. MANUFACTURER	10. STYLES/S.O.	11. VOLTAGE RATING	12. CURRENT RATING
13. EQUIPMENT CLASSIFICATION	14. FREQUENCY	15. WET BULB TEMPERATURE	16. DRY BULB TEMPERATURE

SECTION C – VISUAL AND ELECTRICAL/MECHANICAL INSPECTION

17. CHECK POINT	COND*	NOTES	CHECK POINT	COND*	NOTES
COMPONENT INSPECTION/TESTING			WIRING VISUAL VERIFICATION		
ENERGIZE AND TEST SYSTEM			UTILITY TRIP/GENERATOR BUILDING LOAD TEST		
INSTALLATION INSPECTION/TESTING			TIGHTNESS OF BOLTED CONNECTIONS		
GENERATOR CONTROLS AND FUNCTIONS			CHECK FOR PROPER SIZE BREAKER		
WIRING CONTINUITY TESTING			REFERENCE DRAWINGS		
WORKING CLEARANCE			PROPER PHASING CONNECTIONS AND COLOR CODE		
SWITCHGEAR CONTROL FUNCTIONS					

PERFORM AUTOMATIC TRANSFER SYSTEM (ATS) FUNCTIONS UNDER THE ADJACENT CONTROLLER	A. OPERATE NORMAL POWER		
	B. ALL GENERATORS OPERATE		
	C. GENERATORS 1 AND 2 OPERATE		
	D. GENERATORS 2 AND 3 OPERATE		
	E. GENERATORS 1 AND 3 OPERATE		
	F. RETURN TO NORMAL POWER AFTER EACH OF THE ABOVE TESTS		
	G. PARALLEL WITH UTILITY UPON RETURN TO NORMAL POWER (ITEMS B THROUGH E)		

SECTION D – ELECTRICAL TESTS

18. MEASUREMENT DESCRIPTION	VOLTAGE AND CURRENT MEASUREMENTS										
	VOLTAGE**						CURRENT**				
	A-N	B-N	C-N	A-B	B-C	C-A	A	B	C	N	G
	A-N	B-N	C-N	A-B	B-C	C-A	A	B	C	N	G

19. NOTES

1. CHECK FOR PROPER GROUNDING CONNECTIONS PRIOR TO ENERGIZING.

* CONDITION: A = ACCEPTABLE; R = NEEDS REPAIR, REPLACEMENT OR ADJUSTMENT; C = CORRECTED; NA = NOT APPLICABLE
** NOTE VALUE AND PHASING

NFPA 70B

FIGURE E.25 **Typical Back-Up Power System Inspection Checklist.**

Shaded text = Revisions. Δ = Text deletions and figure/table revisions. • = Section deletions. *N* = New material.

2023 Edition

INSULATION RESISTANCE–DIELECTRIC ABSORPTION TEST SHEET FOR POWER CABLE

Test No. _____

_____ Company   Date _____

_____ Location   Time _____

Circuit		Circuit Length		Aerial Duct Burned
Number of Conductors	Conductor Size	AWG MCM (kcmil)	Belted Shielded	
Insulating Material		Insulating Thickness	Voltage Rating	Age
Pothead or Terminal Type			Location Indoors Outdoors	
Number and Type of Joints				
Recent Operating History				
			Mfr.	
State if Potheads or Terminals Were Guarded During Test				
List Associated Equipment Included in Test				
Misc. Information				

Test Data — Megohms

Part Tested					Test Made	Hours Days	After Shutdown
Grounding Time					Dry-Bulb Temp.		
Test Voltage					Wet-Bulb Temp.		
Test Connections	To Line	To Line	To Line	To Line	Dew Point		
	To Earth	To Earth	To Earth	To Earth	Relative Humidity		%
	To Guard	To Guard	To Guard	To Guard	Absolute Humidity		Gr./#
¼ minute					Equipment Temp.		
½ minute					How Obtained		
¾ minute							
1 minute							
2 minutes					"Megger" Inst.		
3 minutes					Serial No.		
4 minutes					Range		
5 minutes					Voltage		
6 minutes							
7 minutes							
8 minutes							
9 minutes							
10 minutes							
10:1 min. Ratio							

Remarks _____

_____

Tested by: _____

© 2023 National Fire Protection Association   NFPA 70B

Δ **FIGURE E.26**   Typical Insulation Resistance–Dielectric Absorption Test Sheet for Power Cable.

CABLE TEST SHEET

Company _____ Date _____ Job No. _____

Test Location _____ Circuit _____ Air Temp. _____ % Hum. _____

Test Type: Acceptance ☐ Periodic ☐ Special ☐ Date Last _____ Sheet No. _____ Weather _____

Cable Mfr.	
Rated kV	(Gnd., Ungnd.)
Oper. kV	(Gnd., Ungnd.)
Length	
Age	
No. Cond.	
No. Size	
Insul. Material	
Insul. Thickness	
Insul. Type	
Covering	
Installed in	
Factory Test kV	
% Factory Test kV	
Max. Test kV	
Voltmeter kV	

Time Min.	Volts kV	Leakage Current-Microamps		
		Φ1 – ⊙	Φ2 – △	Φ3 – ⊡

Insulation Resistance Test
1 Minute @ 2.5 kV — 1000 Megohms

Φ TO GND.			
Φ 1 TO Φ	—		
Φ 2 TO Φ	—	—	

Authorization of Max.
Test kV and Verifying Voltmeter kV

_____

Signature

Remarks: _____

_____

_____

_____

Test Set No.: _____ Tested by: _____ Sheet No.: _____

© 2023 National Fire Protection Association

NFPA 70B

△ FIGURE E.27   Typical Cable Test Sheet.

Shaded text = Revisions.   △ = Text deletions and figure/table revisions.   • = Section deletions.   N = New material.

2023 Edition

INSULATION RESISTANCE TEST RECORD

Date _____

Scope: Dielectric Absorption Without Temperature Correction

Apparatus _____   Equipment Temp. _____   Ambient Temp. _____

Instrument Used _____   Polarization Index No. _____

Condition _____ 10:1 Min. Ratio _____

Condition		
Dangerous - - - - - - - - Less than 1	Fair - - - - - - - - - 2 to 3	
Poor - - - - - - - - - Less than 1.5	Good - - - - - - - - 3 to 4	
Questionable - - - - - - 1.5 to 2	Excellent - - - - - - - Above 4	

Time in Minutes		0.25	0.5	1	2	3	4	5	6	7	8	9	10
To Ground	Phase 1												
	Phase 2												
	Phase 3												
Between Phases	Phase 1–2												
	Phase 2–3												
	Phase 3–4												

Plot the lowest group reading on graph.

Tested by: _____

© 2023 National Fire Protection Association

NFPA 70B

△ **FIGURE E.28**   **Typical Insulation Resistance Test Record.**

     Shaded text = Revisions.   △ = Text deletions and figure/table revisions.   • = Section deletions.   *N* = New material.

INSULATION RESISTANCE TEST RECORD FOR ROTATING MACHINERY

Reference: ANSI/IEEE 43, *Recommended Practice for Testing Insulation Resistance of Rotating Machinery*

Scope:

Dielectric Absorption — Temperature Corrected

ac machines 1000 kVA or more
dc machines 100 kW or more

Date _____

Apparatus _____   Voltage _____   Rating _____

Test Conditions:

List Associated Test Equipment
Included in Test _____

Winding Grounding Time _____   Test Made _____ Hours After Shutdown

Ambient Temperature _____   Relative Humidity _____ %   Weather _____

Equipment Temperature _____   How Obtained _____

Instrument _____   Range _____   Voltage _____

Test Data:

Minutes	0.25	0.5	1.0	2.0	3.0	4.0	5.0	6.0	7.0	8.0	9.0	10.0
Reading												
Correction												

Polarization No. (10:1 min. ratio) _____   Tested by _____

Remarks: _____
_____
_____
_____

© 2023 National Fire Protection Association   NFPA 70B

△ **FIGURE E.29** **Typical Insulation Resistance Test Record for Rotating Machinery.**

MOTOR TEST INFORMATION

SHEET NO. _____ OF _____
TEST REPORT NO. _____

CUSTOMER _____ DATE _____ PROJECT NO. _____

ADDRESS _____ AIR TEMP. _____ REL. HUMIDITY _____

OWNER/USER _____ DATE LAST INSPECTION _____

ADDRESS _____ LAST INSPECTION _____

EQUIPMENT LOCATION _____

OWNER IDENTIFICATION _____

MOTOR TEST INFORMATION

INSULATION RESISTANCE TEST RESULTS AT _____ VDC IN MEGOHMS

30 SEC.   _____
60 SEC.   _____
10 MIN.   _____
D.A.   _____
P.I.   _____

A. NAME & IDENTIFYING MARK OF MOTOR   _____

B. MANUFACTURER   _____

C. MODEL NUMBER   _____

D. SERIAL NUMBER   _____

E. RPM   _____

F. FRAME SIZE   _____

G. CODE LETTER   _____

H. HORSEPOWER   _____

I. NAMEPLATE VOLTAGE & PHASE   _____

J. NAMEPLATE AMPS   _____

K. ACTUAL VOLTAGE   _____

L. ACTUAL AMPS   _____

M. STARTER MANUFACTURER   _____

N. STARTER SIZE   _____

O. HEATER SIZE, CATALOG # & AMP   _____

P. MANUFACTURER OF DUAL ELEMENT   _____

Q. AMP RATING OF FUSE   _____

R. POWER FACTOR   _____

S. SERVICE FACTOR   _____

REMARKS: _____
_____
_____
_____
_____
_____
_____
_____
_____

TEST EQUIPMENT USED _____ SERIAL # _____

SUBMITTED BY _____ TEST _____

Courtesy of Northeast Electrical Testing   NFPA 70B

FIGURE E.30   Typical Motor Test Information Form.

GROUNDING SYSTEM RESISTANCE TEST

CUSTOMER _____ DATE _____ SHEET NO. _____ OF _____

ADDRESS _____ AIR TEMP. _____ PROJECT NO. _____

OWNER/USER _____ DATE LAST INSPECTION _____ REL. HUMIDITY _____

ADDRESS _____ LAST INSPECTION REPORT NO. _____

LOCATION _____

SEASON	
SOIL TYPE	
SOIL CONDITION	
SINGLE ROD DEPTH	
MULTIPLE RODS (Y/N)	
LONGEST DIMENSION	
BURIED WIRE/STRIPS (Y/N)	
LONGEST DIMENSION	
DIST. TO AUX. ELECTRODE	
OTHER	

AUXILIARY POTENTIAL ELECTRODE

DISTANCE (FEET)	RESISTANCE (OHMS)

DISTANCE (FEET)

RESISTANCE (OHMS)

REMARKS _____
_____
_____
_____
_____

SUBMITTED BY _____ EQUIPMENT USED _____

Courtesy of Northeast Electrical Testing

NFPA 70B

FIGURE E.31   Typical Ground System Resistance Test Report.

GROUND TEST INSPECTION REPORT — HEALTH CARE FACILITIES

SHEET NO. _____ OF _____

CUSTOMER _____ DATE _____ PROJECT NO. _____
ADDRESS _____ AIR TEMP. _____ REL. HUMIDITY _____
OWNER/USER _____ DATE LAST INSPECTION _____
ADDRESS _____ LAST INSPECTION REPORT _____
EQUIPMENT LOCATION _____
OWNER IDENTIFICATION _____

MAXIMUM TEST INTERVALS:
GENERAL CARE: 12 MONTHS
CRITICAL CARE: 6 MONTHS
WET LOCATIONS: 12 MONTHS

*NOTE: MAXIMUM READINGS PERMITTED:
20mV NEW CONSTRUCTION
40mV CRITICAL EXISTING CONSTRUCTION
500mV GENERAL CARE EXISTING CONSTRUCTION
0.1 ohm NEW CONSTRUCTION
0.2 ohm QUIET GROUNDS AND EXISTING CONSTRUCTION

ROOM NO.	DESCRIPTION (C) CRITICAL (G) GENERAL	VOLTAGE MEASUREMENT			IMPEDANCE MEASUREMENT	
		NUMBER OF RECEPTABLES	NUMBER OF OTHER	MAX READING (MILLIVOLTS)	NUMBER OF RECEPTACLES	MAX READING (OHMS)

REMARKS _____
_____
_____

CUSTOMER REPRESENTATIVE _____ TITLE _____

TEST EQUIPMENT _____ SERIAL # _____

SUBMITTED BY _____

Courtesy of Northeast Electrical Testing   NFPA 70B

FIGURE E.32   Typical Ground Test Inspection Report — Health Care Facilities.

LINE ISOLATION MONITOR TEST DATA — HEALTH CARE FACILITIES

SHEET _____ OF _____

CUSTOMER _____ DATE _____ PROJECT NO. _____
ADDRESS _____ AIR TEMP. _____ REL. HUMIDITY _____
OWNER/USE _____ DATE LAST INSPECTION _____
ADDRESS _____ LAST INSPECTION REPORT NO. _____
EQUIPMENT LOCATION _____
CIRCUIT _____

INSTRUMENT OR METER UNDER TEST

TYPE _____ MANUFACTURER _____ VOLTAGE _____

SERIAL NO. _____ MODEL NO. _____

CATALOG NO. _____ STYLE NO. _____

TEST OPERATIONS

CAUTION: NO TEST EQUIPMENT NEEDED FOR THIS SECTION. REMOVE ALL PLUGS FROM MONITOR
DURING THESE TESTS. PATIENT MUST NOT BE SUBJECTED TO HARMFUL TEST VOLTAGES.

		AS FOUND		AS LEFT	
1. AUDIBLE AND VISUAL INDICATORS	SELF TEST				
	SILENCE (MUTE)				
2. CHECK APPROPRIATE BOX IF INDICATOR IS OPERATIONAL	RED				
	GREEN				
	YELLOW				
3. LIM	MANUFACTURER'S SPECIFIED ALARM POINT		MA		MA
	METER READING		MA		MA

TEST OPERATIONS USING TEST EQUIPMENT:

TEST SET _____

		AS FOUND	AS LEFT
4. LINE LEAKAGE TO GROUND	ONE mA		
	TWO mA		
	THREE mA		
	FOUR mA		
	FIVE mA		
5. ARE ALL BREAKERS OPERATIONAL AND CIRCUITS LABELED?			

REMARKS _____
_____
_____
_____
_____

CUSTOMER REPRESENTATIVE _____ TITLE _____
TEST EQUIPMENT _____ SERIAL # _____
SUBMITTED BY _____ TEST CREW _____

Courtesy of Northeast Electrical Testing

NFPA 70B

FIGURE E.33 Typical Line Isolation Monitor Test Data Report — Health Care Facilities.

Shaded text = Revisions.   Δ = Text deletions and figure/table revisions.   • = Section deletions.   N = New material.

2023 Edition

TORQUE VALUE RECORD

SHEET NO. _____ OF _____

CUSTOMER _____ DATE _____ PROJECT NO. _____

ADDRESS _____ AIR TEMP. _____ REL. HUMIDITY _____

OWNER/USER _____ DATE LAST INSPECTION _____

ADDRESS _____ LAST INSPECTION REPORT NO. _____

EQUIPMENT LOCATION _____

OWNER IDENTIFICATION _____

GENERAL INFORMATION:

Equipment ID: _____ Performed By: _____

Location: _____ Torque Marked: ☐ Yes ☐ No Color: _____

Date Performed: _____ Verified By: _____

Torque Wrench Information: ☐ IN-LBS ☐ FT-LBS Verification Marked: ☐ Yes ☐ No Color: _____

Manufacturer: _____ Model: _____ Approved By: _____

No.	No. of Items	Item Description/Location	Vendor Specification		NETA Specification		Torque		Note
			NO.	FT-LB / IN-LB	NO.	FT-LB / IN-LB	NO.	FT-LB / IN-LB	
				FT-LB		FT-LB		FT-LB	
				IN-LB		IN-LB		IN-LB	
				FT-LB		FT-LB		FT-LB	
				IN-LB		IN-LB		IN-LB	
				FT-LB		FT-LB		FT-LB	
				IN-LB		IN-LB		IN-LB	
				FT-LB		FT-LB		FT-LB	
				IN-LB		IN-LB		IN-LB	
				FT-LB		FT-LB		FT-LB	
				IN-LB		IN-LB		IN-LB	
				FT-LB		FT-LB		FT-LB	
				IN-LB		IN-LB		IN-LB	
				FT-LB		FT-LB		FT-LB	
				IN-LB		IN-LB		IN-LB	
				FT-LB		FT-LB		FT-LB	
				IN-LB		IN-LB		IN-LB	
				FT-LB		FT-LB		FT-LB	
				IN-LB		IN-LB		IN-LB	
				FT-LB		FT-LB		FT-LB	
				IN-LB		IN-LB		IN-LB	
				FT-LB		FT-LB		FT-LB	
				IN-LB		IN-LB		IN-LB	
				FT-LB		FT-LB		FT-LB	
				IN-LB		IN-LB		IN-LB	
				FT-LB		FT-LB		FT-LB	
				IN-LB		IN-LB		IN-LB	
				FT-LB		FT-LB		FT-LB	
				IN-LB		IN-LB		IN-LB	

REMARKS _____

_____

CUSTOMER REPRESENTATIVE _____ TITLE _____

TEST EQUIPMENT _____ SERIAL # _____

SUBMITTED BY _____

Courtesy of Northeast Electrical Testing

NFPA 70B

FIGURE E.34 Typical Torque Value Record.

Shaded text = Revisions.   △ = Text deletions and figure/table revisions.   • = Section deletions.   *N* = New material.

MAIN POWER ENERGIZATION CHECKLIST
For use of this form see TM 5-694: the proponent agency is COE.

SECTION A – CUSTOMER DATA

1. PLANT/BUILDING	2. LOCATION	3. JOB NUMBER
4. CIRCUIT DESIGNATION	5. CIRCUIT FED FROM	6. CIRCUIT FED TO · 7. DATE *(YYYYMMDD)*
8. TEST EQUIPMENT TYPE/BRAND AND CALIBRATION DATE		9. TESTED BY

SECTION B – VISUAL AND ELECTRICAL/MECHANICAL INSPECTION

10.

CHECK POINT	COND*	NOTES	CHECK POINT	COND*	NOTES
COMPONENT INSPECTION/TESTING COMPLETED			VERIFY SWITCHGEAR CONTROL FUNCTIONS		
WIRING VISUAL VERIFICATION			CHECK FOR WORKING CLEARANCE		
VERIFY WIRING DIAGRAMS			ENERGIZE AND TEST SYSTEM		
VERIFY CIRCUIT SWITCHER CONTROL FUNCTIONS			TRANSFORMER TRANSFER CONTROL FUNCTIONS		
ENERGIZE AND TEST SYSTEM FOR ALL CONDITIONS			CHECK FOR UNUSUAL SOUNDS AFTER ENERGIZING		
CHECK BUSHING OR TERMINALS			CHECK ANCHORING OF TRANSFORMER SWITCHGEAR AND SWITCHES ENCLOSURE		
CHECK FOR REMOVAL OF PAINT OR HEAVY DENTS			CHECK FOR NORMAL/ABNORMAL SWITCHING OPERATION		

SECTION C – ELECTRICAL TESTS

11.

MEASUREMENT DESCRIPTION	VOLTAGE AND CURRENT MEASUREMENTS										
	VOLTAGE**						CURRENT**				
	A-N	B-N	C-N	A-B	B-C	C-A	A	B	C	N	G
	A-N	B-N	C-N	A-B	B-C	C-A	A	B	C	N	G
	A-N	B-N	C-N	A-B	B-C	C-A	A	B	C	N	G
	A-N	B-N	C-N	A-B	B-C	C-A	A	B	C	N	G
	A-N	B-N	C-N	A-B	B-C	C-A	A	B	C	N	G

12. NOTES

* CONDITION: A = ACCEPTABLE; R = NEEDS REPAIR, REPLACEMENT OR ADJUSTMENT; C = CORRECTED; NA = NOT APPLICABLE
** NOTE VALUE AND PHASING

FIGURE E.35   Typical Main Power Energization Checklist.

Shaded text = Revisions.   Δ = Text deletions and figure/table revisions.   • = Section deletions.   *N* = New material.

Facility Identification   **Job No.**

INSTRUCTIONS TO CONTRACTOR

Date: _____

Contractor Name: _____

Address: _____

City, State, Zip Code: _____

Subject: Project Title: _____

            Project No.: _____

Enclosed is one complete set of the following bid documents covering work for the subject project.

     1. Project Scope of Work, Dated: _____

     2. Proposal Forms for:
         General Maintenance of Electrical Power Equipment, and/or
         Infrared Surveying of Electrical Power Equipment, and/or
         Circuit Breaker Overhaul and Trip Unit Retrofit

     3. Plant Electrical Power Equipment Documentation:
       • **Plant one line diagrams**   **Dwg. Nos.** _____ ,   **Dated** _____
       • **Plant layout drawings**   **Dwg. Nos.** _____ ,   **Dated** _____
       • **Plant equipment list**   **Doc. No.** _____ ,   **Dated** _____
       • **Short circuit analyses and time-current coordination studies**
       • **Equipment manufacturers' requirements will be available at the plant for your use.**

We would appreciate receiving a quote from you for this work on the enclosed Project Scope of Work in strict accordance to the quote documents. Please respond in writing if you do not intend to submit a quote for this project.

One original and copy(s) of your quote will be due not later than _____ at _____ local time.

Fax and send one original of your proposal to: *(Enter Project Engineer's Name, Address,* _____
                                             and Fax No. here) _____

We welcome suggestions regarding changes in specifications and/or modifications in design or production methods that will aid in reducing costs without impairing quality or that will improve the quality, safety, and/or performance of the product on which you are quoting. However, your base bid price must be submitted on the basis of the bid documents. All voluntary alternates are to be presented as a separate price from the base bid.

Pre-Quote Walk Through (if applicable)

You are invited to attend a pre-quote walk through meeting scheduled for:

       Time: _____

       Day: _____

       Date: _____

       Location: _____

If you desire further information addressing the technical specifications or site visitation, please contact *(project engineer)* at *(phone no.).*

Sincerely,

(Enter Project Engineer's Name and Location here) _____

© 2023 National Fire Protection Association   NFPA 70B

△ **FIGURE E.36**   **Instructions to Contractor.**

Facility Identification   **Job No.**

PROJECT SCOPE OF WORK

Introduction

This Scope of Work document will define the maintenance activities to be included in this project. The contractor shall provide all labor, materials, and equipment necessary to perform requested electrical power equipment maintenance. All maintenance activities will be performed in accordance with the applicable Technical Specification and other pertinent portions of facility's Electrical Power Equipment Maintenance Manual. *The costs of premium time, if required, shall be included in this quote.*

If electrical power equipment is found to be within the Manufacturer's specifications for continued service and the required maintenance is unnecessary, clean, adjust, and reassemble the electrical power equipment and perform all Manufacturer recommended procedures for continued service.

If the contractor discovers that the electrical power equipment cannot be brought into compliance with the Manufacturer's specifications for continued service, advise the Owner of the "as found" condition and await further direction. *Save all component parts for Owner inspection.*

General Task Description

_____

_____

_____

_____

_____

_____

_____

_____

_____

_____

_____

_____

_____

_____

_____

Schedule

Time to complete all tasks: _____

Time equipment is available: _____

Time/day to begin work: _____

Time/day to complete work: _____

© 2023 National Fire Protection Association   NFPA 70B (p. 1 of 2)

Δ FIGURE E.37   Project Scope of Work Template.

Facility Identification   **Job No.**

PROJECT SCOPE OF WORK *(continued)*

Specific Task Description

Contractor will perform the specific tasks described in this section.

General Maintenance

The following maintenance activities will be performed in accordance with the Technical Specifications for General Maintenance or Electrical Power Equipment.

_____
_____
_____
_____
_____
_____

Circuit Breaker Overhaul and Trip Unit Retrofit

The following maintenance activities will be performed in accordance with the Technical Specifications for Circuit Breaker Overhaul and Trip Unit Retrofit.

_____
_____
_____
_____
_____
_____

Infrared Surveying

The following maintenance activities will be performed in accordance with the Technical Specifications for Infrared Surveying of Electrical Power Equipment.

_____
_____
_____
_____
_____
_____

Work Not Included (Listed Owner furnished services)

_____
_____
_____
_____
_____

Exceptions to Specifications

_____
_____
_____
_____
_____

© 2023 National Fire Protection Association   NFPA 70B (p. 2 of 2)

Δ **FIGURE E.37** *Continued*

PROJECT SCOPE OF WORK QUOTE FORM

Location: _____   Project No. _____   Purch. Req. No. _____

Contractor: _____   MBO No. _____

The Contractor shall perform the work in strict accordance with the facility's Electrical Power Equipment Maintenance Manual EMM-1 General Maintenance Technical Specification, the Circuit Breaker Overhaul and Trip Unit Retrofit Technical Specification, the plant equipment list, single line diagrams and drawings, and the Project Scope of Work. All alternates shall be fully described with exceptions listed by Item Number, and priced separately. When applicable, General Maintenance Technical Specification (GMTS) codes shall be used on this Proposal Form as they are used in the Project Scope of Work.

Item No.	Maintenance Activity Description and Location of Equipment	GMTS Code	Quantity	Item/Unit Price	Item Total Price
				Page Total	

© 2023 National Fire Protection Association

NFPA 70B

FIGURE E.38   Project Scope of Work Form.

Shaded text = Revisions.   Δ = Text deletions and figure/table revisions.   • = Section deletions.   *N* = New material.

PROJECT SCOPE OF WORK MODIFICATION QUOTE FORM

Location: _____   Project No. _____   Purch. Req. No. _____

                              MBO No. _____   Modification No. _____
Contractor: _____

All modifications shall be fully described with reference to the original Item Number, and priced separately. The Contractor shall perform the work in strict accordance with the facility's Electrical Power Equipment Maintenance Manual EMM-1 General Maintenance Technical Specification, the Circuit Breaker Overhaul and Trip Unit Retrofit Technical Specification, the plant equipment list, single line diagrams and drawings, and the Project Scope of Work. When applicable, General Maintenance Technical Specification (GMTS) codes shall be used on this Proposal Form as they are used in the Project Scope of Work. Contractor shall not begin work until approved by the plant.

Item No.	Maintenance Activity Description and Location of Equipment	GMTS Code	Qty.	Labor	Mat'l	Item Total Price
					Page Total	

Submitted by: _____   Date: _____

Approved by: _____   Date: _____

© 2023 National Fire Protection Association   NFPA 70B

△ **FIGURE E.39**   **Project Scope of Work Modification Form.**

**POWER QUALITY SURVEY
DATA COLLECTION MANUAL**

Installation: _____

Location: _____

Collection Date: _____

Courtesy of U.S. Army Corps of Engineers

NFPA 70B

FIGURE E.40   Cover and Contents.

Shaded text = Revisions.   Δ = Text deletions and figure/table revisions.   • = Section deletions.   *N* = New material.

2023 Edition

POINTS OF CONTACT

Installation: _____

Address: _____

_____

Names	Titles	Office Symbols	Phones
_____	_____	_____	_____
_____	_____	_____	_____
_____	_____	_____	_____
_____	_____	_____	_____
_____	_____	_____	_____
_____	_____	_____	_____
_____	_____	_____	_____
_____	_____	_____	_____

Contractor's Name: _____

Address: _____

Names	Titles	Office Names	Phones
_____	_____	_____	_____
_____	_____	_____	_____
_____	_____	_____	_____
_____	_____	_____	_____
_____	_____	_____	_____
_____	_____	_____	_____
_____	_____	_____	_____
_____	_____	_____	_____

Utilities: _____

Address: _____

_____

Names	Titles	Office Names	Phones
_____	_____	_____	_____
_____	_____	_____	_____
_____	_____	_____	_____
_____	_____	_____	_____

Courtesy of U.S. Army Corps of Engineers

NFPA 70B

FIGURE E.41   Points of Contact.

Shaded text = Revisions.   Δ = Text deletions and figure/table revisions.   • = Section deletions.   *N* = New material.

POWER DISTRIBUTION UNIT (PDU) SURVEY

Date: _____

Installation: _____ Location: _____

Power Distribution Unit (PDU) Identification: _____

Manufacturer: _____ Model/Serial #: _____

Size: _____ kVA   3-Phase: _____   Single-Phase: _____   Frequency: _____ Hz

Input Voltage Rating: _____ V   Input Current Rating: _____ A   Tap Changing Range: _____

Output Voltage Rating: _____ V   Output Current Rating: _____ A

Measured Input Volts	$V_{(IN)A\text{-}B}$ = _____ V	$V_{(IN)B\text{-}C}$ = _____ V	$V_{(IN)C\text{-}A}$ = _____ V	
Input Voltage Harmonic Distortion	$V_{(IN)THD(A\text{-}B)}$ = ____ % 3rd = _____ __th = _____ __th = _____	$V_{(IN)THD(B\text{-}C)}$ = ____ % 3rd = _____ __th = _____ __th = _____	$V_{(IN)THD(A\text{-}C)}$ = ____ % 3rd = _____ __th = _____ __th = _____	
Measured Input Amps	$I_{(IN)A}$ = _____ A	$I_{(IN)B}$ = _____ A	$I_{(IN)C}$ = _____ A	
Input Current Harmonic Distortion	$I_{(IN)THD(A)}$ = ____ % 3rd = _____ __th = _____ __th = _____	$I_{(IN)THD(B)}$ = ____ % 3rd = _____ __th = _____ __th = _____	$I_{(IN)THD(C)}$ = ____ % 3rd = _____ __th = _____ __th = _____	
Measured Output Volts	$V_{(O)A\text{-}N}$ = _____ V $V_{(O)A\text{-}G}$ = _____ V	$V_{(O)B\text{-}N}$ = _____ V $V_{(O)B\text{-}G}$ = _____ V	$V_{(O)C\text{-}N}$ = _____ V $V_{(O)C\text{-}G}$ = _____ V	$V_{(O)N\text{-}G}$ = _____ V
Output Voltage Harmonic Distortion	$V_{(O)THD(A\text{-}N)}$ = ____ % 3rd = _____ __th = _____ __th = _____	$V_{(O)THD(B\text{-}N)}$ = ____ % 3rd = _____ __th = _____ __th = _____	$V_{(O)THD(C\text{-}N)}$ = ____ % 3rd = _____ __th = _____ __th = _____	$V_{(O)THD(N\text{-}G)}$ = ____ % 3rd = _____ __th = _____ __th = _____
Measured Output Amps	$I_{(O)A}$ = _____ A	$I_{(O)B}$ = _____ A	$I_{(O)C}$ = _____ A	$I_{(O)N}$ = _____ A
Output Current Harmonic Distortion	$I_{(O)THD(A)}$ = ____ % 3rd = _____ __th = _____ __th = _____	$I_{(O)THD(B)}$ = ____ % 3rd = _____ __th = _____ __th = _____	$I_{(O)THD(C)}$ = ____ % 3rd = _____ __th = _____ __th = _____	$I_{(O)THD(N)}$ = ____ % 3rd = _____ __th = _____ __th = _____
K Factor	Measured K Factor: _____		Nameplate K Factor: _____	
Ground System	Neutral bus of PDU is connected to ground? ❑ Yes ❑ No Ground bus of PDU is connected to upstream switchgear/switchboard/panel ground bus? _____ to building metal frame? _____ to raised floor frame? _____ Ground current measurement: _____ A Ground resistance measurement: _____ Ω			
Temperature	Transf winding temperature range: _____ Bus temperature range: _____ CBs having temperature higher than 32°C (90°F): _____			
Power Factor	PF: _____ Displacement Power Factor (DPF): _____			

Courtesy of U.S. Army Corps of Engineers

NFPA 70B (p. 1 of 2)

△ **FIGURE E.42** **Power Distribution Unit (PDU) Survey.**

Shaded text = Revisions.   △ = Text deletions and figure/table revisions.   • = Section deletions.   *N* = New material.

2023 Edition

POWER DISTRIBUTION UNIT (PDU) SURVEY *(continued)*

Deficiencies found	
Problems in the past	
Customer's concerns	
Notes	

Courtesy of U.S. Army Corps of Engineers

FIGURE E.42   *Continued*

Shaded text = Revisions.   **Δ** = Text deletions and figure/table revisions.   • = Section deletions.   **N** = New material.

GENERATOR SET SURVEY

Date: _____

Installation: _____ Location: _____

Number of generator sets at this location: _____

Generator Set #1

Physical Conditions: ❑ Good condition   ❑ Damage   ❑ Not in use   ❑ Need repair
❑ Old   ❑ Corrosion   ❑ Need maintenance   ❑ Other:_____

• Designed for: ❑ Prime operation   ❑ Standby operation   ❑ Emergency operation

Engine Data:

• Manufacturer: _____
• Model/Type: _____   Rated Voltage:_____
• Rated hp (or kW): _____   Rated Current: _____
• Power Factor:_____   Frequency: _____

Generator Data:

• Manufacturer:_____
• Model/Type:_____
• Generated Voltages: _____ V   Generated Frequencies: _____ Hz
• Rated kVA: _____   Rated kW: _____
• Rated Currents:_____ A   Efficiency Factor: _____
• Winding Connection (D/W/GW):_____   Power Factor: _____

Batteries

• ❑ Good condition   ❑ Leakage   ❑ Need maintenance   ❑ Dead   ❑ Other:_____
• Measured Voltages: _____ V   Measured Temperatures:_____

Generator Set #2

Physical Conditions: ❑ Good condition   ❑ Damage   ❑ Not in use   ❑ Need repair
❑ Old   ❑ Corrosion   ❑ Need maintenance   ❑ Other:_____

• Designed for: ❑ Prime operation   ❑ Standby operation   ❑ Emergency operation

Engine Data:

• Manufacturer: _____
• Model/Type: _____   Rated Voltage:_____
• Rated hp (or kW): _____   Rated Current: _____
• Power Factor: _____   Frequency: _____

Generator Data:

• Manufacturer:_____
• Model/Type:_____
• Generated Voltages: _____ V   Generated Frequencies: _____ Hz
• Rated kVA: _____   Rated kW: _____
• Rated Currents:_____ A   Efficiency Factor: _____
• Winding Connection (D/W/GW):_____   Power Factor: _____

Batteries

• ❑ Good condition   ❑ Leakage   ❑ Need maintenance   ❑ Dead   ❑ Other:_____
• Measured Voltages: _____ V   Measured Temperatures:_____

Courtesy of U.S. Army Corps of Engineers

NFPA 70B (p. 1 of 2)

Δ **FIGURE E.43   Generator Set Survey.**

Shaded text = Revisions.   Δ = Text deletions and figure/table revisions.   • = Section deletions.   **N** = New material.

GENERATOR SET SURVEY *(continued)*

Generator Set #3

Physical Conditions: ❏ Good condition   ❏ Damage   ❏ Not in use   ❏ Need repair
❏ Old   ❏ Corrosion   ❏ Need maintenance   ❏ Other: _____
- Designed for: ❏ Prime operation   ❏ Standby operation   ❏ Emergency operation

Engine Data:
- Manufacturer: _____
- Model/Type: _____   Rated Voltage: _____
- Rated hp (or kW): _____   Rated Current: _____
- Power Factor: _____   Frequency: _____

Generator Data:
- Manufacturer: _____
- Model/Type: _____
- Generated Voltages: _____ V   Generated Frequencies: _____ Hz
- Rated kVA: _____   Rated kW: _____
- Rated Currents: _____ A   Efficiency Factor: _____
- Winding Connection (D/W/GW): _____   Power Factor: _____

Batteries
- ❏ Good condition   ❏ Leakage   ❏ Need maintenance   ❏ Dead   ❏ Other: _____
- Measured Voltages: _____ V   Measured Temperatures: _____

Generator Operation:
- Can these generators run in parallel with the utility power sources? ❏ Yes ❏ No
- The generators are being used as: ❏ Backup source   ❏ Peak shaving   ❏ Prime source
- Are the generators properly protected against overload? ❏ Yes ❏ No   abnormal conditions? ❏ Yes ❏ No
  or reverse power flow (if generators can run in parallel with utility source)? ❏ Yes ❏ No
- Can the generators automatically start? ❏ Yes ❏ No   and automatically shut off? ❏ Yes ❏ No
- How many times did generator fail to start or break down (with unknown reason) during the last few years? _____

Maintenance:
- Does the generator operation log book exist and is it up to date? ❏ Yes ❏ No
- How often does the generator run for maintenance? _____ times per week/month, ❏ with loads or ❏ without loads.
- How long did the generator run during each maintenance period? _____ minutes
- How often is the generator fuel system checked? _____ times per week/month

Generator Grounding System:
- ❏ Solidly grounded   ❏ High resistance   ❏ Low resistance   ❏ Reactance
- Measured ground impedance in ohms: _____
- Is the generator's neutral bus connected to ground? ❏ Yes ❏ No
- Is the generator frame connected to ground? ❏ Yes ❏ No

Notes:
_____
_____
_____
_____
_____

Courtesy of U.S. Army Corps of Engineers   NFPA 70B (p. 2 of 2)

Δ **FIGURE E.43**   *Continued*

ELECTRICAL PANEL SURVEY Date: _____

Installation: _____ Location: _____

_____

Panel Identification: _____

Manufacturer Name: _____ Panel Type/Model: _____

Voltage Rating: _____ V   Current Rating: _____ A   Phases: _____   # of Wires: _____

Main Breaker: Type/Model: _____   Rating: _____ A   Adjustable Setting Range: _____

Measured Voltages	V_{A-N} = _____ V V_{A-G} = _____ V	V_{B-N} = _____ V V_{B-G} = _____ V	V_{C-N} = _____ V V_{C-G} = _____ V	V_{N-G} = _____ V
Voltage Sine Waves	V_{A-N}	V_{B-N}	V_{C-N}	V_{N-G}
Harmonic Voltage Distortion	$V_{THD(A-N)}$ = ____ % 3rd = _____ % __th = _____ % __th = _____ %	$V_{THD(B-N)}$ = ____ % 3rd = _____ % __th = _____ % __th = _____ %	$V_{THD(C-N)}$ = ____ % 3rd = _____ % __th = _____ % __th = _____ %	$V_{THD(N-G)}$ = ____ % 3rd = _____ % __th = _____ % __th = _____ %
Measured Currents	I_A = _____ A	I_B = _____ A	I_C = _____ A	I_N = _____ A
Current Sine Waves	I_A	I_B	I_C	I_N
Harmonic Current Distortion	$I_{THD(A)}$ = _____ % 3rd = _____ % __th = _____ % __th = _____ %	$I_{THD(B)}$ = _____ % 3rd = _____ % __th = _____ % __th = _____ %	$I_{THD(C)}$ = _____ % 3rd = _____ % __th = _____ % __th = _____ %	$I_{THD(N)}$ = _____ % 3rd = _____ % __th = _____ % __th = _____ %
Power Factor	PF: _____ Displacement Power Factor (DPF): _____			
Grounding System	Ground bus isolated from frame? ____ or bonded to frame? ____ Ground by metal conduits? ____ or by ground conductors? ____ Ground bus bonded to neutral bus? ❑ Yes ❑ No Each branch circuit has separated neutral ❑ Yes ❑ No and ground conductor? ❑ Yes ❑ No Ground current measurement: _____ A Ground resistance measurement: _____ Ω Sketch the existing grounding system (on the back sheet) when it is necessary.			
Temperature	Bus temperature range: _____ Conductor temperature range: _____ CBs having temperature higher than 32°C (90°F): _____			
Entrance Conductor	Phases: _____ MCM Number of conductors per phase: _____			
Sizes	Neutral: _____ MCM Number of conductors per phase: _____ Ground: _____ MCM Number of conductors per phase: _____			
Lightning Protection	Manufacturer: _____ Type: _____ Voltage rating: _____			

© 2023 National Fire Protection Association   NFPA 70B (p. 1 of 2)

FIGURE E.44   Electrical Panel Survey.

ELECTRICAL PANEL SURVEY *(continued)*

Other Circuit Breakers in the Panel	Circuit breaker rating: _____ A 3 Ph or Single:_____ How many CB:_____
	Circuit breaker rating: _____ A 3 Ph or Single:_____ How many CB:_____
	Circuit breaker rating: _____ A 3 Ph or Single:_____ How many CB:_____
	Circuit breaker rating: _____ A 3 Ph or Single:_____ How many CB:_____
	Circuit breaker rating: _____ A 3 Ph or Single:_____ How many CB:_____
	Circuit breaker rating: _____ A 3 Ph or Single:_____ How many CB:_____
	Circuit breaker rating: _____ A 3 Ph or Single:_____ How many CB:_____
	Circuit breaker rating: _____ A 3 Ph or Single:_____ How many CB:_____
Deficiencies Found	
Problems in the Past	
Customer's Concerns	
Notes	

© 2023 National Fire Protection Association

NFPA 70B (p. 2 of 2)

△ **FIGURE E.44**   *Continued*

Shaded text = Revisions.   △ = Text deletions and figure/table revisions.   • = Section deletions.   **N** = New material

INVERTER SURVEY

Date: _____

Installation: _____   Location: _____

Inverter Identification: _____

Number of inverters at this location: _____   Do they all have the same size and characteristics? ❏ Yes ❏ No

Manufacturer: _____   Model: _____   Type: _____   Phases: _____   Wires: _____

Input Voltages	Rated: _____ Measured: _____	
Input Currents	Rated: _____ Measured: _____	
Output Voltages	Rated: _____ Measured: _____	
Output Currents	Rated: _____ Measured: _____	
kVA	Rated: _____ Measured input: _____ Measured output: _____ PF: _____	
kW	Rated: _____ Measured input: _____ Measured output: _____ DPF: _____	
Conductor Sizes	Phases: ( )_____ Neutral: ( )_____ Ground: ( )_____	
Measured Temperatures	Bus temperature range: _____ Conductor temperature range: _____	
Grounding System	Terminal of inverter bonded to ground? ❏ Yes ❏ No Ground bus of inverter bonded to the frame? ❏ Yes ❏ No Ground current measurement: _____ A Ground resistance measurement: _____ Ω Sketch the existing grounding system (on the back sheet) when it is needed.	
Batteries	Manufacturer: _____ Model: _____ Type: _____ Cell voltage: _____ Number of cells: _____ Total battery voltages: _____ V Total battery currents: _____ A Conductor sizes: Phases: ( ) _____ Neutral: ( ) _____ Ground: ( ) _____ Physical conditions: ❏ Damage ❏ Corrosion ❏ Leakage Fluid fill level: _____ Proper mounting: _____ Proper clearance: _____ Battery rack condition: _____ Battery rack grounded? ❏ Yes ❏ No Battery bank terminal grounded? ❏ Yes ❏ No Battery fluid specific gravity last checked: _____	

Measured Cell Battery Voltages and Fluid Temperatures

All temperatures are in _°C _°F

Cell #____ ____ V ____	Cell #____ ____ V ____	Cell #____ ____ V ____	Cell #____ ____ V ____	Cell #____ ____ V ____	Cell #____ ____ V ____	Cell #____ ____ V ____
Cell #____ ____ V ____	Cell #____ ____ V ____	Cell #____ ____ V ____	Cell #____ ____ V ____	Cell #____ ____ V ____	Cell #____ ____ V ____	Cell #____ ____ V ____
Cell #____ ____ V ____	Cell #____ ____ V ____	Cell #____ ____ V ____	Cell #____ ____ V ____	Cell #____ ____ V ____	Cell #____ ____ V ____	Cell #____ ____ V ____
Cell #____ ____ V ____	Cell #____ ____ V ____	Cell #____ ____ V ____	Cell #____ ____ V ____	Cell #____ ____ V ____	Cell #____ ____ V ____	Cell #____ ____ V ____
Cell #____ ____ V ____	Cell #____ ____ V ____	Cell #____ ____ V ____	Cell #____ ____ V ____	Cell #____ ____ V ____	Cell #____ ____ V ____	Cell #____ ____ V ____

© 2023 National Fire Protection Association   NFPA 70B (p. 1 of 2)

FIGURE E.45   Inverter Survey.

INVERTER SURVEY *(continued)*

Deficiencies Found	
Problems in the Past	
Notes	

© 2023 National Fire Protection Association

NFPA 70B (p. 2 of 2)

△ **FIGURE E.45** *Continued*

BUILDING LIGHTNING PROTECTION SURVEY

Date: _____

Installation: _____   Building #: _____

Physical Conditions	❑ Good Condition ❑ Rust/Corrosion ❑ Damaged
Roof	Materials: ❑ Metal ❑ Non-metal Types: ❑ Flat ❑ Gable ❑ Hip ❑ Gambrel ❑ Intermediate Ridges ❑ Domed ❑ Shed
Air Terminals	Size (diameter): _____ inches Height: _____ feet _____ inches Material: ❑ Copper ❑ Copper Alloys ❑ Aluminum Approximate distance between two consecutive air terminals: _____ feet Air terminals securely mounted on appropriate bases? ❑ Yes ❑ No Air terminal bases are of the same material as the air terminals? ❑ Yes ❑ No Air terminal bases properly fastened/anchored to the roof? ❑ Yes ❑ No An air terminal at each corner of the roof? ❑ Yes ❑ No Two paths for currents to flow (to ground) at each air terminal? ❑ Yes ❑ No
Lightning Conductors	Sizes: _____ AWG Material: ❑ Copper ❑ Copper Alloys ❑ Aluminum Approximate distance between two consecutive lightning conductors: _____ feet Interconnected lightning conductors properly bonded together? ❑ Yes ❑ No Any sharp bend curves (less than 8 inch radius and 90° angle)? ❑ Yes ❑ No Lightning conductor securely fastened every 4 feet? ❑ Yes ❑ No
Down Conductors	Size: _____ AWG Material: ❑ Copper ❑ Copper Alloys ❑ Aluminum Are the conductors electrically continuous running down to the ground? ❑ Yes ❑ No Approximate distance between two consecutive down conductors: _____ feet At least 2 down conductors installed at opposite corners of the building? ❑ Yes ❑ No Total number of down conductors installed: _____ Average resistance measurement at down conductors: _____ Ω

Objects on the Roof	Metal object has a thickness less than ³⁄₁₆ inch? ❑ Yes ❑ No
	Metal object is directly bonded to lightning conductors or through an air terminal
	    to lightning conductors? ❑ Yes ❑ No
	The bonding surface has a contact area of not less than 3 sq-inches? ❑ Yes ❑ No
	Non-metal objects on the roof? ❑ Yes ❑ No
	Are they protected with air terminals? ❑ Yes ❑ No
	Does each air terminal provide a two-way path to the ground? ❑ Yes ❑ No
	For non-metal object, is the distance from the farthest corner of the object to the
	    air terminal less than 2 feet? ❑ Yes ❑ No

Grounding System	Separate grounding loop for lightning protection system? ❑ Yes ❑ No Is the grounding loop for lightning protection system bonded to the electrical grounding system? ❑ Yes ❑ No Average ground resistance measurement (at the location where it is connected to electrical grounding system): _____ Ω

© 2023 National Fire Protection Association

NFPA 70B (p. 1 of 2)

FIGURE E.46   Building Lightning Protection Survey.

haded text = Revisions.   Δ = Text deletions and figure/table revisions.   • = Section deletions.   N = New material.

2023 Edition

BUILDING LIGHTNING PROTECTION SURVEY *(continued)*

Deficiencies Found	
Problems in the Past	
Sketch the roof floor plan and mark down the location of air terminals, cross-roof lightning conductors, down conductors, and distances between them.	

© 2023 National Fire Protection Association

NFPA 70B (p. 2 of 2)

Δ **FIGURE E.46**   *Continued*

Shaded text = Revisions.   Δ = Text deletions and figure/table revisions.   • = Section deletions.   *N* = New materi

RECTIFIER SURVEY   Date: _____

Installation: _____   Location: _____

_____

Rectifier Identification: _____

Number of units at this location: _____   Do they all have the same size and characteristics? ❏ Yes ❏ No

Manufacturer: _____   Model: _____   Type: _____   Phases: _____   Wires: _____

Input Voltages	Rated: _____ Measured: _____
Input Currents	Rated: _____ Measured: _____
Output Voltages	Rated: _____ Measured: _____
Output Currents	Rated: _____ Measured: _____
kVA	Rated: _____ Measured input: _____ Measured output: _____ PF: _____
kW	Rated: _____ Measured input: _____ Measured output: _____ DPF: _____
Conductor Sizes	Phases: _____ Neutral: _____ Ground: _____ Number of conductors per phase: _____
Measured Temperatures	Bus temperature range: _____ Conductor temperature range: _____
Grounding System	Terminal of rectifier bonded to ground? ❏ Yes ❏ No Ground bus of rectifier bonded to the frame? ❏ Yes ❏ No Ground current measurement: _____ A Ground resistance measurement: _____ Ω Sketch the existing grounding system (on the back sheet) when it is needed.
Batteries	Manufacturer: _____ Model: _____ Type: _____ Cell voltage: _____ Number of cells: _____ Total battery voltages: _____ V Total battery currents: _____ A Conductor sizes: Phases: ( ) _____ Neutral: ( ) _____ Ground: ( ) _____ Physical conditions: ❏ Damage ❏ Corrosion ❏ Leakage Fluid fill level: _____ Proper mounting: _____ Proper clearance: _____ Battery rack condition: _____ Battery rack grounded? ❏ Yes ❏ No Battery bank terminal grounded? ❏ Yes ❏ No Battery fluid specific gravity last checked: _____

Measured Battery Cell Voltages and Fluid Temperatures

All temperatures are in _°C _°F

Cell #____ ____ V ____	Cell #____ ____ V ____	Cell #____ ____ V ____	Cell #____ ____ V ____	Cell #____ ____ V ____	Cell #____ ____ V ____	Cell #____ ____ V ____
Cell #____ ____ V ____	Cell #____ ____ V ____	Cell #____ ____ V ____	Cell #____ ____ V ____	Cell #____ ____ V ____	Cell #____ ____ V ____	Cell #____ ____ V ____
Cell #____ ____ V ____	Cell #____ ____ V ____	Cell #____ ____ V ____	Cell #____ ____ V ____	Cell #____ ____ V ____	Cell #____ ____ V ____	Cell #____ ____ V ____
Cell #____ ____ V ____	Cell #____ ____ V ____	Cell #____ ____ V ____	Cell #____ ____ V ____	Cell #____ ____ V ____	Cell #____ ____ V ____	Cell #____ ____ V ____
Cell #____ ____ V ____	Cell #____ ____ V ____	Cell #____ ____ V ____	Cell #____ ____ V ____	Cell #____ ____ V ____	Cell #____ ____ V ____	Cell #____ ____ V ____

© 2023 National Fire Protection Association   NFPA 70B (p. 1 of 2)

△ **FIGURE E.47**   **Rectifier Survey.**

RECTIFIER SURVEY *(continued)*

Deficiencies Found	
Problems in the Past	
Customer's Concerns	
Notes	

© 2023 National Fire Protection Association

NFPA 70B (p. 2 of 2)

△ FIGURE E.47 *Continued*

     Shaded text = Revisions.   **△** = Text deletions and figure/table revisions.   • = Section deletions.   ***N*** = New material.

ELECTRICAL PANEL SURVEY

Date: _____

Installation: _____ Location: _____

_____

Panel Identification: _____

Manufacturer Name: _____ Panel Type/Model: _____

Voltage Rating: _____ V   Current Rating: _____ A   Phases: _____   # of Wires: _____

Main Breaker: Type/Model: _____   Rating: _____ A   Adjustable Setting Range: _____

Measured Voltages	$V_{A-N} =$ _____ V $V_{A-G} =$ _____ V	$V_{B-N} =$ _____ V $V_{B-G} =$ _____ V	$V_{C-N} =$ _____ V $V_{C-G} =$ _____ V	$V_{N-G} =$ _____ V
Voltage Sine Waves	V_{A-N}	V_{B-N}	V_{C-N}	V_{N-G}
Harmonic Voltage Distortion	$V_{THD(A-N)} =$ ____ % 3rd = _____ % __th = _____ % __th = _____ %	$V_{THD(B-N)} =$ ____ % 3rd = _____ % __th = _____ % __th = _____ %	$V_{THD(C-N)} =$ ____ % 3rd = _____ % __th = _____ % __th = _____ %	$V_{THD(N-G)} =$ ____ % 3rd = _____ % __th = _____ % __th = _____ %
Measured Currents	$I_A =$ _____ A	$I_B =$ _____ A	$I_C =$ _____ A	$I_N =$ _____ A
Current Sine Waves	I_A	I_B	I_C	I_N
Harmonic Current Distortion	$I_{THD(A)} =$ _____ % 3rd = _____ % __th = _____ % __th = _____ %	$I_{THD(B)} =$ _____ % 3rd = _____ % __th = _____ % __th = _____ %	$I_{THD(C)} =$ _____ % 3rd = _____ % __th = _____ % __th = _____ %	$I_{THD(N)} =$ _____ % 3rd = _____ % __th = _____ % __th = _____ %
Power Factor	PF:_____ Displacement Power Factor (DPF): _____			
Grounding System	Ground bus isolated from frame?____ or bonded to frame?____ Ground by metal conduits?____ or by ground conductors?____ Ground bus bonded to neutral bus? ❑ Yes ❑ No Each branch circuit has separated neutral ❑ Yes ❑ No and ground conductor? ❑ Yes ❑ No Ground current measurement: _____ A Ground resistance measurement: _____ Ω Sketch the existing grounding system (on the back sheet) when it is necessary.			
Temperature	Bus temperature range: _____ Conductor temperature range: _____ CBs having temperature higher than 32°C (90°F): _____			
Entrance Conductor Sizes	Phases: _____ MCM Number of conductors per phase: _____ Neutral: _____ MCM Number of conductors per phase: _____ Ground: _____ MCM Number of conductors per phase: _____			
Lightning Protection	Manufacturer: _____ Type: _____ Voltage rating: _____			

© 2023 National Fire Protection Association   NFPA 70B (p. 1 of 2)

△ FIGURE E.48   Electrical Panel Survey.

ELECTRICAL PANEL SURVEY *(continued)*

Other Circuit Breakers in the Panel	CB rating: _____ A	How many CB: _____	Conductor sizes: _____
	CB rating: _____ A	How many CB: _____	Conductor sizes: _____
	CB rating: _____ A	How many CB: _____	Conductor sizes: _____
	CB rating: _____ A	How many CB: _____	Conductor sizes: _____
	CB rating: _____ A	How many CB: _____	Conductor sizes: _____
	CB rating: _____ A	How many CB: _____	Conductor sizes: _____
	CB rating: _____ A	How many CB: _____	Conductor sizes: _____
	CB rating: _____ A	How many CB: _____	Conductor sizes: _____

Deficiencies Found

_____
_____
_____
_____
_____

Problems in the Past

_____
_____
_____
_____

Customer's Concerns

_____
_____
_____
_____
_____

Notes

_____
_____
_____
_____
_____
_____
_____
_____

© 2023 National Fire Protection Association

NFPA 70B (p. 2 of 2)

△ **FIGURE E.48**   *Continued*

TRANSFER SWITCHES SURVEY

Date: _____

Installation: _____   Location: _____

Transfer Switch Identification: _____

Manufacturer Name: _____   Model/Type: _____   Serial #: _____

Voltage Rating: _____ V   Current Rating: _____ A   Fuse sizes: _____

Automatic or Manual: _____   Phases: _____   # of Poles: _____   # of Wires: _____

Measured Voltages	$V_{A-G} =$ _____ V $V_{A-N} =$ _____ V	$V_{B-G} =$ _____ V $V_{B-N} =$ _____ V	$V_{C-G} =$ _____ V $V_{C-N} =$ _____ V	$V_{N-G} =$ _____ V
Voltage Sine Waves	V_{A-G}	V_{B-G}	V_{C-G}	V_{N-G}
Harmonic Voltage Distortion	$V_{THD(A-G)} =$ ____ % 3rd = _____ % 5th = _____ % __th = _____ %	$V_{THD(B-G)} =$ ____ % 3rd = _____ % 5th = _____ % __th = _____ %	$V_{THD(C-G)} =$ ____ % 3rd = _____ % 5th = _____ % __th = _____ %	$V_{THD(N-G)} =$ ____ % 3rd = _____ % 5th = _____ % __th = _____ %
Measured Currents	$I_A =$ _____ A	$I_B =$ _____ A	$I_C =$ _____ A	$I_N =$ _____ A
Current Sine Waves	I_A	I_B	I_C	I_N
Harmonic Current Distortion	$I_{THD(A)} =$ _____ % 3rd = _____ % 5th = _____ % __th = _____ %	$I_{THD(B)} =$ _____ % 3rd = _____ % 5th = _____ % __th = _____ %	$I_{THD(C)} =$ _____ % 3rd = _____ % 5th = _____ % __th = _____ %	$I_{THD(N)} =$ _____ % 3rd = _____ % 5th = _____ % __th = _____ %

Grounding System	Neutral bus exists? ❏ Yes ❏ No Ground bus exists? ❏ Yes ❏ No Neutral bus bonded to ground bus at the transfer switch? ❏ Yes ❏ No Neutral conductors just run through transfer switch? ❏ Yes ❏ No Ground bus bonded to the frame? ❏ Yes ❏ No Ground bus connected to upstream source ground? ❏ Yes ❏ No Ground bus connected to downstream load ground? ❏ Yes ❏ No Ground resistance measurement: _____ Ω Ground current measurement: _____ A Sketch the existing grounding system (on the back sheet) when it is necessary.
Temperatures	Bus temperatures: _____ Conductor temperatures: _____
Power Factor	PF: _____ Displacement Power Factor (DPF): _____
Conductor Sizes	Normal source: Phases: ( ) _____ Neutral: ( ) _____ Ground: ( ) _____ Emerg/Standby source: Phases: ( ) _____ Neutral: ( ) _____ Ground: ( ) _____ Load side: Phases: ( ) _____ Neutral: ( ) _____ Ground: ( ) _____

© 2023 National Fire Protection Association

NFPA 70B (p. 1 of 2)

△ **FIGURE E.49**   **Transfer Switches Survey.**

Shaded text = Revisions.   △ = Text deletions and figure/table revisions.   • = Section deletions.   *N* = New material.

2023 Edition

TRANSFER SWITCHES SURVEY *(continued)*

Operation Scheme of Transfer Switch	Make before break? ❏ Yes ❏ No Break before make? ❏ Yes ❏ No Time delay available? ❏ Yes ❏ No
Deficiencies Found	
Problems in the Past	
Customer's Concerns	
Notes	

© 2023 National Fire Protection Association   NFPA 70B (p. 2 of 2)

Δ **FIGURE E.49** *Continued*

    Shaded text = Revisions.   **Δ** = Text deletions and figure/table revisions.   • = Section deletions.   **N** = New material

POWER TRANSFORMERS SURVEY
                                                                              Date: _____

Installation: _____   Location: _____

Transformer Identification: _____

Type: ❏ Isolation   ❏ Shielded Isolation   ❏ Dry   ❏ Oil   ❏ Pad or Pole Mounted

Number of units: _____   kVA Rating of each unit: _____   Phases: _____   Impedance: _____ %

Load Tap Changing: ❏ Automatic   ❏ Manual   ❏ None

Cooling System (O/A/FA/etc.): _____   Nameplate Power Factor: _____   Nameplate "k" Factor: _____

Measured Power Factor: _____   Measured Displacement Power Factor: _____   Measured "k" Factor: _____

	High Voltage Sides			*Low Voltage Sides*			
Voltage Rating	_____ V			_____ V			
Current Rating	_____ A			_____ A			
Wiring Connection	(D/Y/GY): _____			*(D/Y/GY):* _____			
Measured Voltages	$V_{A\text{-}B}$	$V_{B\text{-}C}$	$V_{A\text{-}C}$	$V_{a\text{-}n}$	$V_{b\text{-}n}$	$V_{c\text{-}n}$	$V_{n\text{-}g}$
Harmonic Voltages	THD						
	3rd						
	5th						
	__th						
	__th						
Measured Currents	I_A	I_B	I_C	I_a	I_b	I_c	I_n
Harmonic Currents	THD						
	3rd						
	5th						
	__th						
	__th						
Conductor Sizes	Phases: ____ # of Conductors/phase: ____ Neutral: ____ # of Conductors/phase: ____ Ground: ____ # of Conductors: ____			*Phases:* ____ *# of Conductors/phase:* ____ *Neutral:* ____ *# of Conductors/phase:* ____ *Ground:* ____ *# of Conductors:* ____			

© 2023 National Fire Protection Association   NFPA 70B (p. 1 of 2)

FIGURE E.50   Power Transformers Survey.

POWER TRANSFORMERS SURVEY *(continued)*

Temperature	Winding temperature range: _____ Bus temperature range: _____ Enclosure temperature: _____
Physical Conditions	❏ Good condition ❏ Damage ❏ Corrosion ❏ Fluid leakage Proper mounting: _____ Proper clearance: _____ Need maintenance: _____ Sight of burning/overheat (color change): _____
Grounding System	Ground bus connected to transformer frame? ❏ Yes ❏ No Ground bus connected to upstream source ground? ❏ Yes ❏ No Ground bus connected to downstream load ground? ❏ Yes ❏ No Ground bus connected to building metal frame? ❏ Yes ❏ No Ground current measurement: _____ A Ground resistance measurement: _____ Ω
Deficiencies Found	
Problems in the Past	
Customer's Concerns	
Notes	

© 2023 National Fire Protection Association   NFPA 70B (p. 2 of 2)

△ **FIGURE E.50** *Continued*

UNINTERRUPTIBLE POWER SYSTEM SURVEY

Date: _____

Installation: _____ Location: _____

_____

UPS System Identification: _____

_____

Number of modules: _____ Do these modules have the same sizes and characteristics? ❏ Yes ❏ No

Module #1

Manufacturer: _____

Model/Type: _____

Frequencies: Input: _____ Hz   Output: _____ Hz

Power Factor: Input: _____   Output: _____

Wiring Connection: Input: ❏ 3-Phases/3 Wires   ❏ 3-Phases/4 Wires   ❏ Single-Phase

                     Output: ❏ 3-Phases/3 Wires   ❏ 3-Phases/4 Wires   ❏ Single-Phase

Grounding System: Ground Current: _____ A   Ground Resistance: _____ Ω

Input Voltages: Rated: _____ V   Measured $V_{A-B} =$ _____ V $V_{B-C} =$ _____ V $V_{A-C} =$ _____ V

Input Currents: Rated: _____ A   Measured $I_A =$ _____ A $I_B =$ _____ A $I_C =$ _____ A

DC Link Voltages: Rated: _____ V   Measured $V_{A-B} =$ _____ V $V_{B-C} =$ _____ V $V_{A-C} =$ _____ V

DC Link Currents: Rated: _____ A   Measured $I_A =$ _____ A $I_B =$ _____ A $I_C =$ _____ A

Output Voltages: Rated: _____ V   Measured $V_{A-B} =$ _____ V $V_{B-C} =$ _____ V $V_{A-C} =$ _____ V

Output Currents: Rated: _____ A   Measured $I_A =$ _____ A $I_B =$ _____ A $I_C =$ _____ A

kVA: Rated: _____   Measured Input: _____ _____ _____   Measured Output: _____ _____ _____

kW: Rated: _____   Measured Input: _____ _____ _____   Measured Output: _____ _____ _____

Module #2 (If they are of different sizes/characteristics)

Manufacturer: _____

Model/Type: _____

Frequencies: Input: _____ Hz   Output: _____ Hz

Power Factor: Input: _____   Output: _____

Wiring Connection: Input: ❏ 3-Phases/3 Wires   ❏ 3-Phases/4 Wires   ❏ Single-Phase

                     Output: ❏ 3-Phases/3 Wires   ❏ 3-Phases/4 Wires   ❏ Single-Phase

Grounding System: Ground Current: _____ A   Ground Resistance: _____ Ω

Input Voltages: Rated: _____ V   Measured $V_{A-B} =$ _____ V $V_{B-C} =$ _____ V $V_{A-C} =$ _____ V

Input Currents: Rated: _____ A   Measured $I_A =$ _____ A $I_B =$ _____ A $I_C =$ _____ A

DC Link Voltages: Rated: _____ V   Measured $V_{A-B} =$ _____ V $V_{B-C} =$ _____ V $V_{A-C} =$ _____ V

DC Link Currents: Rated: _____ A   Measured $I_A =$ _____ A $I_B =$ _____ A $I_C =$ _____ A

Output Voltages: Rated: _____ V   Measured $V_{A-B} =$ _____ V $V_{B-C} =$ _____ V $V_{A-C} =$ _____ V

Output Currents: Rated: _____ A   Measured $I_A =$ _____ A $I_B =$ _____ A $I_C =$ _____ A

kVA: Rated: _____   Measured Input: _____ _____ _____   Measured Output: _____ _____ _____

kW: Rated: _____   Measured Input: _____ _____ _____   Measured Output: _____ _____ _____

© 2023 National Fire Protection Association   NFPA 70B (p. 1 of 2)

▲ **FIGURE E.51**   Uninterruptible Power System Survey.

UNINTERRUPTIBLE POWER SYSTEM SURVEY *(continued)*

Batteries	Manufacturer: _____ Model: _____ Type: _____
	Number of battery banks: _____ Number of cells per bank: _____
	    Measured total voltage of each bank: _____ _____ _____ _____ _____ V
	    Measured total current of each bank: _____ _____ _____ _____ _____ A
	Battery rack condition: _____ Battery rack properly grounded? ❏ Yes ❏ No
	Battery bank terminal grounded? ❏ Yes ❏ No
	Battery bank switch (3 or 4 poles): _____ Switch properly grounded? ❏ Yes ❏ No
	Conductor sizes: Phases: ( ) _____ Neutral: ( ) _____ Ground: ( ) _____
	Ground current measurement: _____ A Ground resistance measurement: _____ Ω
	Batteries properly mounted? ❏ Yes ❏ No Proper ventilation? ❏ Yes ❏ No
	Fluid level checked: _____ Battery fluid specific gravity last checked: _____
	Battery physical conditions: ❏ Damage ❏ Corrosion ❏ Leakage ❏ Need maintenance

Measured Battery Cell Voltages and Fluid Temperatures

All temperatures are in _°C _°F

Cell #____ ____ V ____	Cell #____ ____ V ____	Cell #____ ____ V ____	Cell #____ ____ V ____	Cell #____ ____ V ____	Cell #____ ____ V ____	Cell #____ ____ V ____
Cell #____ ____ V ____	Cell #____ ____ V ____	Cell #____ ____ V ____	Cell #____ ____ V ____	Cell #____ ____ V ____	Cell #____ ____ V ____	Cell #____ ____ V ____
Cell #____ ____ V ____	Cell #____ ____ V ____	Cell #____ ____ V ____	Cell #____ ____ V ____	Cell #____ ____ V ____	Cell #____ ____ V ____	Cell #____ ____ V ____
Cell #____ ____ V ____	Cell #____ ____ V ____	Cell #____ ____ V ____	Cell #____ ____ V ____	Cell #____ ____ V ____	Cell #____ ____ V ____	Cell #____ ____ V ____
Cell #____ ____ V ____	Cell #____ ____ V ____	Cell #____ ____ V ____	Cell #____ ____ V ____	Cell #____ ____ V ____	Cell #____ ____ V ____	Cell #____ ____ V ____
Cell #____ ____ V ____	Cell #____ ____ V ____	Cell #____ ____ V ____	Cell #____ ____ V ____	Cell #____ ____ V ____	Cell #____ ____ V ____	Cell #____ ____ V ____

Deficiencies Found	_____ _____ _____ _____ _____
Notes	_____ _____ _____ _____ _____ _____

© 2023 National Fire Protection Association   NFPA 70B (p. 2 of 2)

△ **FIGURE E.51** *Continued*

    Shaded text = Revisions.   △ = Text deletions and figure/table revisions.   • = Section deletions.   *N* = New material.

LOW VOLTAGE BREAKER DATA RECORD

Site: _____ Date: _____ Page: _____

No.	Location	Breaker						Relay							
		Mfgr.	Type	Rated Voltage	Frame Rating	Interr. Time	Mfgr.	Type	Long Time Delay		Short Time Delay		Instant	Ground	
									Range	Bands Avail.	Range	Bands Avail.	Range	Range	Bands Avail.

NFPA 70B

© 2023 National Fire Protection Association

FIGURE E.52   Low-Voltage Breaker Data Record.

Shaded text = Revisions.   Δ = Text deletions and figure/table revisions.   • = Section deletions.   N = New material.

RECLOSER DATA RECORD

Site: _____   Date: _____   Page: _____

No.	Location	CT Ratio	Nominal Voltage	Mfgr.	Type	BIL	Continuous Current Rating	Interruption Rating	Minimum Trip	Hydrau or Electro	Operation Sequence Available	Reclosing Times Available	Tripping Curves Available

NFPA 70B

© 2023 National Fire Protection Association

△ **FIGURE E.53**   **Recloser Data Record.**

Shaded text = Revisions.   △ = Text deletions and figure/table revisions.   • = Section deletions.   *N* = New material.

GENERATOR DATA RECORD

Site: _____   Date: _____   Page: _____

No.	Location	Type	kVA Rating	Generated Volts	Rated Current	Speed in RPM	Wiring Connections	Subtrans. Impedance	Ground Impedance	Power Factor

NFPA 70B

© 2023 National Fire Protection Association

FIGURE E.54   Generator Data Record.

Shaded text = Revisions.   Δ = Text deletions and figure/table revisions.   • = Section deletions.   N = New material.

Annex F NEMA Configurations

This annex is not a part of the requirements of this NFPA document but is included for informational purposes only.

F.1 Figure F.1 shows the typical NEMA configurations for general-purpose nonlocking plugs and receptacles.

F.2 Figure F.2 shows the typical NEMA configurations for locking plugs and receptacles.

Shaded text = Revisions. **Δ** = Text deletions and figure/table revisions. • = Section deletions. *N* = New material.

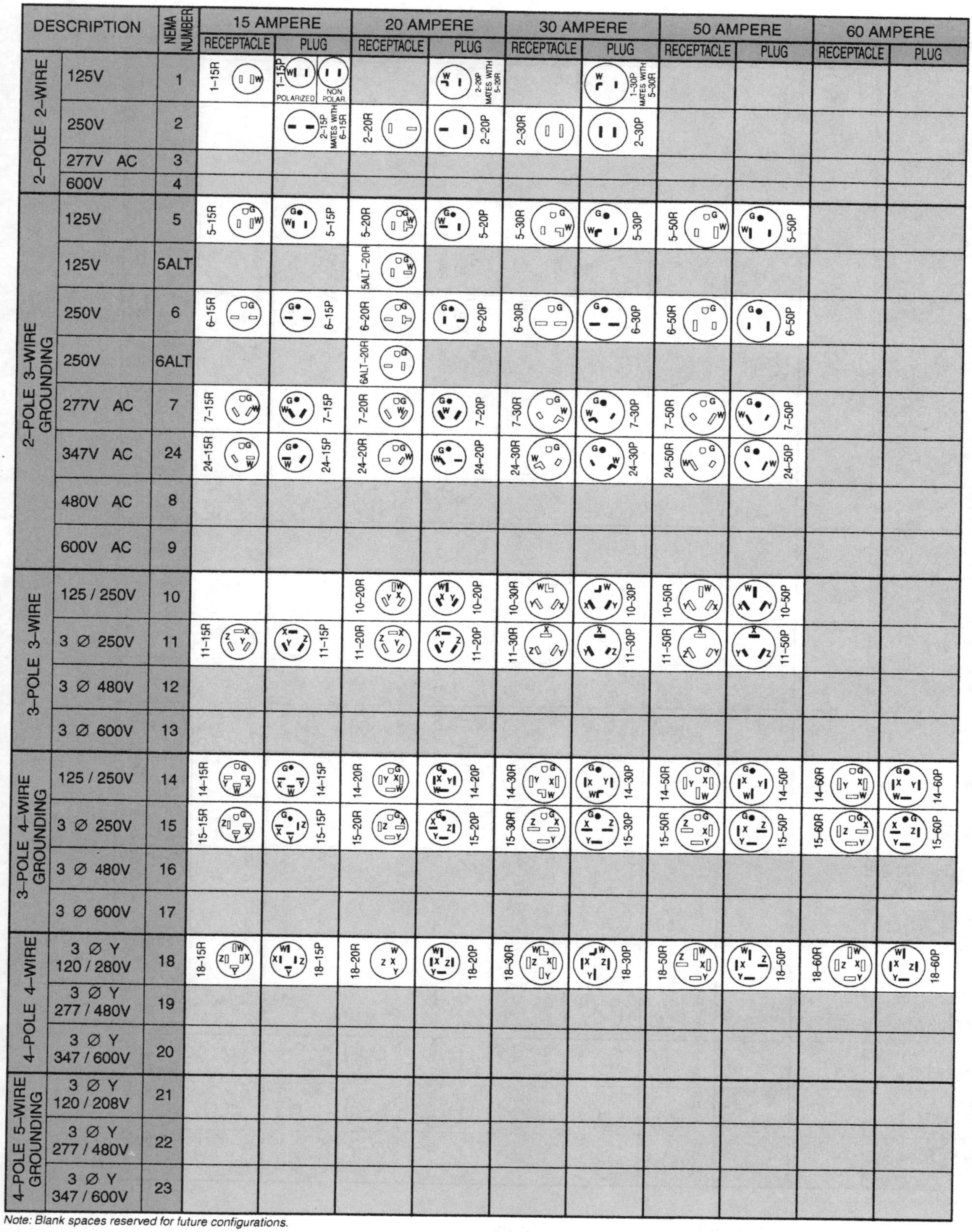

△ FIGURE F.1 NEMA Configurations for General-Purpose Nonlocking Plugs and Receptacles.

Note: Blank spaces reserved for future configurations.

Shaded text = Revisions.   △ = Text deletions and figure/table revisions.   ● = Section deletions.   N = New material.

2023 Edition

Note: Blank spaces reserved for future configurations.

△ **FIGURE F.2**   **NEMA Configurations for Locking Plugs and Receptacles.**

Shaded text = Revisions.   △ = Text deletions and figure/table revisions.   • = Section deletions.   **N** = New material

Annex G Primary Contact Matrix

This annex is not a part of the requirements of this NFPA document but is included for informational purposes only.

G.1 Primary Contact Matrix. Figure G.1 shows a typical primary contact matrix.

PRIMARY CONTACT MATRIX

		Primary Contacts	Other
Facility Manager			
Maintenance Manager			
Information Technology (IT) Manager			
Hazardous Material (Haz Mat) Team			
Site Security			
Medical Response Team			
Fire Response Team			
Other Responders			
System Affected			
Power delivery systems	Generator(s)		
	Power equipment failure (cables, switchgear, circuit breakers, SCADA)		
	UPS systems		
HVAC systems	Make-up water not available		
	Primary components fail (pump, filter, etc.)		
	Make water support equipment (pipes, valves)		
	HVAC controls		
	HVAC zones control (pneumatic)		
	CPU monitored/ controlled		
	HVAC bldg. zone controls		
Building security and egress systems	Video monitoring, personnel entry/exit surveillance systems, exit/egress lighting		
	Fire sensors, pathogens detection-response systems		
	Fire suppression activation/failure		
	Egress system failure (doors, elevation)		

© 2023 National Fire Protection Association

NFPA 70B (1 of 2)

Δ **FIGURE G.1 Primary Contact Matrix.**

PRIMARY CONTACT MATRIX (continued)

		Primary Contacts	Other
Potential emergency/ failures from natural/ human actions	Utility supply		
	Floods (nature), floods (broken piping)		
	Snow		
	Fire (wild and facility)		
Meteorological hazards	Windstorms (hurricanes, tornadoes, cyclones)		
	Temperature extremes		
	Lightning strike/surge events		
Biological events	"Normal" diseases, exotic diseases		
	Animal/insect infestations		
Accidental (human or equipment caused)	Hazards (chemical, radiological, biological) spill or release into environment (air, water)		
	Internal site explosions		
	Fuel/resource outages		
	Internal communications equipment failure, human communication failure		
	HVAC equipment/controls failure		
	CPU server failure		
	Terminal/video readout failure		
	Security equipment failure		
	Fire suppression equipment failure		
	Human/animal sickness		
Accidental external utility related disruptions	Utility power disruptions		
	Domestic water utility disruptions/pollution/ contaminations		
	Fuel gases interruptions		
	External communications failure		

© 2023 National Fire Protection Association   NFPA 70B (2 of 2)

△ **FIGURE G.1** *Continued*

= Revisions.   = Text deletions and figure/table revisions.   • = Section deletions.   = New materia

Annex H Equipment Storage and Maintenance During Construction

This annex is not a part of the requirements of this NFPA document but is included for informational purposes only.

H.1 Introduction. Preferably, all types of electrical equipment should be stored in a clean, heated building affording good physical protection and providing controlled access to prevent unauthorized tampering with the equipment. However, equipment can be stored in other inside and outside environments with proper provisions to satisfy the general recommendations of this section and the recommendations specified in the particular equipment sections. The manufacturer's instructions for the specific equipment and environment should be followed.

H.1.1 Before storage, when equipment is received, it should be inspected for shipping damage, and reports should be made as recommended to recover repair or replacement costs from the carrier in the event damage was sustained. In some cases, visual inspection might indicate a need to test for concealed damage before the equipment is removed from the carrier vehicle.

H.1.2 Covers are recommended unless storage conditions specified in Section H.1 exist. Canvas tarpaulins or the equivalent are preferred over other coverings because they provide better humidity control and enclosure scuff protection.

H.1.3 The manufacturer's shipping skids should be left on the equipment to provide structural support until the equipment is set in its final resting place.

H.1.4 Insulation tests should be conducted and test values recorded when the equipment is received. Periodic tests are recommended in the following sections for particular types of equipment. In all cases, insulation should be retested prior to start-up, with sufficient time provided for any necessary dry-out or repair prior to energizing.

H.1.5 Regular inspections should be made to check the general effectiveness of equipment storage provisions, and improvements should be made as indicated.

H.2 Equipment. Where storage conditions specified in Section H.1 are not available, indoor or outdoor storage should comply with the following paragraphs.

H.2.1 Switchgear, Switchboards, Motor Control, and Other Control Equipment.

H.2.1.1 Metal-enclosed equipment should be stored in the upright position. Good ventilation of the shelter and protection from dirt, moisture, and physical damage should be provided.

H.2.1.2 Space heaters furnished with the equipment should be connected to a continuous source of power of the proper rating.

CAUTION: Where space heaters are supplied from auxiliary power transformers, care should be taken that low-voltage heater circuits are properly isolated before power-source connection to prevent inadvertent energizing of the auxiliary transformer and associated high-voltage primary wiring.

H.2.1.3 Temporary heaters or lamp banks should be used where space heaters are not furnished to maintain temperature at a level approximately 12°C (22°F) above ambient.

H.2.1.4 In humid locations, it might be necessary to remove the equipment from shipping cases to permit adequate ventilation and to avoid mildew.

H.2.1.5 Oil-immersed circuit breakers, starters, and similar items that are shipped dry should be stored indoors or should be filled with insulating liquid as soon as they are received on site. Units filled with liquid can be stored outdoors if raised above grade to prevent any damage from surface water and if a shed roof and tarpaulin siding (or equivalent) are provided.

H.2.1.6 Insulation resistance values of such parts as operating coils should be spot-checked every 6 weeks. If any readings are low, the affected parts should be dried out before they are placed in operation.

H.3 Busway and Associated Fittings.

H.3.1 Busway sections and fittings preferably should be stored in a heated building that has adequate air circulation and is protected from dirt, water, and physical damage. Where this is not possible, sections and fittings should be stored in a clean, dry shelter that has provisions for maintaining temperature uniformity necessary to prevent condensation.

H.3.2 If busway sections and associated fittings are stored outdoors, they should be securely covered for protection from weather and dirt. Temporary electrical heating should be installed beneath the cover to prevent condensation. At least 0.0283 watt/m³ (3 watts/ft³) is adequate for the average environment.

H.3.3 Weatherproof busway should be treated exactly the same as indoor busway until after it is installed. It is not weatherproof until completely and properly installed.

H.4 Motors and Generators.

H.4.1 Indoor storage should be provided for all motors and generators except motors designed for outdoor use, which can be stored outdoors without protective covering. These generally are explosionproof motors, totally enclosed motors, and totally enclosed motors with integral coolers. However, in special cases where they are designed for indoor use only, they should be stored indoors. Other motors can be stored outdoors if protective covering that permits good ventilation is furnished.

H.4.2 For motors and mechanical equipment with motors such as motor-operated valve actuators stored outdoors without protective cover, the following should be observed:

(1) All enclosure openings not intended to be open during operation of the equipment, such as conduit and cable entrances in terminal boxes, should be closed with watertight plugs. Temporary shipping plugs should be replaced with permanent storage plugs.
(2) All motors and mechanical equipment with motors should be stored in their normal operating position (e.g., vertical motors in an upright position with their shaft extension downward).

H.4.3 If space heaters are furnished in the units, they should be connected to a continuous supply of power of the proper rating.

H.4.4 Insulation resistance values of each winding should be measured and should be recorded for future reference. The first set of values should be reasonably consistent with the factory insulation resistance measurement values. These measurements should be taken as soon as possible after a unit arrives at the site.

H.4.5 Brushes should be removed from brush holders and should be stored in a dry, warm place where condensation will not occur.

H.4.6 After installation at the final service location, motors with oil-lubricated bearings and ac motors and generators with collector rings should be protected as follows:

(1) *Oil-lubricated bearings.* All internal surfaces of bearing housing should be coated with rust preventative. Vent and drain connections should be plugged, capped, or blinded, as applicable, using steel fittings. The internal surfaces should be recoated (by fill, fill and drain, slushing, spraying, or rotation, as appropriate) at 1-month intervals.
(2) *Collector rings.* Applied protective coatings should be examined and renewed if not intact.

H.4.7 Every 3 months, insulation resistance values of each winding of units rated 2300 volts and higher should be measured and recorded. Temperature and weather conditions should be recorded at time of reading. If resistance is low and cables have been connected, the cables should be disconnected and the measurements repeated. If resistance of winding insulation only is low, leads in a unit's terminal box should be dried out by removing the cover and exposing them to dry, clear weather or by placing an electric lamp or heater in the terminal box. If these measures do not result in acceptable insulation resistance values, the windings should be dried out by an approved method until acceptable values are obtained.

H.4.8 Six weeks or less before start-up, insulation resistance values of each winding of all units should be measured and recorded. Temperature and weather conditions should be recorded at time of reading. If resistance is low, the recommendations of H.4.7 should be followed.

H.4.9 If grease-lubricated units are on site more than 1 year from the date of shipment from the factory without having been operated, the bearing grease should be inspected. If there has been any visible deterioration of the lubricating properties of the grease, the grease should be cleaned out and the bearings replaced per the manufacturer's recommendations.

H.4.10 Immediately before start-up, the following should be performed:

(1) Insulation values of all units with cables connected should be measured and recorded. If readings are low, the units should be dried out before starting.
(2) Protective coatings should be cleaned from collector ring surfaces.
(3) Surfaces of commutators should be cleaned per manufacturer's instructions.

H.5 Transformers.

H.5.1 Indoor storage should be provided for all transformers except the following:

(1) Transformers intended for outdoor installation can be stored outdoors without protective covering.
(2) Large indoor units can be stored outdoors if raised above grade to prevent any damage from surface water and if a shed roof and tarpaulin siding (or equivalent) are provided.

H.5.2 Ventilated dry-type units should have the same storage conditions as indoor switchgear.

H.5.3 Drums of insulating liquid stored outdoors should be laid on their sides with the large bung downward. Drums should be placed so that the large bung is at about a 45-degree angle from the bottom center position, to minimize contamination by moisture or other liquids.

H.5.4 Transformers Filled with Insulating Liquid. If a transformer is shipped with its main tank filled with insulating liquid (except for expansion space), the level of the liquid and the ambient temperature should be measured and recorded when the unit arrives on site. Levels should be within recommended tolerances. The transformer should be regularly inspected to verify the absence of leaks.

H.5.5 Transformer Gas Blanket. If a transformer is shipped with its main tank filled with insulating liquid and blanketed with gas under pressure or filled with gas under pressure, the gas pressure and the ambient temperature should be measured and recorded when the unit arrives on site and every month thereafter. Pressures should be kept within specified tolerances. If leaks are suspected, they should be found and repaired.

H.5.6 Primary Disconnect Switches. Primary disconnect switches should be handled in accordance with the recommendations for switchgear, motor control, and control equipment.

H.6 Cables.

H.6.1 Reels of paper-insulated, lead-sheathed cable should be rotated 90 degrees every 2 weeks. Sealed ends should be checked for leaks and patched if necessary.

H.6.2 Low-pressure, gas-filled cable should be handled as follows:

(1) Gas pressure should be measured and recorded when the cable is received at the site and every month thereafter. The pressure should be between 34.48 kPa (5 psig) and 89.64 kPa (13 psig). If falling pressure indicates a leak in the cable, a cylinder of dry nitrogen should be connected to the cable to maintain pressure until the leak is located and sealed.
(2) Nitrogen used to maintain pressure during storage, if needed, should be in accordance with ASTM D1933, *Standard Specification for Nitrogen Gas as an Electrical Insulating Material.* Where available, nitrogen type III is preferred. Manufacturer's recommendations should be followed during installation and operation of any nitrogen cylinders.

H.6.3 Physical protection from vehicles or striking objects is recommended for solid dielectric types (XLP or EPR) on reels. Cable ends should be sealed at the factory and maintained until cables are terminated properly.

H.7 Storage Batteries.

H.7.1 All batteries should be stored indoors, in a dry place.

H.7.2 Batteries that have been shipped dry and charged should have the seals inspected when they are received at the site. Any seals that are damaged should be renewed per the manufacturer's instructions.

Shaded text = Revisions. Δ = Text deletions and figure/table revisions. • = Section deletions. *N* = New material.

Δ **H.7.3** Batteries that have been shipped wet should be handled in accordance with the manufacturer's instructions. Lead-acid batteries that have been shipped wet should be handled as follows:

(1) Electrolyte levels should be inspected when batteries are received at the site. Electrolyte should be added to the proper level, if any has been lost.

(2) Three months after the date of shipment from the factory, and every three months thereafter, batteries should be given a freshening charge to restore the voltage to 2.15 volts per cell and the specific gravity to 1.21 at 25°C (77°F). The charging rate should not exceed the manufacturer's recommended value; batteries should not be overcharged.

Annex I   Reliability Centered Maintenance

This annex is not a part of the requirements of this NFPA document but is included for informational purposes only.

I.1 Definitions. These definitions are referenced in several reliability publications and the formulas can be verified in MIL-HNDK-508, *Wiring and Wiring Devices for Combat and Tactical Vehicles, Selection and Installation of,* or in IEEE 100, *Authoritative Dictionary of IEEE Standards Terms.*

I.1.1 Availability. The probability that a system or product will be available to perform its intended mission or function when called upon to do so at any point in time. It can be measured in one of several ways.

I.1.1.1 Function of Uptime. Availability can be considered as the percent of total time that a system is available. It is measured using Equation I.1.1.1 (note that the period of time over which this measure of availability is made must be defined). Downtime includes administrative time and delays, as well as time for maintenance and repair.

$$[I.1.1.1]$$

$$\text{Availability} = \frac{\text{Uptime}}{\text{Downtime} + \text{Uptime (Total time)}}$$

I.1.1.2 Operational Availability.

I.1.1.2.1 Another equation for availability directly uses parameters related to the reliability and maintainability characteristics of the item as well as the support system. Equation I.1.1.2.1 reflects this measure.

$$[I.1.1.2.1]$$

$$\text{Operational Availability} = \frac{\text{Mean Time Between Maintenance (MTBM)}}{\text{Mean Downtime} + \text{MTBM}}$$

I.1.1.2.2 In Equation I.1.1.2.1, mean time between maintenance (MTBM) includes all maintenance required for any reason, including repairs of actual design failures, repairs of induced failures, cases where a failure cannot be confirmed, and preventive maintenance.

I.1.1.3 Inherent Availability. When only maintenance required to correct design failures is counted and the effects of the support system are ignored, the result is inherent availability, which is given by Equation I.1.1.3.

$$[I.1.1.3]$$

$$\text{Inherent Availability} = \frac{\text{Mean Time Between Failures (MTBF)}}{\text{Mean Time to Repair} + \text{MTBF}}$$

I.1.2 RCM Maintenance. Those activities and actions that directly retain the proper operation of an item or restore that operation when it is interrupted by failure or some other anomaly. (Within the context of RCM, proper operation of an item means that the item can perform its intended function.) These activities and actions include removal and replacement of failed items, repair of failed items, lubrication, servicing (includes replenishment of consumables such as fuel), and calibrations. Other activities and resources are needed to support maintenance. These include spares, procedures, labor, training, transportation, facilities, and test equipment. These activities and resources are usually referred to as logistics. Although some organizations might define maintenance to include logistics, it is used in this section in the more limited sense and does not include logistics.

I.1.2.1 Corrective Maintenance. Actions required to restore a failed item to proper operation. Restoration is accomplished by removing the failed item and replacing it with a new item, or by fixing the item by removing and replacing it with a new item, or by fixing the item by removing and replacing internal components or by some other repair action.

I.1.2.2 Preventive Maintenance. Scheduled activities based on an interval to ensure safety, reduce the likelihood of operational failures, and obtain as much useful life as possible from an item.

I.1.2.3 Condition-Based Maintenance. Actions performed on the basis of observed wear or on predicting when the risk of failure is excessive.

I.1.2.3.1 Some items exhibit wear as they are used. If the probability of failure can be related to a measurable amount of wear, it might be possible to prescribe how much wear can be tolerated before the probability of failure reaches some unacceptable level. If so, then this point becomes the criterion for removal or overhaul. Measurement can be done using a variety of techniques depending on the characteristic being measured. The temperature of electrical equipment, for example, can be measured using infrared thermography.

I.1.2.3.2 In predictive maintenance, a given operating characteristic of the item, current, or temperature, for example, is trended and compared with the known "normal" operating levels. An acceptable range is established with either upper and lower limits or some maximum or minimum level. As long as the trend data remain inside the acceptable values, any variation is considered to be normal deviation due to variances in materials, operating environment, and so forth. When the trend line intersects the "unacceptable" limit line, preventive maintenance is required to avoid a failure in the future. The limits are based on knowledge of the normal operating characteristics and the level of risk of failure that is acceptable.

I.1.3 Reliability. The probability that an item will perform its intended function(s) without failure for a specified time under stated conditions.

I.1.4 Reliability-Centered Maintenance (RCM). A logical, structured framework for determining the optimum mix of applicable and effective maintenance activities needed to sustain the operational reliability of systems and equipment while ensuring their safe and economical operation and support.

I.2 Benefits of RCM.

I.2.1 Reduced Costs. Savings have been achieved by industries for equipment when going from a traditional to an RCM-based PM program. It is important to note that these costs savings were achieved with no reduction in safety.

I.2.2 Increased Availability. For many systems, availability is of primary importance. The level of availability achieved in actual use of a product is a function of how often it fails and how quickly it can be restored to operation. The latter, in turn, is a function of how well the product was designed to be maintainable, the amount of PM required, and the logistics resources and infrastructure that have been put in place to support the product. RCM directly contributes to availability by reducing PM to that which is essential and economic.

I.3 Relationship of RCM to Other Disciplines.

I.3.1 Reliability. Much of the analysis needed for reliability provides inputs necessary for performing an RCM analysis. The fundamental requirement of the RCM approach is to understand the failure characteristics of an item. As used herein, failure characteristics include the consequences of failure, and whether or not the failure manifests itself and, if it does, how. Reliability is measured in different ways, depending on one's perspective: inherent reliability, operational reliability, mission (or functional) reliability, and basic (or logistics) reliability. RCM is related to operational reliability.

I.3.1.1 Inherent Versus Operational Reliability. From a designer's perspective, reliability is measured by "counting" only those failures that are design-related. When measured in this way, reliability is referred to as "inherent reliability." From a user's or operator's perspective, any event that causes the system to stop performing its intended function is a failure event. These events include all design-related failures that affect the systems' function. Also included are maintenance-induced failures, no-defect-found events, and other anomalies that might have been outside the designer's contractual responsibility or technical control. This type of reliability is called "operational reliability."

I.3.1.2 Mission-Critical or Functional Reliability Versus Basic or Logistics Reliability. Any failure that causes the product to fail to perform its function or critical mission is counted in "mission-critical reliability." Redundancy improves mission-critical reliability. Consider a case where one part of a product has two elements in parallel where only one is needed (redundant). If a failure of one element of the redundant part of the product fails, the other continues to function, allowing the product to do its job. Only if both elements fail will a mission-critical failure occur.

I.3.1.3 Basic Reliability. In "basic" reliability, all failures are counted, whether or not a mission-critical or functional failure has occurred. This measure of reliability reflects the total demand that will eventually be placed on maintenance and logistics.

I.3.1.3.1 Safety. RCM specifically addresses safety and is intended to ensure that safety is never compromised.

I.3.1.3.2 Environmental Concerns. In the past several years, environmental concerns and issues involving regulatory bodies have been accorded importance in the RCM approach for some items that are equal (or nearly so) to safety. Failures of an item that can cause damage to the environment or that result in some federal or state law being violated can pose serious consequences for the operator of the item. So the RCM logic can be modified to specifically address environmental or other concerns.

I.3.1.3.3 Maintainability. RCM is a method for prescribing PM that is effective and economical. Whether or not a given PM task is effective depends on the reliability characteristics of the item in question. Whether or not a task is economical depends on many factors, including how easily the PM tasks can be performed. Ease of maintenance, corrective or preventive, is a function of how well the system has been designed to be maintainable. This aspect of design is called maintainability. Providing ease of access, placing items requiring PM where they can be easily removed, providing means of inspection, designing to reduce the possibility of maintenance-induced failures, and other design criteria determine the maintainability of a system.

I.4 Supporting Data. Data are critical to the success of an RCM analysis. Since conducting an RCM analysis requires an extensive amount of information, and much of this information is not available early in the design phase, RCM analysis for a new product cannot be completed until just prior to production. The data fall into four categories: failure characteristics, failure effects, costs, and maintenance capabilities and procedures. Table I.4 illustrates reliability and maintainability information crucial to an RCM analysis.

I.5 Reliability, Inherent Availability, and Operational Availability Data. Table I.5 is provided to help you understand and properly apply the data categories in your analysis. The summary information calculated from the individual equipment records is also included. Calculation formulas for each category are given in Table I.4. These definitions are referenced in several reliability publications, and the formulas can be verified in MIL-HNDK-508, *Wiring and Wiring Devices for Combat and Tactical Vehicles, Selection and Installation of*, or in the IEEE standard definition publication.

Table I.4 Reliability and Maintainability Information for RCM Analysis

Calculated Data	Formula for Calculation
Ao, Operational Availability	$Ao = MTBM/(MTBM+MDT)$
Ai, Inherent Availability	$Ai = MTBF/(MBTF+MTTR)$
R(t), Reliability (for time interval t)	$R(t) = e^{-\lambda t}$
MTBF, Mean Time Between Failures (h)	$MTBF = Tp/Tf$
BTTR, Mean Time To Repair (h)	$MTTR = Rdt/Tf$
MTTM, Mean Time To Maintain (h)	$MTTM = Mdt/Tma$
MDT, Mean Downtime (h)	$MDT = (Rdt + Rlt + Mdt)/Tde$
Probability of satisfactory start, prob_s_s	$Prob\_s\_s = total\_start/ total\_attempt$
Probability of failure to start, prob_f_s	$Prob\_f\_s = total\_fail\_start/ total\_attempt$
Hrdt/Year, Hours Downtime per Year	$Hrdt/Year = (1 - Ao) \times 8760$

Table I.5 Reliability, Inherent Availability, and Operational Availability Data

Roll Up Report by Category, Class, and Item				
CATEGORY[a]	CLASS[b]	Reliability[c]	Inherent Availability[d]	Operational Availability[e]
Accumulator		0.993467721	0.999993849	0.999884828
	Accumulator, Pressurized.	0.993913727	0.999992102	0.999841861
	Accumulator, Unpressurized.	0.992345933	0.999998246	0.999992983
Air Compressor		0.964395571	0.999966392	0.999377084
	Air Compressor, Electric.	0.926805720	0.999919556	0.999207149
	Air Compressor, Fuel.	0.989726301	0.999996935	0.999487902
Air Dryer		0.997716217	0.999998695	0.999926162
	Air Dryer, All Types.	0.997716217	0.999998695	0.999926162
Air Handling Unit		0.989056337	0.999997032	0.999875595
	Air Handling Unit, Non-humid wo/Drive.	0.989056337	0.999997032	0.999875595
Arrester		0.998679474	0.999999397	0.999999397
	Arrester, Lightning.	0.998679474	0.999999397	0.999999397
Battery		0.993006248	0.999990299	0.999969547
	Battery, Gel Cell-Sealed, Strings.	0.980061731	0.999995402	0.999967422
	Battery, Lead Acid, System.	0.992563514	0.999972627	0.999968207
	Battery, Nickel-Cadmium.	0.999399558	0.999999292	0.999971403
Blower		0.999825378	1.000000000	0.999960812
	Blower, wo/Drive.	0.999825378*	1.000000000	0.999960812
Boiler		0.878642210	0.999360697	0.995132436
	Boiler, Hot Water, Gravity and Circulated.	0.959008598	0.999985268	0.999501894
Steam		0.842870823	0.999064090	0.993057393
	Boiler, Steam, High Pressure.	0.928026957	0.999619462	0.991492148
	Boiler, Steam, Low Pressure.	0.719936234	0.998154400	0.995621239
Bus Duct		0.999696290	1.000000000	1.000000000
	Bus Duct, All types, (100 ft).	0.999696290*	1.000000000	1.000000000
Cabinet Heaters		0.999897930	0.999999994	0.999978224
	Cabinet Heaters, Forced Air Flow, Steam or Hot Water.	0.999897930	0.999999994	0.999978224
Cable		0.998149212	0.999998818	0.999987869
Above Ground		0.999509398	0.999999527	0.999998357
	Cable, Above Ground, In Conduit, ≤600V, Per 1000 ft.	0.999932074	0.999999938	0.999990264
	Cable, Above Ground, In Conduit, >600V ≤5kV, Per 1000 ft.	0.999463225	0.999999476	0.999998707
	Cable, Above Ground, No Conduit, ≤600V, Per 1000 ft.	0.999879838	0.999999966	0.999999904
	Cable, Above Ground, No Conduit, >600V ≤5kV, Per 1000 ft.	0.999244433	0.999999655	0.999999655
	Cable, Above Ground, Trays, ≤600V, Per 1000 ft.	0.968468243*	1.000000000	1.000000000
	Cable, Above Ground, Trays, >600V ≤5kV, Per 1000 ft.	0.997171966*	1.000000000	1.000000000
Aerial		0.988381339	0.999997295	0.999997259
	Cable, Aerial, ≤15kV, Per Mile.	0.953928762	0.999990218	0.999990218
	Cable, Aerial, >15kV, Per Mile.	0.995896395	0.999998806	0.999998762
Below Ground		0.994225869	0.999995527	0.999928197
	Cable, Below Ground, Duct, ≤600V, Per 1000 ft.	0.999875009	0.999999766	0.999999697
	Cable, Below Ground, Duct, >600V ≤5kV, Per 1000 ft.	0.987125021*	1.000000000	1.000000000
	Cable, Below Ground, In Conduit, ≤600V, Per 1000 ft.	0.997994901	0.999997428	0.999991686

(continues)

Shaded text = Revisions.   △ = Text deletions and figure/table revisions.   • = Section deletions.   N = New material.

2023 Edition

Table I.5   *Continued*

Roll Up Report by Category, Class, and Item				
CATEGORY[a]	CLASS[b]	Reliability[c]	Inherent Availability[d]	Operational Availability[e]
	Cable, Below Ground, In Conduit >600V ≤5kV, per 1000 ft.	0.997646877	0.999995779	0.999987126
	Cable, Below Ground, Insulated, >5kV, Per 1000 ft.	0.980031515	0.999988193	0.999674546
	Cable, Below Ground, Insulated, ≤600V, Per 1000 ft.	0.973653295	0.999976836	0.999976836
Insulated		0.992748496	0.999998338	0.999998338
	Cable, Insulated, DC, Per 100 ft.	0.992748496	0.999998338	0.999998338
Cable Connection		0.999629261	0.999999968	0.999999968
Capacitor Bank		0.839937440	0.999954142	0.999942075
	Capacitor Bank, Power Factor Corrector, (in kVAR).	0.839937440	0.999954142	0.999942075
Charger		0.992621004	0.999999577	0.999986472
	Charger, Battery.	0.992621004	0.999999577	0.999986472
Chiller		0.888515818	0.999829779	0.997620632
	Chiller, Absorption.	0.841986658	0.999769437	0.995132437
	Chiller, Centrifugal, 600–1000 Tons.	0.955142622	0.999923928	0.997604888
	Chiller, Reciprocating, Closed, w/Drive, 50–200 Tons.	0.879941865	0.999809524	0.998734968
	Chiller, Reciprocating, Open, wo/Drive, 50–200 Tons.	0.826705884	0.999775088	0.999312485
	Chiller, Rotary, 600–1000 Tons.	0.986993503	0.999964132	0.996197991
	Chiller, Screw, >300 Tons.	0.956286690	0.999510164	0.996566046
Circuit Breaker, 600V 3 Phase, Fixed		0.999996752	0.999999582	0.999983888
		0.999996551	0.999999899	0.999992732
	Circuit Breaker, 600V, 3 Phase, Fixed, Including molded case, ≤600 amp, Normally Closed, Trp. Ckt. Incl.	0.999984307*	1.000000000	0.999997443
	Circuit Breaker, 600V, 3 Phase, Fixed, Including molded case, ≤600 amp, Normally Open, Trp. Ckt. Incl.	0.999887215	0.999999760	0.999990187
	Circuit Breaker, 600V, 3 Phase, Fixed, Including molded case, >600 amp, Normally Closed, Trp. Ckt. Incl.	0.999994218*	1.000000000	0.999992509
	Circuit Breaker, 600V, 3 Phase, Fixed, Including molded case, >600V ≤5kV.	0.996576534	0.999985320	0.999880051
Drawout (Metal Clad)		0.998892235	0.999999605	0.999837990
	Circuit Breaker, 600V, Drawout (Metal Clad), <600 amp, Normally Closed, Trp. Ckt. Incl.	0.999792091	0.999999858	0.999798004
	Circuit Breaker, 600V, Drawout (Metal Clad), <600 amp, Normally Open, Trp. Ckt. Incl.	0.997456731	0.999998256	0.999860901
	Circuit Breaker, 600V, Drawout (Metal Clad), >600 amp, Normally Closed, Trp. Ckt. Incl.	0.998150509	0.999999894	0.999954301
	Circuit Breaker, 600V, Drawout (Metal Clad), >600 amp, Normally Open, Trp. Ckt. Incl.	0.994487152	0.999998738	0.999927638
Vacuum		0.980129686	0.999975385	0.999852780
	Circuit Breaker, 5kV, Vacuum, <600 amp, Normally Closed, Trp. Ckt. Incl.	0.997191564	0.999997432	0.999960511
	Circuit Breaker, 5kV, Vacuum, <600 amp, Normally Open, Trp. Ckt. Incl.	0.998887668*	1.000000000	0.999983060
	Circuit Breaker, 5kV, Vacuum, >600 amp, Normally Closed, Trp. Ckt. Incl.	0.976752059	0.999960259	0.999619774
	Circuit Breaker, 5kV, Vacuum, >600 amp, Normally Open, Trp. Ckt. Incl.	0.961020019	0.999957368	0.999854272

(continues)

Table I.5 *Continued*

Roll Up Report by Category, Class, and Item				
CATEGORY[a]	CLASS[b]	Reliability[c]	Inherent Availability[d]	Operational Availability[e]
Compressor		0.986548811	0.999986587	0.999865676
	Compressor, Refrigerant, >1 Ton.	0.995193627	0.999998075	0.999907183
	Compressor, Screw Type.	0.946328222	0.999931777	0.999667651
Condensers		0.900083857	0.999913810	0.999583534
	Condensers, Double Tube.	0.973573588	0.999992357	0.999758971
	Condensers, Propeller Type Fans/Coils, DX.	0.733621551	0.999734138	0.999393134
	Condensers, Shell and Tube.	0.998878743*	1.000000000	0.999614286
Control Panel		0.994698171	0.999998908	0.999800824
	Control Panel, Generator, wo/Switchgear.	0.988952766	0.999997330	0.999980962
	Control Panel, HVAC/Chillers/AHUs, wo/Switchgear.	0.999848787*	1.000000000	0.999982209
	Control Panel, Switchgear Controls.	0.980568763	0.999997149	0.998160003
Convectors		0.999913016	1.000000000	0.999998481
	Convectors, Fin Tube Baseboard, Electric.	0.999582861*	1.000000000	0.999999626
	Convectors, Fin Tube Baseboard, Steam or Hot Water.	0.999890105*	1.000000000	0.999998180
Cooling Tower		0.968333522	0.999702865	0.997170520
	Cooling Tower, Atmospheric Type, wo/Fans, Motors, Pumps, Valves, etc.	0.928543791	0.999247479	0.994184363
	Cooling Tower, Evaporative Type, wo/Fans, Motors, Pumps, Valves, etc.	0.994195540	0.999988924	0.999046330
Damper Assembly		0.999971953	0.999999975	0.999990131
	Damper Assembly, Motor.	0.999966919*	1.000000000	0.999989337
	Damper Assembly, Pneumatic.	0.999277503	0.999999835	0.999994555
Diesel Engine Generator Packaged		0.589772164	0.998540049	0.993985981
		0.775917369	0.999329810	0.997272882
	Diesel Engine Generator, Packaged, 250kW-1.5MW, Continuous.	0.558396351	0.998287624	0.996927250
	Diesel Engine Generator, Packaged, 250kW-1.5MW, Standby.	0.883822868	0.999742312	0.997409685
Unpackaged		0.317735957	0.996759289	0.986574653
	Diesel Engine Generator, Unpackaged, 750kW-7MW, Continuous.	0.162719469	0.994801067	0.980739869
	Diesel Engine Generator, Unpackaged, 750kW-7MW, Standby.	0.531004159	0.998262059	0.991052357
Drive		0.978172315	0.999958316	0.999925947
	Drive, Adjustable Speed.	0.978172315	0.999958316	0.999925947
Evaporator Coil		0.995968933	0.999993228	0.999908962
		0.995812835	0.999992633	0.999899263
	Evaporator, Coil, Direct Expansion.	0.995812835	0.999992633	0.999899263
Shell Tube		0.997036799	0.999997290	0.999975270
	Evaporator, Shell Tube, Direct Expansion.	0.997036799	0.999997290	0.999975270
Fan		0.987559807	0.999971610	0.999351118
	Fan, Centrifugal.	0.981021428	0.999946483	0.999770440
	Fan, Propeller/Disc.	0.989640193	0.999957798	0.999093547
	Fan, Tubeaxial.	0.989938879	0.999990870	0.999055744
	Fan, Vaneaxial.	0.996408668*	1.000000000	1.000000000
Filter		0.999898973	1.000000000	0.999903911
	Filter, Electrical Tempest.	0.998510134*	1.000000000	1.000000000
Mechanical		0.999891630	1.000000000	0.999896927
	Filter, Mechanical, Air Regulator Set.	0.999840000*	1.000000000	0.999981949

(continues)

Table I.5   *Continued*

			Inherent	Operational
CATEGORY[a]	**CLASS[b]**	**Reliability[c]**	**Availability[d]**	**Availability[e]**
	Filter, Mechanical, Fuel Oil.	0.999271146*	1.000000000	0.999910729
	Filter, Mechanical, Lube Oil.	0.999377566*	1.000000000	0.999554311
Fuse		0.997969725	1.000000000	1.000000000
	Fuse, >5kV ≤15kV.	0.999341365*	1.000000000	1.000000000
	Fuse, 0-5kV.	0.998627456*	1.000000000	1.000000000
Gas Turbine Generator		0.647849145	0.998890863	0.990692798
Packaged		0.587787144	0.998689955	0.989043771
	Gas Turbine Generator, Packaged, 750kW-7MW, Continuous.	0.177710554	0.994598022	0.983584136
	Gas Turbine Generator, Packaged, 750kW-7MW, Standby.	0.829472916	0.999868149	0.990615770
Unpackaged		0.994155201	0.999775158	0.997950995
	Gas Turbine Generator, Unpackaged, 750kW-7MW, Continuous.	0.994155201	0.999775158	0.997950995
Gauge		0.999042094	1.000000000	0.999999785
	Gauge, Fluid Level.	0.999042094*	1.000000000	0.999999785
Heat Exchanger		0.989034610	0.999997303	0.998935596
	Heat Exchanger, Boiler System, Steam.	0.971835048	0.999998369	0.997231137
	Heat Exchanger, Lube Oil.	0.996596565	0.999995330	0.999740960
	Heat Exchanger, Water To Water.	0.996130029*	1.000000000	0.999861134
Heater		0.947826981	0.999984168	0.994164558
	Heater, Electric, Lube/Fuel Oil Or Jacket.	0.947826981	0.999984168	0.994164558
Humistat		0.984575905	0.999998226	0.999998226
	Humistat, Assembly.	0.984575905	0.999998226	0.999998226
Inverters		0.995190512	0.999985691	0.999598793
	Inverters, All Types.	0.995190512	0.999985691	0.999598793
Meter		0.998913484	0.999993988	0.999993961
	Meter, Electric.	0.999635167	0.999999958	0.999999958
	Meter, Fuel.	0.946014073	0.999543853	0.999543853
	Meter, Water.	0.999621152	0.999999870	0.999999697
Motor Generator Set		0.975052652	0.999978501	0.993070544
	Motor Generator Set, 3 Phase, 400 Hz.	0.995075131	0.999995491	0.999628032
	Motor Generator Set, 3 Phase, 60 Hz.	0.957963867	0.999963722	0.987366458
Motor Starter		0.999147052	0.999995416	0.999944527
	Motor Starter, ≤600V.	0.998167781*	1.000000000	0.999984223
	Motor Starter, >600V.	0.996875738	0.999991427	0.999909983
Motor, Electric		0.999032041	0.999973300	0.999930849
	Motor, Electric, DC.	0.985531708	0.999031729	0.998182336
Induction		0.981918899	0.999992950	0.999724259
	Motor, Electric, Induction, ≤600V.	0.988992708	0.999998736	0.999957372
	Motor, Electric, Induction, >600V.	0.974689985	0.999986993	0.999484292
Single Phase		0.999980411	0.999999987	0.999988267
	Motor, Electric, Single Phase, ≤5 amp.	0.999979878*	1.000000000	0.999996192
	Motor, Electric, Single Phase, >5 amp.	0.998550210	0.999999503	0.999696847
Synchronous		0.998653401	0.999978284	0.999857033
	Motor, Electric, Synchronous, ≤600V.	0.996555656*	1.000000000	0.999777580
	Motor, Electric, Synchronous, >600V.	0.991366824	0.999964367	0.999907948
Motor, Mechanical		0.195448823	0.999809717	0.998810724
Diesel		0.904562026	0.999953538	0.991433654
	Motor, Mechanical, Diesel.	0.904562026	0.999953538	0.991433654

(continues)

     Shaded text = Revisions.   **Δ** = Text deletions and figure/table revisions.   • = Section deletions.   **N** = New material.

ble I.5   *Continued*

Roll Up Report by Category, Class, and Item

CATEGORY[a]	CLASS[b]	Reliability[c]	Inherent Availability[d]	Operational Availability[e]
Gas		0.161029030	0.999791533	0.999743425
	Motor, Mechanical, Gas.	0.161029030	0.999791533	0.999743425
pe		0.981888041	0.999994337	0.999991952
	Pipe, Flex, Non-Reinforced, >4 in.	0.985560776	0.999994466	0.999990038
	Pipe, Flex, Reinforced, >4 in.	0.977618384	0.999994186	0.999994186
ping		0.999960899	0.999998770	0.999676366
Refrigerant		0.999954550	0.999999430	0.999990919
	Piping, Refrigerant, <1 in.	0.999925556*	1.000000000	0.999993884
	Piping, Refrigerant, <2 in.	0.997181886	0.999996564	0.999986684
	Piping, Refrigerant, >2 in.	0.999822269*	1.000000000	1.000000000
	Piping, Refrigerant, 1-3 in.	0.993176045	0.999993747	0.999895362
Water		0.999720116	0.999994706	0.997739077
	Piping, Water, ≤2 in.	0.998834378*	1.000000000	1.000000000
	Piping, Water, >12 in.	0.939385452*	1.000000000	1.000000000
	Piping, Water, >2 ≤4 in.	0.979679275	0.999966994	0.999966994
	Piping, Water, >4 ≤8 in.	0.998103531*	1.000000000	1.000000000
	Piping, Water, >8 ≤12 in.	0.999374866*	1.000000000	0.994961083
essure Control		0.993091820	0.999995568	0.999938101
	Pressure Control, Assembly.	0.993091820	0.999995568	0.999938101
essure Regulator		0.999163441	1.000000000	0.999993069
Hot Gas		0.999163441	1.000000000	0.999993069
	Pressure Regulator, Hot Gas.	0.999163441*	1.000000000	0.999993069
mp		0.993705867	0.999994889	0.999826613
Centrifugal		0.994206434	0.999995523	0.999903450
	Pump, Centrifugal, Integral Drive.	0.992515450	0.999993654	0.999897429
	Pump, Centrifugal, wo/Drive.	0.995791244	0.999997272	0.999909083
	Pump, Positive Displacement.	0.991821538	0.999992500	0.999537023
diators		0.987545587	0.999977760	0.999934189
	Radiators, Small Tube.	0.987545587	0.999977760	0.999934189
ctifiers		0.995540658	0.999991837	0.998972976
	Rectifiers, All Types.	0.995540658	0.999991837	0.998972976
nding Unit		0.999566658	0.999999536	0.999999258
Air Velocity		0.998867884	0.999998707	0.999997599
	Sending Unit, Air Velocity.	0.998867884	0.999998707	0.999997599
	Sending Unit, Pressure.	0.997916028	0.999997883	0.999997089
	Sending Unit, Temperature.	0.999980697*	1.000000000	1.000000000
ftware Con. ADAS Sys.		0.642221250	0.999854564	0.999658784
	Software Con. ADAS Sys., ≤1000 Acquisition Points.	0.777690112	0.999954199	0.999888246
	Software Con. ADAS Sys., >1000 Acquisition Points.	0.428800729	0.999644282	0.999174503
ainer		0.999943310	1.000000000	0.999916767
	Strainer, Coolant.	0.998861684*	1.000000000	0.999333463
	Strainer, Duplex Fuel/Lube Oil.	0.995679886*	1.000000000	0.999861421
	Strainer, Fuel Oil.	0.998766615*	1.000000000	0.999924447
	Strainer, Lube Oil.	0.999529759*	1.000000000	0.999881981
Water		0.999926442	1.000000000	0.999960363
	Strainer, Water, ≤4 in.	0.999920044*	1.000000000	0.999999893
	Strainer, Water, >4 in.	0.999081068*	1.000000000	0.999505864
itch		0.993744427	0.999996988	0.999960651

(continues)

aded text = Revisions.   Δ = Text deletions and figure/table revisions.   • = Section deletions.   *N* = New material.

2023 Edition

Table I.5   *Continued*

			Inherent	Operational
CATEGORY[a]	**CLASS**[b]	**Reliability**[c]	**Availability**[d]	**Availability**[e]
Automatic Transfer		0.950118163	0.999976051	0.999857315
	Switch, Automatic Transfer, >600 amp., ≤600V.	0.968631015	0.999994046	0.999809981
	Switch, Automatic Transfer, 0-600 amp., ≤600V.	0.917774618	0.999943753	0.999942269
Disconnect		0.999846881	0.999999966	0.999961037
	Switch, Disconnect, Enclosed, ≤600V.	0.999394569*	1.000000000	0.999938186
	Switch, Disconnect, Enclosed, >5kV.	0.998257804	0.999999801	0.999939288
	Switch, Disconnect, Enclosed, >600V ≤5kV.	0.997942528*	1.000000000	0.999867230
	Switch, Disconnect, Fused, DC, >600 amp., ≤600V.	0.999408178*	1.000000000	1.000000000
	Switch, Disconnect, Fused, DC, 0-600 amp., ≤600V.	0.999367257*	1.000000000	0.999987568
	Switch, Electric, On/Off Breaker Type, Non-knife., ≤600V.	0.999358198	0.999999927	0.999999780
Float		0.997716932	0.999999478	0.999985388
	Switch, Float, Electric.	0.997716932	0.999999478	0.999985388
Manual Transfer		0.999129111	1.000000000	0.999966262
	Switch, Manual Transfer, ≤600 amp., ≤600V.	0.997919138*	1.000000000	0.999952908
	Switch, Manual Transfer, >600 amp., ≤600V.	0.998503402*	1.000000000	0.999975863
	Switch, Oil Filled, ≥5kV.	0.998241979*	1.000000000	0.999996849
Static		0.997748999	0.999996656	0.999919287
	Switch, Static, >1000 amp., ≤600V.	0.996326697	0.999989918	0.999739539
	Switch, Static, >600 ≤1000 amp., ≤600V.	0.992336720	0.999998244	0.999994731
	Switch, Static, 0-600 amp. ≤600V.	0.998950665*	1.000000000	0.999999648
Switchgear		0.991916417	0.999974462	0.999585725
Bare Bus		0.989863408	0.999968286	0.999579123
	Switchgear, Bare Bus, ≤600V, All Cabnets, Ckt. Bkrs. Not Included.	0.990554799	0.999992098	0.999455269
	Switchgear, Bare Bus, >5kV, All Cabnets, Ckt. Bkrs. Not Included.	0.982216877	0.999995342	0.999839597
	Switchgear, Bare Bus, >600V ≤5kV, All Cabnets, Ckt. Bkrs. Not Included.	0.997007868	0.999872746	0.999607036
Insulated Bus		0.999613608	0.999989619	0.999601929
	Switchgear, Insulated Bus, ≤600V, All Cabnets, Ckt. Bkrs. Not Included.	0.998420947*	1.000000000	0.999468794
	Switchgear, Insulated Bus, >5kV, All Cabnets, Ckt. Bkrs. Not Included.	0.995913049	0.999982547	0.999626621
	Switchgear, Insulated Bus, >600V ≤5kV, All Cabnets, Ckt. Bkrs. Not Included.	0.996224761	0.999996546	0.999696028
Tank		0.995965564	0.999991636	0.999971186
Day		0.994810377	0.999997030	0.999974756
	Tank, Day, Genset Fuel.	0.994810377	0.999997030	0.999974756
Fuel		0.993549151	0.999955673	0.999872929
	Tank, Fuel.	0.993549151	0.999955673	0.999872929
Receiver		0.997280535	0.999997824	0.999996891
	Tank, Receiver, Air.	0.997280535	0.999997824	0.999996891
Water		0.996377265	0.999999793	0.999989539
	Tank, Water.	0.996377265	0.999999793	0.999989539
Thermostat		0.998319168	0.999999398	0.999997565
	Thermostat, Radiator.	0.998319168	0.999999398	0.999997565
Transducer		0.999978470	0.999999933	0.999998552
Flow		0.996713345	1.000000000	0.999986736
	Transducer, Flow.	0.996713345*	1.000000000	0.999986736
Pressure		0.997477750	0.999999423	0.999987243
	Transducer, Pressure.	0.997477750	0.999999423	0.999987243

(continue

Shaded text = Revisions.   Δ = Text deletions and figure/table revisions.   • = Section deletions.   *N* = New materia

Table I.5 *Continued*

	Roll Up Report by Category, Class, and Item			
CATEGORY[a]	CLASS[b]	Reliability[c]	Inherent Availability[d]	Operational Availability[e]
Temperature		0.998242572	0.999999950	0.999999026
	Transducer, Temperature.	0.998242572	0.999999950	0.999999026
Transformer, Dry Air Cooled		0.999953743	0.999995817	0.999971899
		0.999882198	1.000000000	0.999944571
	Transformer, Dry, Air Cooled, ≤500kVA.	0.999775100*	1.000000000	0.999995570
	Transformer, Dry, Air Cooled, >1500kVA ≤3000kVA.	0.999393210*	1.000000000	0.999745124
	Transformer, Dry, Air Cooled, >500kVA ≤1500kVA.	0.999582527*	1.000000000	0.999987102
Isolation		0.997166548	0.999993113	0.999989567
	Transformer, Dry, Isolation, Delta Wye, <600V.	0.997166548	0.999993113	0.999989567
Transformer, Liquid Forced Air		0.994797669	0.999950735	0.998990580
		0.989259891	0.999836759	0.996601877
	Transformer, Liquid, Forced Air, ≤10,000kVA.	0.992879584	0.999797696	0.990915913
	Transformer, Liquid, Forced Air, ≤5,000kVA.	0.987452327	0.999994736	0.999987215
	Transformer, Liquid, Forced Air, >10,000kVA ≤50,000kVA.	0.994329760	0.999065253	0.985856760
Non-Forced Air		0.997113141	0.999998203	0.999985412
	Transformer, Liquid, Non-Forced Air, ≤3000kVA.	0.998891114	0.999999367	0.999996102
	Transformer, Liquid, Non-Forced Air, >10000kVA ≤50000kVA.	0.982624792	0.999987813	0.999893406
	Transformer, Liquid, Non-Forced Air, >3000kVA ≤10000kVA.	0.994771048	0.999999402	0.999985038
UPS Rotary		0.999078297	0.999998349	0.999951289
		0.995983397	1.000000000	0.999895500
	UPS, Rotary.	0.995983397*	1.000000000	0.999895500
Small Computer Room Floor		0.990661925	0.999997858	0.999967870
	UPS, Small Computer Room Floor.	0.990661925	0.999997858	0.999967870
Valve 3-way		0.999995192	0.999999568	0.999977752
		0.999727982	1.000000000	0.999987577
	Valve, 3-way, Diverting/Sequencing.	0.999257278*	1.000000000	0.999999501
	Valve, 3-way, Mixing Control.	0.999570876*	1.000000000	0.999980689
Ball		0.999807822	0.999999957	0.999999204
	Valve, Ball, N.C.	0.999516658*	1.000000000	0.999998106
	Valve, Ball, N.O.	0.998749718	0.999999929	0.999999929
Butterfly		0.998692271	0.999999513	0.999995506
	Valve, Butterfly, N.C.	0.991788585	0.999996931	0.999990199
	Valve, Butterfly, N.O.	0.999965510*	1.000000000	0.999996507
Check		0.999742108	0.999999971	0.999980199
	Valve, Check.	0.999742108	0.999999971	0.999980199
Control		0.999937125	0.999999943	0.999996490
	Valve, Control, N.C.	0.999922211	0.999999929	0.999997478
	Valve, Control, N.O.	0.999832761*	1.000000000	0.999992325
Expansion		0.999742991	1.000000000	1.000000000
	Valve, Expansion.	0.999742991*	1.000000000	1.000000000
Gate		0.999827547	0.999999888	0.999999642
	Valve, Gate, N.C.	0.999421886	0.999999934	0.999998647
	Valve, Gate, N.O.	0.999872337	0.999999883	0.999999752
Globe		0.999980570	1.000000000	0.999921533
	Valve, Globe, N.C.	0.999975654*	1.000000000	0.999901776
	Valve, Globe, N.O.	0.999903788*	1.000000000	0.999999612
Plug		0.990331504	0.999997992	0.999997984
	Valve, Plug, N.C.	0.986191497	0.999997832	0.999997819

(continues)

Shaded text = Revisions. Δ = Text deletions and figure/table revisions. • = Section deletions. *N* = New material.

2023 Edition

Table I.5   *Continued*

			Inherent	Operational
CATEGORY[a]	**CLASS**[b]	**Reliability**[c]	**Availability**[d]	**Availability**[e]
	Valve, Plug, N.O.	0.996093704	0.999998213	0.999998213
Reducing		0.998490771	1.000000000	0.999972616
	Valve, Reducing, Makeup Water.	0.998490771*	1.000000000	0.999972616
Relief		0.998671145	0.999999696	0.999994763
	Valve, Relief.	0.998671145	0.999999696	0.999994763
Suction		0.998214603	0.999998521	0.999994094
	Valve, Suction.	0.998214603	0.999998521	0.999994094
Valve Operator		0.992808232	0.999991177	0.999971677
	Valve Operator, Electric.	0.990159307	0.999979209	0.999934083
Hydraulic		0.915817948	0.999969884	0.999601804
	Valve Operator, Hydraulic.	0.915817948	0.999969884	0.999601804
Pneumatic		0.995224402	0.999998361	0.999997541
	Valve Operator, Pneumatic.	0.995224402	0.999998361	0.999997541
Voltage Regulator		0.964377637	0.999690405	0.999644857
	Voltage Regulator, Static.	0.964377637	0.999690405	0.999644857
Water Cooling Coil		0.999577258	0.999999879	0.999993176
Fan Coil Unit		0.999577258	0.999999879	0.999993176
	Water Cooling Coil, Fan Coil Unit.	0.999577258	0.999999879	0.999993176

[a]Represents the category of the item, for example, Boiler.
[b]Represents the Class of the item, for example, Boiler, Hot Water.
[c]This column represents the probability of the item failing in 1 year.
[d]Inherent Availability considers down time as a result of failure. No maintenance down time is considered. Ref: RAC publications, *Reliability Toolkit*, page 12.
[e]Operational Availability considers down time as a result of maintenance and failure. Ref: RAC publications, *Reliability Toolkit*, page 12.

I.6 FMECA Procedure as Part of an RCM Program.

I.6.1 Part of an effective RCM program is to determine the failure modes effects and conduct criticality analysis (FMECA) of all systems, determine the risk priority based on the product of the severity level of a component, failure occurrence level, and detection level.

I.6.2 Determine the failure modes associated with each system (e.g., chilled water supply can have no water flow or degraded flow). Assign a failure mechanism to each failure mode (e.g., degraded flow can be the result of leaky gasket, low supply voltage to motor) and determine the failure effects on system (e.g., no effect, decrease in chiller water temperature). Severity levels are assigned along with probability of failure and a risk priority is determined. This provides for greater emphasis and funding to be assigned to systems that have a greater risk of failure. Therefore systems with higher risk priority would receive more preventive and predictive maintenance than systems with lower risk priorities.

I.6.3 Risk priority is classified with a number, risk priority number (RPN). This is equal to the product of severity level of a component, occurrence, and detection level as noted below with the sum of RPNs for each component within a critical system:

[I.6.3]

$$\text{sum} \frac{\overset{i}{S} (RPN)n; \text{ where } RPN = O \times S \times D}{(\text{Occurrence} \times \text{Severity} \times \text{Detection})}$$
$$n=1$$

I.6.4 The purpose of preventive maintenance is not to prevent every component failure from occurring but to prevent the system operational failure. Critical components/sub-systems that compromises system operation should receive a high degree of preventive and predictive maintenance. These are critical components or subsystems. A component/sub-system that represents a single point failure that does not compromise the system would receive less preventive and predictive maintenance or even just run to failure.

I.6.5 There are several FMECA methods that can be used to categorize components and subsystems. This depends on how much data is available for the particular systems. A basic block diagram of the RCM process is shown in Figure I.6.5.

I.6.5.1 Define the system: Identify each systems indenture levels. This identifies each system functional item and its associated failure modes for each functional output. These would be considered your different maintenance areas of concern.

I.6.5.2 Define ground rules and assumptions: The ground rules apply to mission system/equipment, analysis methods (what do we wish to prevent main power outage, operating time during mission stage, source of data).

I.6.5.3 Construct equipment tree. This is a block diagram of operation between indenture levels (function items) that provides different types of failure modes and effects.

I.6.5.4 Identify failure modes.

I.6.5.5 Analyze failure effects.

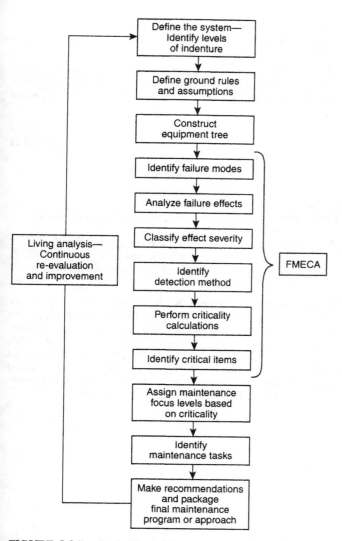

FIGURE I.6.5   Basic Block Diagram of the RCM Process.

I.6.5.6 Classify effect severity

(1) Identify detection method.
(2) Perform criticality calculations
(3) Identify critical items.
(4) Assign maintenance focus based on criticality
(5) Identify maintenance tasks.
(6) Make recommendations and package final maintenance program or approach.

I.6.6 Example of FMECA.

I.6.6.1 Detection Method.

I.6.6.1.1 When system controls, automation configurations, and system safeguards are unknown, Detection Method Level can be assumed to be 1. This assumes and stresses that, for a mission critical facility, all item and system level function losses should and will be apparent.

I.6.6.1.2 Although this is an acceptable approach for initial analysis and demonstration purposes, it should be understood that the presence, or absence, of detection method in a systems has a direct effect on the risk associated with the operation of that system. Therefore, consideration of detection method will provide more accurate and resolute analysis results and recommendations. Furthermore, an understanding of current detection method provisions, along with results of an analysis which considered detection method and component level failure modes, can and should be utilized to make recommendations on future detection method provisions.

I.6.6.2 Occurrence.

I.6.6.2.1 Equipment specific PREP database availability numbers will provide indication of failure frequency. These metrics will help to provide less subjective item and system risk assessments. However, they must be adjusted to account for system redundancy, and ranked into discrete occurrence levels to be used in qualitative equipment criticality calculations.

I.6.6.2.2 By design and purpose, a redundant system is more reliable and less vulnerable than a single point, with respect to system function and mission requirements. Therefore, the occurrence level for a single point function must be weighted to reflect the operation, presumed reliability, and severity of loss of function of the redundant component system as accurately as possible.

I.6.6.2.3 The following formula is used to calculate the adjusted availability of a given subsystem due to a level of component or subsystem redundancy.

$$[I.6.6.2.3]$$

$$Ai^1 = \sum_{k=m}^{n} \frac{n!}{k!(n-k)!} (Ai)^k (1-Ai)^{(n-k)}$$

where:
Ai = Initial inherent component availability
Ai^1 = Adjusted redundant component availability level
m = Minimum number of components needed
n = Number of components available
k = Current component in redundant system being analyzed

I.6.6.2.4 With availability metrics representative of system configuration now available, component availability is ranked to provide discrete subsystem occurrence levels, as shown in Table I.6.6.2.4.

I.6.6.3 Severity.

I.6.6.3.1 It is also important to consider the concept of failure severity. Severity pertains to and ranks the consequences of

Table I.6.6.2.4 Component Availability Rankings

Availability (nines)	Occurrence Rank	Occurrence Description
≥0.999999999	1	Almost Never
0.99999999	2	Remote
0.9999999	3	Very Slight
0.999999	4	Slight
0.99999	5	Low
0.9999	6	Medium
0.999	7	Moderately High
0.99	8	High
0.9	9	Very High
0	10	Almost Certain

system level failure mode effects. For example, a highly probable failure may occur for a subsystem of a piece of critical equipment without severe consequences.

I.6.6.3.2 Severity rankings used are as shown in Table I.6.6.3.2.

Table I.6.6.3.2 Severity Rankings

Ranking	Effect	Comment
1	None	No reason to expect failure to have any effect on safety, health, environment, or mission
2	Very Low	Minor disruption to mission
3	Low	Minor disruption to mission
4	Low to Moderate	Moderate disruption to mission
5	Moderate	Moderate disruption to mission
6	Moderate to High	Moderate disruption to mission
7	High	High disruption to mission
8	Very High	High disruption to mission
9	Hazard	Extremely high disruption to mission
10	Hazard	Extremely high disruption to mission

I.6.6.4 RPN Calculations and Ranking Methods for Flexible Analysis.

I.6.6.4.1 Severity, occurrence, and detection method levels are then utilized to produce a subsystem risk assessment as follows:

$$[I.6.6.4.1]$$

$$RPN = O \times S \times D$$

where:
RPN = Risk associated with failure mode (Risk Priority Number)

S = Severity level for failure mode
O = Occurrence level for failure mode
D = Detection method level (1)

I.6.6.4.2 This calculation will be performed for every subsystem item in the master equipment listing. With this information, Risk Priority Numbers for sub-systems and systems can be obtained as follows:

$$[I.6.6.4.2]$$

$$RPN_s = \sum_{n=1}^{j} (RPNc)n$$

where:
RPN_s = Risk Priority Number for the current system being analyzed
RPN_c = Risk Priority Number for the current subsystem
n = The current subsystem being analyzed
j = Total number of components in the subsystem or system

I.6.6.4.3 Results — System X. Item and system risk assessments can now be utilized to apply RCM decision logic (see Table I.6.6.4.3), and to build maintenance tasking programs. Items and systems assessed to be of high operational risk should, especially, be applied to the decision logic and should receive high levels of maintenance focus. Items having extremely low operation risk will receive low levels of maintenance focus, and may be allowed to run to failure.

Table I.6.6.4.3 Example of Risk Priority Number Calculation

Facility Identifier	Equipment Type	Parent System	M	N	PREP ID	A	A'	O' Ranked	S	RPN
A-1	A	X	1	2	13	0.999988924	0.9999999999	1	1	9
A-2	A	X	1	2	13	0.999988924	0.9999999999	1	9	9
B-1	B	X	1	4	163	0.999993654	1.00000000000	1	9	9
B-2	B	X	1	4	163	0.999993654	1.00000000000	1	9	9
B-3	B	X	1	4	163	0.999993654	1.00000000000	1	9	9
B-4	B	X	1	4	163	0.999993654	1.00000000000	1	9	9

Annex J   Power Quality

This annex is not a part of the requirements of this NFPA document but is included for informational purposes only.

J.1 Introduction. Power quality is an assessment of voltage, waveform, and frequency of the power system. Some level of aberration can be tolerable. Objectionable levels of power quality disturbances should be investigated and corrected. Definitions of the power quality descriptors used in this annex can be found in Chapter 3. Understanding the types of power quality problems, their causes, and their solutions is essential to incorporating power quality into a maintenance program.

J.1.1 Poor power quality is an undesirable deviation or interruption of the ideal power supply. Alternating-current (ac) power could be distorted due to nonsinusoidal (nonlinear) waveforms in the three phases of a 3-phase circuit. These commonly differ slightly in size and shape, and circuit voltage can change as the load on the circuit changes. Equipment with electronic components is more susceptible to power quality problems. Some equipment, like adjustable speed drives, conduct current during only part of the power frequency cycle. These are nonlinear loads and create harmonics. Switch-mode power supplies and arcing devices, including fluorescent lamps, are other examples of nonlinear loads. Power quality problems can be caused by equipment or conditions on the customer's premises or on the utility side. Utility side issues include neighboring capacitor switching, load switching, or lightning and weather events. Poor power quality can result in the following

1) Electrical faults
2) Damage or reduced life of electrical and electronic equipment
3) Increased fire hazard
4) Reduced equipment performance and productivity
5) Degraded data and communications

Power quality disturbances can include the following:

1) Harmonics imposed on the fundamental sine wave
2) Voltage transients
3) Voltage sags and swells
4) Long-duration undervoltage and sustained voltage interruptions
5) Unbalanced voltages and single phasing (partial interruption)
6) Inadvertent and inadequate grounding
7) Electrical noise
8) Interharmonics
9) Voltage fluctuations (light flicker)

Examples demonstrate waveforms with common disturbances [Figure J.1.1(a)], a waveform of a sag cleared by the supply line circuit breaker [Figure J.1.1(b)], and a waveform with transient from power factor capacitor switching [Figure J.1.1(c)].

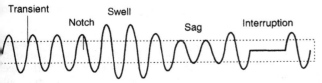

FIGURE J.1.1(a)   Common Power System Disturbances.

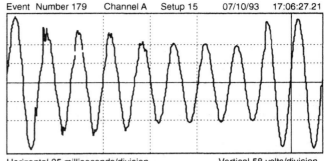

FIGURE J.1.1(b)   Waveform of Sag Cleared by Supply Line Breaker Operation.

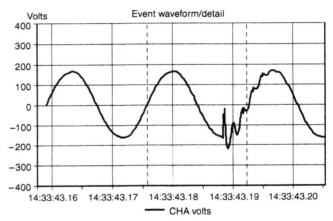

BV rel. trans. norm to hi at 14:33:43.175
Threshold crossed: 50.00 V
Out of limit max./min.: 81.39 V

FIGURE J.1.1(c)   Waveform with Transient from Power Factor Capacitor Switching.

N **J.2 Harmonics.** Harmonics are typically caused by nonlinear loads, which are loads where the wave shape of the steady-state current does not follow the wave shape of the applied voltage. Harmonics are multiples of the fundamental frequency and are identified by their frequency multiple of the harmonic. A harmonic with frequency of 180 Hz on a 60 Hz power system is a third harmonic.

N   **[J.2a]**

$$Harmonic\ \# = \frac{Harmonic\ frequency}{Fundamental\ frequency}$$

Harmonics distort and change the rms magnitude of the waveform. [See Figure J.2(a).]

Total harmonic distortion (THD) of a voltage waveform is stated as a percentage and can be represented by the formula shown in Equation J.2b.

N   **[J.2b]**

$$THD = \left(\frac{100 \times \sqrt{\sum V_h^2}}{V_f} \right) \%$$

where:

THD = total harmonic distortion (percent)

V_h = rms voltage of the individual harmonic (V)

V_f = rms voltage of the fundamental frequency (V)

Line voltage notching is a form of harmonic distortion, as shown in Figure J.2(b). Line voltage notching can occur from phase-controlled rectifiers; the commutation notches can adversely affect electronic equipment.

See Section J.9 for information on interharmonics.

***N* J.2.1 Harmonic Symptoms/Effects.** Symptoms/effects created by harmonics might include the following:

(1) Excessive neutral current

(2) Overheating of transformers, motors, generators, solenoid coils, and lighting ballasts

(3) Nuisance operation of protective devices

(4) Unexplained blowing of fuses on power-factor correction capacitors

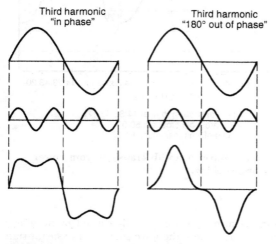

FIGURE J.2(a)   **Harmonics and the Fundamental Waveform.**

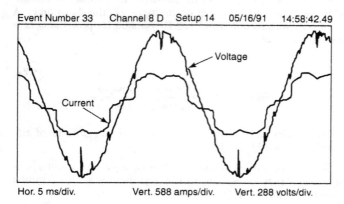

FIGURE J.2(b)   **Line Voltage Notching Harmonic Distortion.**

(5) Unusual audible noise in electrical switchgear or on telephone circuits

(6) Misoperation or failure of solid-state electronic equipment

(7) Loss or corrupt data on computer systems

(8) False operation of control systems

(9) Failure of uninterruptible power supply (UPS) system transfer

(10) Shaft voltages and currents on electric motors resulting in bearing failures

Odd triplen harmonics (third, ninth, and fifteenth) are additive at the neutral circuit. Triplen harmonics on transformer wye secondaries can cause circulating currents on delta-wound primary windings.

Power system capacitance can combine with circuit inductance to establish a resonant condition when harmonics are present. Resonance can cause high voltages to appear across elements of the power system and can cause high currents to flow.

Analysis of harmonics involves determining the amount of harmonic current from nonlinear loads and the system response to these harmonic currents. The interaction of shunt capacitor banks (power-factor correction capacitors) with the transformers (inductive elements) are common combinations that lead to resonance. An example of frequency response characteristic is shown in Figure J.2.1.

The resonance occurs at the frequency where the shunt capacitive reactance is equal to the inductive source reactance and can be expressed in terms of the 60 Hz values as shown in Equation J.2.1.

N   **[J.2.1]**

$$h = \sqrt{\frac{X_c}{X_{sc}}} = \sqrt{\frac{kVA_{sc}}{kVARcap}}$$

where:

h = resonant frequency as a multiple of the fundamental frequency (Hz)

X_c = shunt capacitive reactance of capacitor (ohms)

X_{sc} = short-circuit reactance of source (ohms)

kVA_{sc} = short-circuit apparent power of source (kVA)

kVARcap = capacitor rating (kVAR)

This provides a first check of whether harmonics are likely to be a problem. Overvoltage conditions can occur when the resonance approaches the fifth or seventh harmonic.

More often, typical problems with harmonics are overheated motors, transformers, and neutral conductors, audible distortion on telephone circuits, timing errors for multiple zero crossing, inadequate ride-through due to clipping (flat topping) of waveforms, and overheating of capacitors due to harmonic equivalent surge resistance (ESR) losses. In addition, the problem with the resonance is the excessive voltage generated by the resonance. The harmonics are the stimulus of the resonance.

Harmonics can cause overheating, overvoltage, and excessive noise in transformers and motors. Overheating is a compound effect of increased winding I^2R power losses due to both excessive current and skin effect and increased eddy current and hysteresis losses in the transformer core.

Higher impedance of transformers increases susceptibility to overvoltage and core saturation in the presence of harmonics, causing increased current flow and resultant additional heating. Voltages above the rated primary voltage can cause excessive 60 Hz hum, and harmonics can contribute higher-pitched audible noise.

Motors are also subject to overheating in the presence of harmonics, because of skin effect and increased iron losses. Where fifth harmonics are present, negative-sequence currents will also flow in opposition to the current necessary pace to develop the torque required for rotation. This counter torque is an additional heating factor and can result in pulsating torque and excessive vibration.

Generators equipped with solid-state controls can also operate erratically in the presence of harmonics if the controls incorporate zero-crossing sensing circuits. Generators can cause harmonics due to internal construction. The type of generating winding pitch can determine the magnitude and types of harmonics generated. Generators operating in parallel should have the same winding pitch to minimize problems. Generators operating in parallel with a common neutral, third harmonic currents can circulate between the machines and cause overheating. High resistance grounding of parallel generators can limit the harmonic neutral current.

Electrical panels and cables can become discolored due to overheating from excessive neutral current. Harmonics can also cause conductor-insulation failure because of voltage stress and corona discharge.

The presence of harmonics can contribute to inaccurate readings (high or low) of induction disc meters.

Instrumentation transformers such as current and potential transformers can transfer harmonics from a primary to a secondary, resulting in misoperation of instrumentation, protective relaying, and control circuits.

Computers, electronic equipment, and programmable logic controllers (PLCs) are susceptible to harmonic-distorted waveforms. Neutral-to-ground voltages in excess of 2 volts measured at the equipment can be a sign of harmonic issues. Harmonics on electronic equipment can result in data errors, misoperation, or total failure.

Audible noise can be induced in conductors that parallel conductors containing harmonic currents. Analog voice communication lines should be shielded or rerouted for wider separation. ANSI/IEEE 519, *Recommended Practice and Requirements for Harmonic Control in Electrical Power Systems*, and ANSI/IEEE 1100, *Recommended Practice for Powering and Grounding Electronic Equipment (IEEE Emerald Book)*, contain additional information on the telephone interference factor (TIF).

J.2.2 Causes of Harmonic Distortion. All equipment operating on the principle of ferromagnetics produces harmonics when operating in the saturation region of the magnetic core. This equipment includes transformers, motors, generators, induction heaters, solenoid coils, lifting magnets, and iron-core arc-discharge lighting ballasts.

Arc-producing equipment, such as welding machines and arc furnaces, also develops harmonics. Arc-discharge lamps produce harmonics over and above those introduced by the lamp ballast.

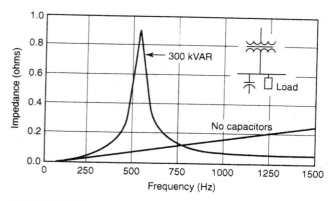

FIGURE J.2.1   Example of Frequency Response Characteristic for a 1500 kVA, 13.8/0.48 kV, 6.0 Percent Transformer and a 300 kVAR, 480 Volt Capacitor Bank.

Electronic equipment, especially equipment that utilizes a rectified-input switching-mode power supply, is a common source of harmonics. The wave-chopping operation develops current waveforms that do not conform to the applied voltage waveform, creating harmonics. This type of equipment includes ac and dc adjustable-speed motor drives, electronic lighting ballasts.

J.2.3 Harmonic Surveying and Testing.

J.2.3.1 Where harmonics are suspected as the cause of problems, it is necessary to determine the magnitude of the harmonic frequencies and their contribution to THD. This information will define the extent of the harmonic problem and identify the source of the harmonics.

If a feasible solution cannot be found, the data can permit calculation of transformer derating factors in accordance with ANSI/IEEE C57.110, *Recommended Practice for Establishing Liquid Immersed and Dry-Type Power and Distribution Transformer Capability When Supplying Nonsinusoidal Load Currents*.

J.2.3.2 The extent of harmonic surveying and testing will vary widely depending on the severity of the problem, available resources, and the facility's particular needs. Simple testing can be performed to confirm or refute the existence of harmonics.

J.2.3.3 The presence of odd triplen harmonics (third, ninth, fifteenth, etc.) can be readily determined on 4-wire wye circuits by measuring neutral current with a true rms responding ammeter and comparing it with current to be expected on the basis of rms phase currents. Neutral-to-ground voltages in excess of 2 volts measured at the equipment can also indicate the presence of triplen harmonics.

J.2.3.4 Instruments useful in harmonic analysis include oscilloscopes, harmonic analyzers, and spectrum analyzers. These instruments can provide visual observation of the waveform to determine if it deviates from a sine wave or if line voltage notching exists.

CAUTION: Because one side of the oscilloscope probe might be common to the case, a line isolation device should be used between the probe and the line voltage being measured.

Spectrum analyzers provide detailed waveform analysis indicating the harmonic frequencies imposed on the fundamental.

Shaded text = Revisions.   Δ = Text deletions and figure/table revisions.   • = Section deletions.   N = New material.

2023 Edition

Harmonic analyzers function the same but can provide THD at the various frequencies.

N J.2.3.5 Harmonic distortion can vary significantly with load. Therefore, readings should be taken under different load conditions. Measurements should be taken to determine the location and extent of harmonics. Readings should be taken on all phases and neutrals, especially on 3-phase circuits that serve single-phase loads.

N J.2.3.6 Each facility differs in its tolerance to harmonic distortion. There are guidelines that can be followed to determine if harmonics are within acceptable limits, including the following:

(1) ANSI/IEEE 519, *Recommended Practice and Requirements for Harmonic Control in Electrical Power Systems*
(2) ANSI/IEEE C57.110, *Recommended Practice for Establishing Liquid Immersed and Dry-Type Power and Distribution Transformer Capability When Supplying Nonsinusoidal Load Currents*
(3) ANSI/IEEE 1100, *Recommended Practice for Powering and Grounding Electronic Equipment (IEEE Emerald Book)*
(4) IEEE 3002.8, *Recommended Practice for Conducting Harmonic Studies and Analysis of Industrial and Commercial Power Systems*

N J.2.4 Solutions/Measures to Harmonic Problems. Recommended solutions or measures to address harmonic problems include any or all of the following:

(1) Derating of existing equipment
(2) Replacement of existing equipment with higher rated equipment
(3) Use of delta-wye- or delta-delta-connected transformers as appropriate
(4) Use of equipment specifically rated for harmonic circuits
(5) Better selection and application of protective and metering devices
(6) Use of rms-sensing protective devices
(7) Balancing of single-phase loads on 3-phase systems
(8) Use of 3-phase rectifiers instead of single-phase rectifiers
(9) Relocating power-factor improvement capacitors
(10) Shielding of conductors and electronic equipment
(11) Isolation of harmonic-sensitive loads
(12) Use of filters to block or shunt off harmonics
(13) Specification of new equipment for low harmonic content
(14) Periodic surveys and power-system adjustments/modifications
(15) Increased neutral conductor size
(16) Replacement or repair of harmonic producing equipment
(17) Utilization of a motor or generator with an insulated bearing

N J.3 Transients (Surges). Transient voltages, or voltage surges, can damage electrical equipment. Transients are covered in ANSI/IEEE C62.41, *Recommended Practice for Surge Voltages in Low-Voltage AC Power Circuits.*

N J.3.1 Transient Symptoms and Effects. Problems associated with transients include the following:

(1) Unusual equipment damage due to insulation failures or arc-over
(2) Damage to electronic equipment components
(3) Total failure, lock-up, or misoperation of computer or other microprocessor-based equipment

N J.3.2 Causes of Transients. Transient voltages in low-voltage ac power circuits usually originate from lightning events on the power system or from switching operations. Lightning strikes can cause severe transients on the power system from direct strike or induced by nearby strikes. Lightning can also produce a transient on the grounded and grounding systems.

Transients can be caused by the switching of inductive or capacitive loads, such as motors, ballasts, transformers, or capacitor banks. Arcing contacts can also cause transients.

Transients can result from phase-to-phase or phase-to-ground short circuits.

N J.3.3 Transient Monitoring. Monitoring can be used to identify power anomalies including voltage transients. Oscilloscopes or power disturbance analyzers specifically designed for transients are useful monitoring tools. Monitoring might be needed over an extended period of time to characterize the nature of the transients.

N J.3.3.1 Monitoring is often performed at specific locations where a sensitive load is connected or is to be connected. Other devices on the monitored circuit, such as the power quality monitor itself, can contain surge-protection devices that limit transients and distort the results. If possible, use an alternative power source for powering monitoring equipment.

N J.3.3.2 Monitoring can be required phase-to-phase, phase-to-ground, phase-to-neutral, and neutral-to-ground to develop a complete profile of the system.

The index for voltage sag quantification is the system average rms (variation) frequency index voltage (SARFI).

N J.3.4 Solutions to Transient Problems.

N J.3.4.1 Devices intended to limit damage from transients are typically rated in units of joules (watt-seconds).

Proper grounding of all circuits intended to be grounded is needed for correct operation of these devices. The manufacturer's instructions should be followed when any of these devices is installed.

N J.3.4.2 Surge arresters are intended to be installed ahead of the service entrance equipment for limiting transient voltage by discharging or bypassing transient currents to ground. They typically provide protection for the effects of lightning.

N J.3.4.3 Surge capacitors are placed in a circuit to slow the transient voltage rise time. By spreading out the voltage increase over a longer time span, less electrical stress occurs to equipment subjected to the transient.

N J.3.4.4 Surge protectors are commonly gas-tube devices or assemblies composed of one or more gas-tube devices. They are used for low-voltage applications (up to 1000 volts rms or 1200 volts dc).

N J.3.4.5 A transient voltage surge suppressor (TVSS) is a device intended for installation on the load side of the main overcurrent protection in circuits not exceeding 600 volts rms. These devices comprise any combination of linear or nonlinear circuit elements (i.e., varistors, avalanche diodes, and gas tubes) and limit transient voltages by diverting or limiting surge current. Typical locations for transient protection are

Shaded text = Revisions.   **Δ** = Text deletions and figure/table revisions.   • = Section deletions.   **N** = New material

service entrance, communication circuits entering the building, computer room power, and at susceptible loads.

J.4 Voltage Sags and Swells. Figure J.4 is an example of a susceptibility curve for a specific piece of equipment. See Section J.10 for information on voltage fluctuations and flicker.

J.4.1 Symptoms of Sags and Swells. A sag duration longer than three cycles is visible with lighting output reduced. Sags often are not distinguishable from momentary interruptions, and the effects to the equipment can be the same. Sensitive equipment, such as computers, can experience intermittent lockups or corrupt data. Even relays and contactors in motor starters can be sensitive to voltage sags, resulting in shutdown of a process when they drop out. Equipment used in industrial plants (e.g., process controllers, programmable logic controllers, adjustable-speed drives, and robotics) is increasingly sensitive to voltage sags as the equipment becomes more complex. Voltage sags can cause the loss of stored data in programmable electronic systems.

The effects of a voltage swell can be more physically destructive to the equipment than those of a voltage sag. The overvoltage can cause breakdown of components in the power supplies of the equipment. This can be a gradual, cumulative effect.

N J.4.2 Causes of Voltage Sags and Swells. Sags and swells can occur in utility transmission and distribution systems or in a facility's power distribution system. A common, underlying cause is a sudden change of current flow.

N J.4.2.1 Sag Causes — Transmission Systems. Severe weather, construction accidents, transportation accidents, or animals can cause faults that result in sags.

N J.4.2.2 Sag Causes — Utility Distribution Systems. Tree limbs contacting distribution systems, vehicle contact with poles or animal contact can all cause voltage sags. A fault on a single feeder can result in an interruption to loads on that feeder, as well as a sag on the other feeders. Typically, distribution system sags are 6 cycles to 20 cycles. Repeated sags can occur with reclosing on a fault. Depending on the number of reclosures, feeders can experience several voltage sags in succession.

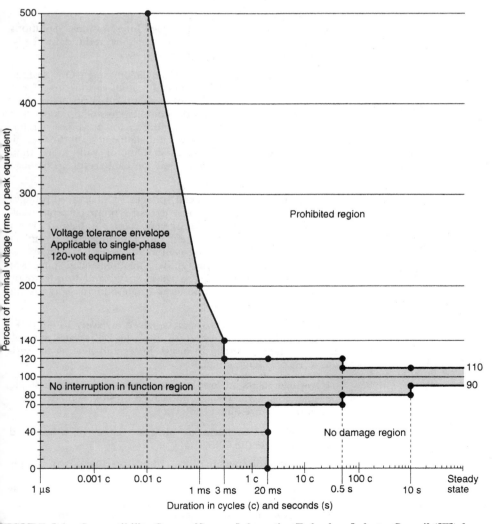

FIGURE J.4   Susceptibility Curve. *[Source: Information Technology Industry Council (ITI).]*

N J.4.2.3 Sag Causes — Facility Power Systems. Sudden increases in the current demand within a facility, such as startup of a large motor, can cause sags until the large current demand decreases. A sudden increase in current can also be the result of an electrical fault. A utility fault can create a severe voltage sag that will last until the fault is cleared.

N J.4.2.4 Swell Causes. Swells are usually associated with system faults. A line-to-ground fault can result in a temporary voltage rise on the unfaulted phases. Swells can also be generated by sudden load decreases. Switching on a large capacitor bank can also cause a swell, although it more often causes a high-frequency transient.

N J.4.3 Monitoring and Testing for Sags and Swells. The timing and magnitude of the sag or swell can often identify the source of the initiating condition. If the phase current levels of the load did not change prior to the voltage sag, the source is more likely to be upstream. When the magnitude of the sag is severe, it is likely that the source was close by. A power-factor correction capacitor being switched on can result in an oscillatory transient followed by a swell. It is common practice to begin monitoring at the point where the utility service connects to the facility equipment.

N J.4.4 Solutions for Sags and Swells. A transformer tap change can be used to raise or lower the nominal voltage level and make the system less susceptible to sags or swells.

N J.4.4.1 Different transformer configurations can be used to minimize the effects of events that cause sags and swells. A delta-delta configuration tends to hold voltage levels higher than a delta-wye or wye-delta configuration.

N J.4.4.2 Fault current limiters, zero voltage independent pole closing capacitor switches, and high-energy surge arresters can be added to the electric system.

N J.4.4.3 Ferroresonant transformers, also called constant-voltage transformers, can handle most short-duration voltage sags. They provide excellent regulation but have limited overload capacity and poor efficiency at low loads.

N J.4.4.4 UPS units can provide isolation from power line disturbances, in addition to providing ride-through during a sag.

N J.4.4.5 Static transfer switches are capable of transferring the supply voltage from one voltage source to another within a quarter-cycle.

N J.5 Long-Duration Undervoltages and Sustained Voltage Interruptions. Facility utilization equipment can be designed and rated to operate within the range of supply system voltage while allowing for voltage drop in the plant system. *[See ANSI/NEMA C84.1, American National Standard for Electric Power Systems and Equipment — Voltage Ratings (60 Hertz).]* It is strongly recommended that plant distribution system voltage drops be kept to a reasonable level.

N J.5.1 Symptoms of Long-Duration Undervoltage. Undervoltage might not be readily apparent. Depending on the length and magnitude of the undervoltage, there can be a detrimental effect on electric and electronic equipment. Equipment such as induction motors might run hotter. Electronic equipment such as computers or microprocessor-based devices might function erratically.

N J.5.2 Causes of Long-Duration Undervoltage. A long-duration undervoltage can originate on the electric utility system or on the plant electrical system. The utility system can be stressed due to line or equipment failure or system load conditions exceeding the supply capability. The plant electrical system or connected loads can result in unacceptable voltage drops even though the voltage is normal at the service point.

N J.5.3 Monitoring and Testing of Long-Duration Undervoltages. Monitoring systems can be sophisticated or a simple voltage-sensing relay. The monitor can be located at the facility service entrance or at sensitive equipment.

N J.5.4 Solutions for Long-Duration Undervoltages. Sensitive equipment should be shut down during extended long-duration undervoltages to prevent damage. Alternative power supplies can be used in order to keep sensitive equipment operational.

N J.5.5 Symptoms of a Sustained Voltage Interruption. A sustained voltage interruption is obvious because electric power is unavailable for an extended period of time, except for equipment served by an alternative power source.

N J.5.6 Causes of Sustained Voltage Interruption. Sustained voltage interruptions can be caused by power system disruptions including downed power lines, equipment failure on the utility's distribution system, or a fault condition causing a circuit protective device to open.

N J.5.7 Solutions for Sustained Voltage Interruptions. Solutions include alternate power sources such as redundant feeds, generator sets, and battery banks.

N J.6 Unbalanced Voltages and Single Phasing. On 3-phase circuits, unbalanced voltages can cause serious problems, particularly to motors, transformers, and other inductive devices. Single phasing, which is the complete loss of a phase, is the worst-case voltage unbalance condition for a 3-phase circuit. Industry guidance limits voltage unbalance at a motor's terminals to 1 percent. Operation of a motor with more than 5 percent unbalance condition will probably result in damage to the motor.

N J.6.1 Symptoms of Unbalanced Voltages. Unbalanced voltages at a motor's terminals can cause excessive phase current unbalance, from 6 to 10 times the percent voltage unbalance. For a voltage unbalance of 2 percent, the resulting current unbalance could range from 12 percent to 20 percent, causing excessive heat and shortening motor life. The unbalanced voltages at the motor terminals will also cause speed and torque to be reduced. Noise and vibration levels can also increase as a result of voltage unbalance.

Insulation life is approximately halved for every 10°C (18°F) increase in winding temperature. Table J.6.1 illustrates the typical percentage increases in motor losses and heating for various levels of voltage unbalance.

Overload relays are one means of protection against single phasing. Relays for voltage imbalance or single-phase detection provide more direct protection.

N J.6.2 Causes of Unbalanced Voltages. Causes of unbalanced voltages include the following:

(1) Unequal impedance in conductors of power supply wiring
(2) Unbalanced distribution of single-phase loads such as lighting
(3) Heavy reactive single-phase loads such as welders

Table J.6.1 Voltage Unbalance Versus Temperature Rise at Average Voltage of 230

Percent Unbalanced Voltage	Percent Unbalanced Current	Increased Temperature Rise	
		°C	°F
0.3	0.4	0	0
2.3	17.7	30	54
5.4	40	40	72

(4) Unbalanced incoming utility supply
(5) Unequal transformer tap settings
(6) Large single-phase load on the system
(7) Open phase on the primary of a 3-phase transformer
(8) Open delta-connected transformer banks
(9) A blown fuse on a 3-phase bank of power factor correction capacitors

N J.6.3 Monitoring and Testing of Unbalanced Voltages.

N J.6.3.1 Measuring. Line-to-line voltages should be measured at the machine terminals. The current in each supply phase should be measured for unbalance.

N J.6.4 Solutions for Unbalanced Voltages.

N J.6.4.1 Possible solutions for unbalanced voltages can include balancing the load distribution among phases or derating equipment connected to unbalanced loads.

N J.6.4.2 Automatic voltage regulators (AVR) can be used to correct minor undervoltage, overvoltage, and voltage unbalance.

N J.6.4.3 Negative sequence voltage relays can be installed to detect single phasing, phase-voltage unbalance, and reversal of supply phase rotation. Reverse phase or phase sequence relays provide limited single-phasing protection by preventing the starting of a motor with one phase of the system open.

N J.6.4.4 Transformer tap settings should be checked and corrected as needed.

N J.6.4.5 An unsymmetrical transformer bank should be replaced, and an open delta bank can be replaced with a three-transformer bank.

N J.6.4.6 Fuses and protective devices in each phase should be checked and replaced as needed.

N J.7 Inadequate Grounding.

N J.7.1 Symptoms of Inadequate Grounding. (Reserved)

N J.7.2 Causes of Inadequate Grounding. (Reserved)

N J.7.3 Monitoring and Testing for Inadequate Grounding. The electrical connection to earth can be measured using methods found in ANSI/IEEE 142, *Recommended Practice for Grounding of Industrial and Commercial Power Systems (IEEE Green Book)*. Other testing and inspections of the grounding system include the following:

(1) Visual inspection of the grounding and bonding conductors and associated connections.
(2) Impedance test of the equipment-grounding conductor.
(3) Voltage measurements between the equipment-grounding conductor and the grounded conductor.

(4) Measurement for current magnitudes on the equipment-grounding conductor.

N J.7.4 Solutions for Inadequate Grounding. The grounded conductor should be connected to the equipment-grounding conductor only as permitted by Article 250 of *NFPA 70*.

N J.7.4.1 Breaking the ground loop current path minimizes ground currents on signal circuits. This can be accomplished by one or more of the following:

(1) Grounding at only a single point per system
(2) Fiber-optic transmission/optical isolators
(3) Isolation transformers

N J.8 Noise in Electrical and Electronic Systems. Noise is undesirable in electrical signals in an electrical or electronic circuit. It can be random or continuous in nature. Noise can be introduced into a circuit from various sources and can cause equipment malfunction or data corruption.

Electromagnetically coupled interference into a wiring system is called electromagnetic interference (EMI), and capacitively coupled interference is called radio frequency interference (RFI).

N J.8.1 Symptoms of Noise. Electrical noise usually manifests itself in the form of data corruption or unexplained equipment malfunction. Electrical noise can create "hum" in a telephone system or "snow" in a video image or cause electronic equipment to lock up.

N J.8.2 Causes of Noise. Causes of noise in electrical and electronic systems can include the following:

(1) Transformer-generated magnetic fields
(2) Long cable runs acting as an antenna
(3) Switch-mode power supplies
(4) Intermittent connections creating electrical noise

N J.8.3 Monitoring and Testing of Noise. Determining the amplitude and frequency of the noise signal is essential in identifying the source. Test equipment useful to identify the nature of the noise includes the following:

(1) Spectrum analyzer — capable of measuring a wide range of frequencies
(2) Conducted RFI/EMI recorder — capable of measuring noise levels superimposed on the voltage waveform
(3) Radiated RFI/EMI recorder — capable of measuring electrical noise levels present in the air
(4) Digital storage oscilloscope
(5) Power-quality monitor

N J.8.4 Solutions for Noise. Isolation or elimination of noise is the best solution; however, attenuation or filtering might be more practical. Some methods of attenuating or filtering out noise include the following:

(1) Shielding of equipment and conductors
(2) Tuned noise filters
(3) The use of twisted pair and shields in low-power signal cables
(4) Electromagnetic shielding mounted on walls, floors, or ceilings if properly grounded.
(5) Active cancellation systems employing Helmholtz coils.

N J.9 Interharmonics. Interharmonics are signal components that have frequencies between the harmonic frequencies. A special class are called subharmonics, which are frequencies below the fundamental frequency. See Section J.2 for information on harmonics.

N J.9.1 Symptoms of Interharmonics. Isolation or elimination of noise is the best solution; however, attenuation or filtering might be more practical. Some methods of attenuating or filtering out noise include the following:

(1) Misoperation of equipment or control devices
(2) Overheating of transformers or motors
(3) CT saturation
(4) CRT flicker
(5) Overload of tuned filters, outlet strip filters
(6) Communications interference

N J.9.2 Causes of Interharmonics. Loads that draw current that are not synchronized to the power line frequency can result in interharmonic voltages and currents. Types of equipment include static frequency converters, induction motors, arc furnaces, and arc welders. Loads that draw current that are not synchronized to the power line frequency can result in interharmonic voltages and currents. Types of equipment include static frequency converters, induction motors, arc furnaces, and arc welders.

N J.9.3 Monitoring and Testing of Interharmonics. Spectrum analyzers or harmonic analyzers with interharmonic capabilities should be used to measure for this condition.

N J.9.4 Solutions for Interharmonics. The solutions for minimizing the effects of interharmonics, like harmonics, include filtering, impedance reduction, derating of transformers and motors, and isolation of sensitive equipment.

N J.10 Voltage Fluctuations and Flicker. Voltage fluctuations are variations in the rms voltage that are lower in magnitude than those that would be considered a sag. These generally do not cause equipment to malfunction but often result in light flicker. Flicker is the change in light output from a lamp, caused by the fluctuation of the supply voltage in the frequency range of 0.5 Hz to 30 Hz, where as little as a quarter of a percent voltage fluctuation at nine times per second can be perceived. Figure J.10 is an example of voltage fluctuation on a sine wave.

See Section J.4 for information on voltage sags and swells.

N J.10.1 Voltage Fluctuations Symptoms. Voltage fluctuations normally are perceived as an annoyance and distraction when the lights flicker but can also cause variations in industrial processes.

N J.10.2 Voltage Fluctuations Causes. Common sources of voltage fluctuations include the following:

(1) Lamp dimmers
(2) Resistance welding machines
(3) Large electric motors with variable loads
(4) Arc furnaces and arc welders
(5) Switching of PF correction capacitors
(6) Magnetic-based imaging machines (X-ray, MRI, CAT scan)

N J.10.3 Voltage Fluctuations Monitoring and Testing. To measure the effect of voltage fluctuations on lighting, a flickermeter is used to quantify the perception of the light flickering. A luminescence meter can be used to measure light output. Oscilloscopes or power quality monitors can be useful in identifying the frequency and magnitude of the fluctuations, which can help identify the source.

N J.10.4 Solutions. Three solutions to minimize the effects of voltage fluctuation on lighting are as follows:

(1) Reduce the magnitude and/or change the frequency of the load current
(2) Reduce the source impedance
(3) Change the type of lighting (e.g., from an incandescent lamp to a fluorescent lamp)

N J.11 Power Quality Audit. Power quality audits are overall studies used to evaluate the overall power quality of the system. These audits are often performed at the following times:

(1) Prior to installing new equipment into a facility

    When commissioning a new facility
(2) When implementing a routine maintenance program to look for changes or trends
(3) When implementing a routine maintenance program to look for changes or trends

Typical parameters to monitor include those found in Table J.11.

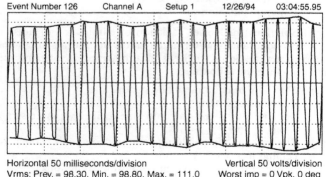

Graphical and Harmonic Analysis

Event Number 126   Channel A   Setup 1   12/26/94   03:04:55.95

Horizontal 50 milliseconds/division   Vertical 50 volts/division
Vrms: Prev. = 98.30, Min. = 98.80, Max. = 111.0   Worst imp = 0 Vpk, 0 deg

FIGURE J.10   Example of a Flicker Sine Wave. *(Source: Dranetz Technologies, Inc.)*

N Table J.11 Typical Power Quality Parameters to be Monitored

No.	Power Quality Parameter	Recommended Measurement(s)
	Timeplots with minimum/maximum/average	
1	Voltage rms	L-N, L-L, N-G where applicable
2	Current rms	Phase, neutral, residual, net
3	Voltage harmonic distortion	V_{thd}, selective harmonics as percent of fundamental
4	Current harmonic distortion	Selective harmonics in amps
5	Voltage unbalance	Either rms deviation from average or negative sequence/ positive sequence method
6	Current unbalance	Either rms deviation from average or negative sequence/ positive sequence method
7	Frequency	
	PQ disturbances	
8	Transients	
9	RMS variations	Sags, swells, interruptions with magnitude/ duration, rms envelope, waveforms
10	Activity chart	Time of day of disturbances
	Demand and energy timeplots with minimum/maximum/ average	
11	Watts	Per phase and total
12	Volt-amperes	Per phase and total
13	Volt-ampere-reactive	Per phase fundamental VARs per phase and total
14	Demand	
15	Energy	

Annex K   Electrical Disaster Recovery

This annex is not a part of the requirements of this NFPA document but is included for informational purposes only.

△ K.1 Introduction. When electrical systems are faced with a natural or man-made disaster, a very specific and detailed sequence of events should occur prior to returning the electrical system to operation in a safe and expeditious manner. Actions can also be taken to reduce the damage to the system and to shorten the system recovery time frame. After a disaster event, it is especially critical to analyze and repair the electrical power system in a safe and logical sequence. This annex describes recovery steps for an electrical power system and related equipment that should be followed before and after an electrical disaster event occurs.

K.2 Catastrophic Event Categories. The events surrounding a disaster can be detailed into the following specific event phases:

(1) Initial event
(2) Securing the facility to limit damage
(3) Mobilization of recovery personnel
(4) Developing a safety plan
(5) Temporary and emergency power generation
(6) Initial damage assessment
(7) Documentation
(8) Equipment
(9) Re-energization of the facility
(10) System commissioning
(11) Project summary

K.2.1 The Initial Event. Disaster recovery efforts can be a result of both natural and man-made disasters. Disaster scenarios including, but not limited to, the following inflict damage of varying degrees to facilities:

(1) Fire: soot, material and equipment damage, water damage, structural damage
(2) Flooding: water damage, structural damage
(3) Hurricane: water damage, structural damage, utility infrastructure damage
(4) Tornado: water damage, structural damage, utility infrastructure damage
(5) Earthquake: structural damage, utility infrastructure damage

K.2.2 Securing the Facility to Limit Damage. If possible, a facility should be secured prior to the disaster event to limit electrical and mechanical damage to equipment and systems. Electrical equipment should be placed into an electrically safe work condition, and critical components should be removed or preserved. Examples of tasks to limit damage are as follows:

(1) Remove critical equipment from their base and raise them above the flood line or remove them from the flood site.
(2) De-energize power to prevent electrical short circuit and arcing damage.
(3) Secure storage tanks and other large devices that can float away.
(4) Sandbag the fronts of electrical equipment rooms to limit water and debris entry.
(5) Remove critical computer and electronic equipment from the site.
(6) Remove all electrical equipment, drawings, manuals, and supplies stored at ground level.
(7) Shut down and control mechanical systems.

K.2.3 Mobilization of Recovery Personnel. During large-scale disaster events, one of the biggest challenges for a commercial or industrial facility is providing enough qualified contractors and disaster recovery specialists to perform required remediation to the facility. Prior to a disaster event occurring, a preplan should be developed for the mobilization of recovery personnel. Consideration should also be given to personnel needs during disaster recovery, including a plan to address physical needs and basic provisions such as transportation, food, shelter, and hygiene.

K.2.3.1 In-House Personnel. Before a disaster event occurs, personnel responsible for the disaster recovery operations and facility repair should be designated and have possession of any applicable action plans. Depending on the magnitude of the

Shaded text = Revisions.   △ = Text deletions and figure/table revisions.   • = Section deletions.   **N** = New material.

2023 Edition

event, the recovery effort can be done solely with in-house personnel or with the assistance of professional restoration companies.

K.2.3.2 Outsourced (Contract) Personnel. Prior to a disaster event, facilities should consider establishing master service agreements (MSAs) with multiple qualified vendors who specialize in electrical disaster recovery services. Doing so prevents confusion and delays in the recovery efforts. Decide who will perform the cleanup (debris removal and electrical equipment restoration) and supply support equipment (e.g., flood pumps, heavy equipment and operators, emergency power equipment, and temporary electrical services). Qualified repair facilities should be identified prior to a disaster recovery event.

K.2.3.3 Notification to Insurance Carrier. As soon as feasible, the site insurance carrier's claims representative should be notified of the event.

K.2.4 Developing a Safety Plan. A site-specific safety plan should be developed before a disaster occurs. When performing recovery of electrical equipment, safety, health, and environmental are paramount. Lockout/tagout, test before touch, and the application of safety grounds are typically covered in site electrical safety plans. While these are key safety aspects of placing equipment into an electrically safe condition, there are other items of safety that need to be addressed and integrated into the safety plan, such as the following:

(1) Air quality
(2) Structural issues
(3) Chemical and biological hazard spill exposure
(4) Site-specific hazards
(5) Site-specific PPE requirements

Δ K.2.5 Temporary and Emergency Power Generation. When disaster events occur, there is often a loss of normal utility power. This creates a unique safety and logistical challenge to provide the required electrical power in a facility for critical systems and lighting. The temporary power portion of the project should be managed to reduce the risk of shock and arc flash hazards. There should be dedicated personnel responsible for temporary power, and they should develop all written standards and procedures to be followed. Typical emergency power procedures should identify elements such as the following:

(1) Potential backfeeding of equipment
(2) Individual motor starters for pumps
(3) Temporary signage and barricades
(4) Site generator location maps.
(5) Fueling schedules
(6) Written request form for the addition of electrical power
(7) Access
(8) Safe exhaust venting of combustion-powered equipment

K.2.6 Initial Damage Assessment. One of the first tasks in assessing equipment and system damage to electrical equipment involved in a disaster event is to perform a walk-through and initial assessment of the entire electrical infrastructure. All pertinent drawings and documentation available should be used to aid in this task.

K.2.6.1 Drawings, Schematics, Equipment Documentation. In some instances drawings and documentation are not available due to destruction from the disaster event. All equipment instruction books, operation and maintenance (O&M)

manuals, and documentation should be identified and centrally located. Electronic versions should be made of documents for secure off-site access.

K.2.6.2 Priority Assessment. Equipment repair priorities should be assessed with a focus on the highest priority equipment. Examples of typical equipment priority categories are as follows:

(1) Category 1: medium-voltage equipment including distribution transformers
(2) Category 2: low-voltage distribution equipment
(3) Category 3: electric motors
(4) Category 4: power and control wiring
(5) Category 5: balance of the plant electrical equipment

K.2.7 Documentation. All electrical components or equipment should be properly documented prior to removal to ensure the equipment is reinstalled properly as found. The documentation process includes the following:

(1) Tag each piece of equipment.
(2) Label all control and power wires.
(3) Take a digital picture of each piece of equipment.
(4) Sketch an accurate diagram of each piece of equipment on the electrical equipment drawing sheet.
(5) Fill out the electrical equipment tracking form.
(6) Save all pictures on a local database.
(7) File the electrical equipment drawing sheet.
(8) Create a master electrical equipment tracking document.
(9) Collect and retain shipping documents of all electrical equipment.

K.2.7.1 Service Shop–Related Activities. If equipment is to be removed from the affected facility for repair at an offsite service center, the equipment should be tagged, identified, and tracked and the status updated on a master equipment repair database.

K.2.7.2 Equipment Tag. Information on each tag should include a unique sequence number, plant identification number, plant description, date, power center, or room number. The tag should be filled out with a medium point permanent marker so the information is legible. The tag should be attached to the equipment with a secure plastic wire-tie.

K.2.7.3 Labeling of Wires. All control wires should be labeled with wire numbers and the power wires with colored phasing tape. Make sure that each side of the termination, both wire and connected device, is identified. This will ensure the wiring will be reconnected as it was originally installed.

K.2.7.4 Photographs of Equipment. After the equipment is tagged and the wires are labeled, a minimum of three photographs should be taken of each piece of equipment. The first photo should include the equipment tag in the picture, making sure the tag is legible and the picture is clear. The second photo is an overall view for the sole purpose of wire clarification/documentation during the reinstallation process and should include all wiring associated with the applicable device. The third photograph should be of the equipment nameplate. Additional photographs should be taken as deemed appropriate.

K.2.7.5 Field Sketch. An accurate field sketch of the electrical equipment should be generated. The sketch should be recorded on a site-specific electrical equipment drawing sheet template. This drawing sheet should include the job name, job number, power center, sequence number, plant equipment number, plant equipment number, plant description, technician name, date, and enough room to sketch the piece of equipment.

K.2.7.6 Equipment Tracking Sheet. After a sketch is made of the piece of equipment, the equipment should be added to an electrical equipment tracking sheet. The electrical equipment tracking sheet should be customized and detailed. The tracking sheet should include general information such as overall condition, item number, sequence number, priority, area of the plant, power center or room number, transformer, substation, cell position, equipment type, circuit identification, plant identification number, manufacturer, model number, frame size, and voltage. Field tracking information should also include entries for each piece of equipment listing the date pulled, shipped, returned, and installed and any quality assurance procedures performed.

K.2.7.7 Repair or Replace. During the documentation process, initial decisions should be made pertaining to each piece of equipment that is damaged. Seeking the services of qualified equipment assessment personnel, whether manufacturer representatives or subject matter experts, is important in the decision-making process.

K.2.7.7.1 Repair or Replace Decisions. Each piece of equipment should be assessed for repair or replacement. Some considerations are as follows:

(1) Can the equipment be satisfactorily repaired?
(2) Can the repair be done adequately and time efficiently on site?
(3) Should the equipment be replaced?

K.2.7.7.2 Repair or Replace Factors. Some of the factors that can affect the repair or replace decision are as follows:

(1) Is the equipment currently manufactured?
(2) Are there long lead times to replace with new?
(3) Will equipment performance be compromised if repaired?
(4) What is the age of the equipment?
(5) What is the reliability requirement?
(6) Can it be effectively repaired?
(7) Is the manufacturer still in business?
(8) Is the repair contractor qualified for the task?
(9) Will the authority having jurisdiction allow repair or replacement?
(10) What is the financial impact?
(11) What is the total outage time required?

K.2.7.7.3 Industry Standards and Guidelines. Industry standards and guidelines should be referred to for information. Information is available from the following:

(1) Electrical Apparatus Service Association (EASA), ANSI/EASA AR100, *Recommended Practice for the Repair of Rotating Electrical Apparatus*
(2) Federal Emergency Management Agency (FEMA), FEMA P-348, *Protecting Building Utility Systems From Flood Damage: Principles and Practices for the Design and Construction of Flood Resistant Building Utility Systems*
(3) Institute of Electrical and Electronic Engineers (IEEE), IEEE 3007.1, *Recommended Practice for the Operation and Management of Industrial and Commercial Power Systems*
(4) Institute of Electrical and Electronic Engineers (IEEE), IEEE 3007.2, *Recommended Practice for the Maintenance of Industrial and Commercial Power Systems*

(5) National Electrical Manufacturers Association (NEMA), NEMA GD 1, *Evaluating Water-Damaged Electrical Equipment*
(6) InterNational Electrical Testing Association (NETA), ANSI/NETA ATS, *Standard for Acceptance Testing Specifications for Electrical Power Distribution Equipment and Systems*
(7) InterNational Electrical Testing Association (NETA), ANSI/NETA MTS, *Standard for Maintenance Testing Specifications for Electrical Power Distribution Equipment and Systems*
(8) National Fire Protection Association (NFPA), *NFPA 70* and NFPA *70E*
(9) *Flood Repair of Electrical Equipment*, Pat Beisert, Shermco Industries, PowerTest Annual Technical Conference, March 12, 2009.
(10) National Electrical Manufacturers Association (NEMA), NEMA GD 2, *Evaluating Fire- and Heat-Damaged Electrical Equipment*

Δ **K.2.8 Equipment.**

N **K.2.8.1 Medium-Voltage Equipment.** Medium-voltage equipment typically serves as the backbone to the electrical power system and should be the primary focus of the initial recovery activities.

K.2.8.2 Low-Voltage Distribution Equipment. Affected components of low-voltage equipment should be removed to facilitate cleaning and drying of the structures. During the removal of the equipment, care should be taken to keep all wiring for each component well marked and together.

Δ **K.2.8.3 Electric Motors.** When a disaster event involves water, electric motor repair is a major component of a flood recovery project. The documentation process is very similar to other electrical equipment but there are additional items that should be documented. The documentation process should include the following:

(1) Record nameplate data and location of the motor.
(2) Tag the motor mounting base and the motor with a unique sequence number.
(3) Mark and record electrical connections.
(4) Record coupling information and condition of coupling.
(5) Mark and record shim information.
(6) Collect all mounting hardware, couplings, and shims and store in its own labeled container. This equipment associated hardware should stay on site and be stored in a central location.

Δ **K.2.8.4 Power and Control Wiring.** Power and control wiring should be tested to determine serviceability.

K.2.8.5 Balance of Plant Electrical Repair. The balance of electrical devices consists of all equipment other than medium-voltage equipment, low-voltage distribution equipment, and motors. These devices are typically repaired rather than replaced.

K.2.8.6 Re-energization of the Facility. Initial re-energization to utility power of a facility damaged by a disaster event should be carefully planned and methodically implemented. Utility energization should occur only after all affected equipment has been repaired or replaced in order to reduce the possibility of unintended energization of equipment unless careful measures are taken to prevent this potential hazard.

△ **K.2.8.7 System Commissioning.** During the re-energization of the facility, equipment operation and performance should be verified. A period of monitoring should be established to verify and document that proper operation has been restored.

K.2.8.8 Project Summary. After a disaster recovery event there is information gathered that should be available for future reference. The final project report should contain this data and should include information such as the following:

(1) As-found conditions of the electrical infrastructure
(2) Listing of equipment repaired or replaced
(3) Test results of all equipment tested before and after service or repairs
(4) Assessment of individual equipment condition
(5) Long-term equipment replacement plan

Annex L   Case Histories

This annex is not a part of the requirements of this NFPA document but is included for informational purposes only.

The case histories in this annex support the need for qualified maintenance personnel and the implementation of an EMP. There are several types of case histories in this annex. These case histories illustrate that it is good business practice to devote the personnel and monetary resources to keep electrical equipment properly maintained. Limiting resources committed to regular maintenance could result in significant monetary consequences, such as equipment replacement, lost production, personnel injuries, death settlements, OSHA fines, legal fees, and losses not covered by insurance. These case histories can be used as a tool to demonstrate the positive effects of routine maintenance and the potential consequences of not having an adequate preventative maintenance program.

L.1 Oil Contamination Causes Transformer Failure. The failure of a transformer caused a total plant shutdown at an industrial facility. Contamination of the transformer's insulating oil caused the failure. The contamination went undetected because the oil had not been tested for several years. Fire damage and equipment replacement costs amounted to $50,000 (US), exclusive of the cost of plant downtime. This amount would have paid for the cost of operating an EMP covering the entire plant's electrical distribution system for several years.

L.2 Lack of Cleaning Program Causes Switchgear Damage. Damage amounting to $100,000 (US) was attributed to the failure of the main switchgear at an industrial facility. Fouling by dirt, gummy deposits, and iron filings caused the failure. The cost of this failure would have supported a comprehensive EMP covering all of the plant's electrical distribution system for several years.

L.3 Failure to Maintain Extension Cord Causes Fire. A large exhibition hall in Chicago was destroyed by a fire believed to have been started because of a defective extension cord serving a display booth. Direct property loss was $60 million (US), and loss of the facility cost an additional $100 million (US) to the economy in the Chicago area. This fire might have been prevented if a program had been in effect to manage the integrity of the cords.

L.4 Clogged Cooling Ducts Cause Motor Failure. The failure of a large motor shut down an entire industrial plant for 12 days. The cause of the failure was overheating resulting from dust-plugged cooling ducts. An EMP inspection would likely have detected the clogged ducts and averted the failure and accompanying plant outage.

L.5 Lack of Maintenance Causes Failure of Multiple Circuit Breakers. A company had their protective relays on their 13.8 kV power system calibrated regularly each year, but did not have the circuit breakers tested or maintained. When a maintenance contractor pointed out that the circuit breakers as well as the protective relays needed maintenance, the company responded: "The circuit breakers are like brand new. We never operate them." One year, several months after the relays were calibrated, an underground feeder cable failed and the fault cascaded through six circuit breakers before it was cleared.

The company was certain the root cause was improper calibration of the protective relays. Upon inspection, however, the company found that all of the operations indicators (flags) on all of the protective relays had dropped, showing that the relays operated correctly. The root cause was determined to be the circuit breaker operating mechanisms. The mechanisms were so dry from lack of lubricant that the opening coils burned up on all six of the circuit breakers that did not operate when the relays signaled the circuit breakers to open. *[See Figure L.5(a) through Figure L.5(f).]*

L.6 Hospital Electrical Panel Fire. A fire necessitated the evacuation of patients on two floors of a healthcare and emergency services hospital. The fire originated in an electric panel on the wall of a patient's room. There was never any routine inspection or preventive maintenance performed on these low

FIGURE L.5(a)   A 20 cal/cm² Arc Flash Suit Hanging on the Wall was Reduced to Ashes. *(Courtesy of Shermco Industries, Inc.)*

voltage panels. Fire and smoke damage resulted and business was interrupted due to the loss of use of those floors for patient care during the cleanup and restoration period. Costs exceeded $300,000 (U.S.).

L.7 Failure to Have Entire Critical System Acceptance Tested Results in $5.2 Million (US) Loss. Critical devices must be acceptance tested as well as periodically tested on a regular basis, even if the costs associated with testing exceed the replacement cost of an item. It's not just the cost of testing that is important, but the criticality of the equipment to be tested as well.

A manufacturing company installed a new 13.8 kV transformer, switchgear, and battery bank with charging system to support expanded production. The electrical equipment manufacturer provided the acceptance testing in accordance with the manufacturing company's specifications in their contract. The molded-case circuit breakers that supplied the

△ **FIGURE L.5(d)   All Bus Terminations and Insulation Were Destroyed.** *(Courtesy of Shermco Industries, Inc.)*

FIGURE L.5(b)   All Six Circuit Breakers and Their Enclosures Were Destroyed. *(Courtesy of Shermco Industries, Inc.)*

FIGURE L.5(e)   All Metal Inside the Circuit Breaker Was Vaporized or Melted. *(Courtesy of Shermco Industries, Inc.)*

FIGURE L.5(c)   Intense Heat Burned the Ceramic in the Arc Extinguishers. *(Courtesy of Shermco Industries, Inc.)*

battery charging system in the outdoor substation were not included in the acceptance testing specifications, presumably because it would cost more to test them than to replace them.

A few months after start-up, one of the underground feeder cables failed and sent fault current through the transformer and reactor, destroying both. The brand-new 13.8 kV switchgear circuit breakers failed to operate and the upstream main circuit breaker had to clear the fault, causing a plant-wide outage. The root cause was traced back to a low-voltage, 100 A two-pole molded-case circuit breaker that when tested after the incident, tripped in 70 seconds with only 45 A of current flowing through it. This circuit breaker fed the battery bank charger that supplied the dc tripping power for the 13.8 kV protective system. With no dc power available, the 13.8 kV circuit breakers were unable to trip. The situation could have been identified and rectified before the fault, but because it was a new installation and just tested, no one at the manufacturing company checked the status of the battery bank. When

△ **FIGURE L.5(f)   Switchgear Could Not Be Repaired and Had to Be Replaced.** *(Courtesy of Shermco Industries, Inc.)*

FIGURE L.7(b)   Transformer (foreground) and Reactor Destroyed by Fault Current. *(Courtesy of Shermco Industries, Inc.*

the circuit breaker feeding the battery bank tripped, the batteries were depleted and could not be recharged. *[See Figure L.7(a) and Figure L.7(b).]*

This failure cost the manufacturing company over $5.2 million (US), not including legal fees. If the acceptance testing in the installation contract had included the circuit breaker supplying the battery charger, this incident and monetary loss would likely not have occurred.

△ **L.8 Refrigeration Compressor Fails Unexpectedly as a Result of Improper Maintenance.** A 25-story office building located in a major metropolitan, warm-climate city was constructed in the early 1920s. The building's air-conditioning system (with one central compressor) was installed in the 1960s. During the hottest time of the year, the compressor motor failed due to a shorted coil winding and the internal temperatures of the building reached over 32°C (90°F). The timeline for repairs to the air-conditioning system was three months. Tenants fled the

building and revenue losses initially increased to over $250,0((US). Long-term revenue losses could not be tracked. Th repair costs of the air-conditioning system and compresso motor approached $200,000 (US) due to the emergency ser ice.

The following is the preventative maintenance schedule th was used when the failure occurred:

Resistive measurements of the motor windings wer performed and recorded for six years. Examples of resistiv measurements recorded were: "good," "not performed," "0.5 and "3." Oil sampling was performed for the past three year The oil sampling revealed evidence of increasing metal wea but under a predetermined action level.

Ignoring trending data from the oil sampling and not accu rately documenting resistive measurements from testin allowed this failure to occur at an unscheduled downtime.

△ **L.9 Explosion in an Electrical Room.** In a plant, two electri cians were servicing programmable logic controller (PLC equipment in the main motor control center (MCC). Durin the electricians' break, an explosion occurred in the mai circuit breaker section of the MCC. One of the electricians ha his back to the enclosure when the explosion occurred. H clothes caught fire and he was severely burned and eventuall died from his injuries. The second electrician suffered smok inhalation, minor burns, and PTSD. The forensic investigatio into this failure revealed the MCC's owner never maintaine nor inspected the MCC during its over 25 years of servic despite requests from the plant's own maintenance staff. Th failure occurred at the 1200 amperes main circuit breaker load side lugs. Two lawsuits were initiated from this explosio The first lawsuit resulted in an eight-figure settlement awarde to the deceased electrician's family. The second lawsuit resulte in a seven-figure settlement awarded to the injured electricia The second lawsuit also required the owner of the MCC to pa the repair costs for the damage to the local electric utility facilities caused by this failure and the local utility's legal fe incurred for the second lawsuit. *[See Figure L.9(a) and Figur L.9(b).]*

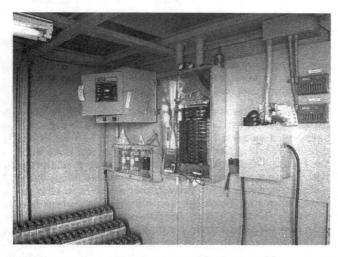

FIGURE L.7(a)   The Circuit Breaker Fed This Battery Bank, which Lost All Power. *(Courtesy of Shermco Industries, Inc.)*

FIGURE L.9(a)   Overview of the MCC.

FIGURE L.9(b)   Close-up View of Main Circuit Breaker Lug Failure.

L.10 Infrared Inspection Prevents Potential Failure and Outage of 20 MVA Transformer. The observation at the initial infrared survey indicated the transformer was not cooling properly. The infrared image showed an uneven heat pattern on the transformer cooling fins. This condition could result in the transformer overheating and a breakdown of the oil. Failure of this substation transformer would result in loss of power to businesses and homeowners.

After consultations between the owner and repair firms, it was determined that there could be several causes for this cooling problem: the transformer could be low on oil, the transformer could have shifted (tilted on an angle), or sludge could be causing a blockage in the cooling fins.

When the observation port at the top of the transformer was opened, inspectors noted that approximately half of the radiator tubes were covered with oil. The initial infrared image

showed an uneven heat pattern. The cooling fins properly filled with oil showed a hotter surface temperature than those cooling fins that were not properly filled with oil. After adding the appropriate amount of oil to the transformer and recharging the nitrogen blanket, another infrared image was taken. The infrared image after the repair indicated an even heat pattern across the cooling fins. Detection of the abnormal condition and the corrective actions prevented potential failure and loss of power, and improved the reliability of the owner's operations.

Δ L.11 Office Building Drive System Loose Connection Results in Arcing Fault. A centrifugal chiller unit failed at a commercial real estate office building. The building engineer noted an odor, typical of electrical damage in the chiller room. It was discovered that there was no power to the chiller panel and the 800 A breaker that powered the chiller had tripped. Basic troubleshooting did not reveal any faults. There was some spattering around the load side of the circuit breaker, but it was not determined if this was old or new and no tests were performed on the circuit breaker. No further investigation was conducted at the time because the chiller was not needed.

The chiller panel cabinet door was closed, and the circuit breaker reset. As soon as the circuit breaker was closed, a severe arcing fault occurred within the panel. A service company was then called in and determined that the unit could not be repaired. The 800 A circuit breaker for the chiller system suffered an arcing fault due to a loose connection. Costs exceeded $100,000 (US).

It's possible that a regular preventive maintenance program that included visual inspection, cleaning, testing, and infrared inspection could have identified and corrected the root cause for this event.

L.12 Hospital MCC Fails and Air Conditioning Down. The plant operator heard a loud bang and found smoke coming from the chiller plant MCC. Failure of the MCC for the chiller plant resulted in the loss of critical air conditioning to a hospital's operating room and the entire facility. Due to the failure, procedures in the operating room were cancelled. Lead times for replacement MCC parts were 6 to 8 weeks. Emergency temporary repairs that included a transformer rental needed to be made to restore partial operations. The fuses for the dry-type transformer that provided power to the MCC had two open fuses and extensive arcing damage was found along the MCC bus bar. The MCC was considered aged as it was 30 years old. Costs exceeded $400,000 (US).

Periodic infrared inspection was conducted on the MCC by a contractor. It was not known if any abnormal conditions were identified during those inspections. Infrared testing is only part of a preventive maintenance program and is helpful in identifying defects on exposed energized parts that have a load at the time of inspection. A comprehensive PM program that includes other testing, like ultrasound and electrical tests, visual inspection, and checking for tightness and proper torque, particularly on the bus bar for the MCC, could have identified the defect or problem before failure. Age of equipment should also be considered in determining frequency of maintenance intervals.

Annex M Informational References

M.1 Referenced Publications. The documents or portions thereof listed in this annex are referenced within the informational sections of this standard and are not part of the requirements of this document unless also listed in Chapter 2 for other reasons.

M.1.1 NFPA Publications. National Fire Protection Association, 1 Batterymarch Park, Quincy, MA 02169-7471.

NFPA 70®, National Electrical Code®, 2023 edition.

NFPA *70E®, Standard for Electrical Safety in the Workplace®*, 2021 edition.

NFPA 110, *Standard for Emergency and Standby Power Systems*, 2022 edition.

NFPA 111, *Standard on Stored Electrical Energy Emergency and Standby Power Systems*, 2022 edition.

NFPA 496, *Standard for Purged and Pressurized Enclosures for Electrical Equipment*, 2021 edition.

NFPA 780, *Standard for the Installation of Lightning Protection Systems*, 2023 edition.

NFPA 791, *Recommended Practice and Procedures for Unlabeled Electrical Equipment Evaluation*, 2021 edition.

M.1.2 Other Publications.

M.1.2.1 ASTM Publications. ASTM International, 100 Barr Harbor Drive, P.O. Box C700, West Conshohocken, PA 19428-2959.

ASTM D923, *Standard Practices for Sampling Electrical Insulating Liquids*, 2015.

ASTM D924, *Standard Test Method for Dissipation Factor (or Power Factor) and Relative Permittivity (Dielectric Constant) of Electrical Insulating Liquids*, 2015.

ASTM D971, *Standard Test Method for Interfacial Tension of Insulating Liquids Against Water by the Ring Method*, 2020.

ASTM D974, *Standard Test Method for Acid and Base Number by Color-Indicator Titration*, 2014e2.

ASTM D1298, *Standard Test Method for Density, Relative Density, or API Gravity of Crude Petroleum and Liquid Petroleum Products by Hydrometer Method*, 2012b, reapproved 2017.

ASTM D1500, *Standard Test Method for ASTM Color of Petroleum Products (ASTM Color Scale)*, 2012, reapproved 2017.

ASTM D1524, *Standard Test Method for Visual Examination of Used Electrical Insulating Liquids in the Field*, 2015.

ASTM D1533, *Standard Test Method for Water in Insulating Liquids by Coulometric Karl Fischer Titration*, 2020.

ASTM D1816, *Standard Test Method for Dielectric Breakdown Voltage of Insulating Liquids Using VDE Electrodes*, 2012, reapproved 2019.

ASTM D1933, *Standard Specification for Nitrogen Gas as an Electrical Insulating Material*, 2003, reapproved 2017.

ASTM D5837, *Standard Test Method for Furanic Compounds in Electrical Insulating Liquids by High-Performance Liquid Chromatography (HPLC)*, 2015.

N **M.1.2.2 EASA Publications.** Electrical Apparatus Service Association, Inc., 1331 Baur Blvd, St. Louis, MO 63132.

ANSI/EASA AR100, *Recommended Practice for the Repair of Rotating Electrical Apparatus*, 2015.

N **M.1.2.3 FEMA Publications.** Federal Emergency Management Agency, US Department of Homeland Security, 500 C Street, SW, Washington, DC 20472.

FEMA P-348, *Protecting Building Utility Systems From Flood Damage: Principles and Practices for the Design and Construction of Flood Resistant Building Utility Systems*, 2017.

Δ **M.1.2.4 IEC Publications.** International Electrotechnical Commission, 3, rue de Varembé, P.O. Box 131, CH-1211 Geneva 20, Switzerland. (In the United States, IEC publications are available from ANSI.)

IEC 62446-2, *Photovoltaic (PV) systems — Requirements for testing, documentation and maintenance — Part 2: Grid connected systems — Maintenance of PV systems*, 2020.

Δ **M.1.2.5 IEEE Publications.** IEEE, 3 Park Avenue, 17th Floor, New York, NY 10016-5997.

IEEE C2, *National Electrical Safety Code® (NESC®)*, 2017.

ANSI/IEEE C37.20.7, *Guide for Testing Switchgear Rated Up to 52 kV for Internal Arcing Faults*, 2017.

IEEE C37.23, *Standard for Metal-Enclosed Bus*, 2015.

ANSI/IEEE 43, *Recommended Practice for Testing Insulation Resistance of Rotating Machinery*, 2013.

IEEE C57.12.91, *Standard Test Code for Dry-Type Distribution and Power Transformers*, 2020.

IEEE C57.104, *Guide for the Interpretation of Gases Generated in Mineral Oil-Immersed Transformers*, 2019.

ANSI/IEEE C57.110, *Recommended Practice for Establishing Liquid Immersed and Dry-Type Power and Distribution Transformer Capability when Supplying Nonsinusoidal Load Currents*, 2018.

ANSI/IEEE C62.41, *Recommended Practice for Surge Voltages in Low-Voltage AC Power Circuits*, 1991.

IEEE 80, *Guide for Safety in AC Substation Grounding*, 2013.

IEEE 100, *Authoritative Dictionary of IEEE Standards Terms*, 2000 (withdrawn).

ANSI/IEEE 141, *Recommended Practice for Electric Power Distribution for Industrial Plants (IEEE Red Book)*, 1993.

ANSI/IEEE 142, *Recommended Practice for Grounding of Industrial and Commercial Power Systems (IEEE Green Book)*, 2007.

ANSI/IEEE 241, *Recommended Practice for Electric Power Systems in Commercial Buildings (IEEE Gray Book)*, 1990.

ANSI/IEEE 242, *Recommended Practice for Protection and Coordination of Industrial and Commercial Power Systems (IEEE Buff Book)*, 2001.

IEEE 315, *Graphic Symbols for Electrical and Electronics Diagrams*, 1975 (1993).

ANSI/IEEE 399, *Recommended Practice for Industrial and Commercial Power Systems Analysis (IEEE Brown Book)*, 1997.

Shaded text = Revisions.   **Δ** = Text deletions and figure/table revisions.   • = Section deletions.   *N* = New material.

ANSI/IEEE 400, *Guide for Field Testing and Evaluation of the Insulation of Shielded Power Cable Systems Rated 5 kV and Above*, 2012.

IEEE 450, *Recommended Practice for Maintenance, Testing, and Replacement of Vented Lead-Acid Batteries for Stationary Applications*, 2010.

ANSI/IEEE 493, *Recommended Practice for the Design of Reliable Industrial and Commercial Power Systems (IEEE Gold Book)*, 2007.

ANSI/IEEE 519, *Recommended Practice and Requirements for Harmonic Control in Electrical Power Systems*, 2014.

ANSI/IEEE 1100, *Recommended Practice for Powering and Grounding Electronic Equipment (IEEE Emerald Book)*, 2005.

IEEE 1106, *Recommended Practice for Installation, Maintenance, Testing, and Replacement of Vented Nickel-Cadmium Batteries for Stationary Applications*, 2015.

IEEE 1159, *Recommended Practice for Monitoring Electric Power Quality*, 2019.

IEEE 1188, *Recommended Practice for Maintenance, Testing, and Replacement of Valve-Regulated Lead-Acid (VRLA) Batteries for Stationary Applications*, 2005 (2010 with 2014 amendment).

IEEE 1584™, *Guide for Performing Arc-Flash Hazards Calculations*, 2018.

IEEE 1578, *Recommended Practice for Stationary Battery Electrolyte Spill Containment and Management*, 2018.

IEEE 1657, *Recommended Practice for Personnel Qualifications for Installation and Maintenance of Stationary Batteries*, 2018.

IEEE 3000 Standards: *Fundamentals*.

IEEE 3001 Standards: *Power Systems Design*.

IEEE 3002 Standards: *Power Systems Analysis*.

IEEE 3002.8, *Recommended Practice for Conducting Harmonic Studies and Analysis of Industrial and Commercial Power Systems*, 2018.

IEEE 3003 Standards: *Power Systems Grounding*.

IEEE 3004 Standards: *Protection & Coordination*.

IEEE 3005 Standards: *Energy & Standby Power Systems*.

IEEE 3006 Standards: *Power Systems Reliability*.

IEEE 3007 Standards: *Maintenance, Operations & Safety*.

IEEE 3007.1, *Recommended Practice for the Operation and Management of Industrial and Commercial Power Systems*, 2010.

IEEE 3007.2, *Recommended Practice for the Maintenance of Industrial and Commercial Power Systems*, 2010.

IEEE 3007.3, *Recommended Practice for Electrical Safety in Industrial and Commercial Power Systems*, 2012.

M.1.2.6 NEMA Publications. National Electrical Manufacturers Association, 1300 North 17th Street, Suite 900, Arlington, VA 22209.

NEMA AB-4, *Guidelines for Inspection and Preventive Maintenance of Molded-Case Circuit Breakers Used in Commercial and Industrial Applications*, 2017.

NEMA BU1.1, *General Instructions for Handling, Installation, Operation, and Maintenance of Busway Rated 600 Volts or Less*, 2010.

ANSI/NEMA C84.1, *American National Standard for Electric Power Systems and Equipment — Voltage Ratings (60 Hz)*, 2020.

NEMA GD 1, *Evaluating Water-Damaged Electrical Equipment*, 2019.

NEMA GD 2, *Evaluating Fire- and Heat-Damaged Electrical Equipment*, 2016.

NEMA KS-3, *Guidelines for Inspection and Preventive Maintenance of Switches Used in Commercial and Industrial Applications*, 2010.

ANSI/NEMA WD 6, *Wiring Devices — Dimensional Specifications*, 2016.

M.1.2.7 NETA Publications. InterNational Electrical Testing Association, 3050 Old Centre Ave., Suite 101, Portage, MI 49024.

ANSI/NETA ATS, *Standard for Acceptance Testing Specifications for Electrical Power Distribution Equipment and Systems*, 2021.

ANSI/NETA MTS, *Standard for Maintenance Testing Specifications for Electrical Power Distribution Equipment and Systems*, 2019.

M.1.2.8 UL Publications. Underwriters Laboratories Inc., 333 Pfingsten Road, Northbrook, IL 60062-2096.

UL 489, *Molded-Case Circuit Breakers, Molded-Case Switches, and Circuit Breaker Enclosures*, 2016.

UL 857, *Busways*, 2009.

UL 943, *Ground-Fault Circuit-Interrupters*, 2016.

UL 943C, *Outline of Investigation for Special Purpose Ground-Fault Circuit-Interrupters*, 2012.

UL 1053, *Ground-Fault Sensing and Relaying Equipment*, 2015.

UL 1066, *Low-Voltage AC and DC Power Circuit Breakers Used in Enclosures*, 2017.

N **M.1.2.9 US Government Publications.** US Government Publishing Office, 732 North Capitol Street, NW, Washington, DC 20401-0001.

OSHA Safety & Health Information Bulletin (SHIB), "Certification of Workplace Products by Nationally Recognized Testing Laboratories."

Title 29, Code of Federal Regulations, Part 1910, "Safety and Health Regulations for Construction."

Title 29, Code of Federal Regulations, Part 1910.94(a), "Ventilation — Abrasive Blasting."

Title 29, Code of Federal Regulations, Part 1910.146, "Permit-Required Confined Spaces."

Title 29, Code of Federal Regulations, Part 1910.242(b), "Hand and Portable Powered Tools and Equipment, General — Compressed Air Used for Cleaning."

Title 29, Code of Federal Regulations, Part 1910.269(e), "Electric Power Generation, Transmission, and Distribution, Enclosed Spaces."

Title 29, Code of Federal Regulations, Part 1926, "Occupational Safety and Health Standards."

Title 29, Code of Federal Regulations, Part 1926.56, "Illumination."

Toxic Substances Control Act, US Environmental Protection Agency, 1976.

TM 5-698-1, *Reliability/Availability of Electrical and Mechanical Systems for Command, Control, Communications, Computer, Intelligence, Surveillance, and Reconnaissance (C4ISR) Facilities*, 2007.

TM 5-698-2, *Reliability-Centered Maintenance (RCM) for Command, Control, Communications, Computer, Intelligence, Surveillance, and Reconnaissance (C4ISR) Facilities*, 2006.

TM 5-698-3, *Reliability Primer for Command, Control, Communications, Computer, Intelligence, Surveillance, and Reconnaissance (C4ISR) Facilities*, 2005.

△ M.1.2.10 Other Publications.

Flood Repair of Electrical Equipment, Pat Beisert, Shermco Industries, PowerTest Annual Technical Conference, March 12, 2009.

The Lighting Library, Illuminating Engineering Society of North America (IESNA).

MIL-HNDK-508, *Wiring and Wiring Devices for Combat and Tactical Vehicles, Selection and Installation of*, April 21, 1998, available from DLA Document Services, 700 Robbins Avenue, Building 4D, Philadelphia, PA 19111-5094. (Supersedes MIL-STD-339)

ISO 31000, *Risk Management — Principles and Guidelines*, 2009.

△ M.2 Informational References.
The following documents or portions thereof are listed here as informational resources only. They are not a part of the requirements of this document.

This bibliography lists some of the more widely recognized sources of maintenance and testing information. Because they are so numerous, many excellent textbooks by individual authors are not listed; information on them is available from the various publishers.

For those who are interested in implementing an effective EMP or improving an existing one, a suitable reference library should be readily available. The size of the plant and the extent of its maintenance and servicing operations will determine the desired publications for the reference library.

The need to use the manufacturer's service manuals and instructions furnished with specific equipment or apparatus has been previously mentioned and cannot be overemphasized. Additionally, there are many sources of helpful information on general and specific maintenance, troubleshooting, test methods, test instruments, and their use. Some of these are available without cost, but most entail a nominal charge. Publishers of technical and trade magazines are another important source of pertinent literature. Some can provide, without charge, reprints of specific articles or, for a nominal fee, a compilation of reprints of articles on a particular subject.

M.2.1 Eaton's Crouse-Hinds Publications. Eaton's Crouse-Hinds Division, 1201 Wolf Street, Syracuse, NY 13208.

Crouse-Hinds 2017 Code Digest, *Article 500-516 of the National Electrical Code with product recommendations for use in hazardous (classified) areas*, 2017.

M.2.2 FM Global Publications. FM Global, 270 Central Avenue, P.O. Box 7500, Johnston, RI 02919.

FM Global Data Sheets, www.fmglobal.com/datasheets.

△ **M.2.3 IEC Publications.** International Electrotechnical Commission, 3, rue de Varembé, P.O. Box 131, CH-1211 Geneva 20, Switzerland. (In the United States, IEC publications are available from ANSI.)

IEC No. 60417-DB-HS, *Graphical Symbols for Use on Equipment*, 2008.

△ **M.2.4 IEEE Publications.** IEEE, 3 Park Avenue, 17th Floor, New York, NY 10016-5997.

ANSI/IEEE 67, *Guide for Operation and Maintenance of Turbine Generators*, 2005.

ANSI/IEEE 315 (ANSI Y32.2-75), *Graphic Symbols for Electrical and Electronics Diagrams*, 1975, reaffirmed 1993.

ANSI/IEEE 432, *Guide for Insulation Maintenance for Rotating Electrical Machinery (5 HP to less than 10,000 HP)*, 1992 (withdrawn).

IEEE 1250, *IEEE Guide for Identifying and Improving Voltage Quality in Power Systems*, 2011.

IEEE 1409, *Guide for Application of Power Electronics for Power Quality Improvement on Distribution Systems Rated 1 kV Through 38 kV*, 2012.

IEEE 1453, *IEEE Recommended Practice — Adoption of IEC 61000-4-15:2010, Electromagnetic compatibility (EMC) — Testing and measurement techniques — Flickermeter — Functional and design specifications*, 2015.

IEEE 1458, *Recommended Practice for the Selection, Field Testing, and Life Expectancy of Molded Case Circuit Breakers for Industrial Applications*, 2017.

IEEE 1564, *Guide for Voltage Sag Indices*, 2014.

IEEE C37.41, *Standard Design Tests for High-Voltage (>1000 V) Fuses and Accessories*, 2016.

ANSI/IEEE C37.95, *Guide for Protective Relaying of Utility-Consumer Interconnections*, 2014.

IEEE C37.96, *Guide for AC Motor Protection*, 2012.

IEEE C57.94, *Recommended Practice for Installation, Application, Operation, and Maintenance of Dry-Type Distribution and Power Transformers*, 2015.

ANSI/IEEE C57.106, *Guide for Acceptance and Maintenance of Insulating Oil in Equipment*, 2006.

IEEE C57.111, *Guide for Acceptance and Maintenance of Silicone Insulating Fluid and Its Maintenance in Transformers*, 2009.

ANSI/IEEE C57.121, *Guide for Acceptance and Maintenance of Less Flammable Hydrocarbon Fluid in Transformers*, 1998, reaffirmed 2009.

△ M.2.5 McGraw-Hill Publications.
McGraw-Hill Publishing Co., 1221 Avenue of the Americas, New York, NY 10020.

Beeman, D., *Industrial Power Systems Handbook*, 1955.

Dugan, R. C., et al., *Electrical Power Systems Quality*, McGraw Hill, 3rd Edition, 2012.

Hubert, C. I., *Preventative Maintenance of Electrical Equipment*, 1969.

Smeaton, R. W., *Motor Applications and Maintenance Handbook*, 1986.

M.2.6 NECA Publications.
National Electrical Contractors Association, 1201 Pennsylvania Ave., NW, Suite 1200, Washington, DC 20004.

Total Energy Management — A Practical Handbook on Energy Conservation and Management, Index No. 2095.

M.2.7 NEMA Publications.
National Electrical Manufacturers Association, 1300 North 17th Street, Suite 900, Arlington, VA 22209.

NEMA 280, *Application Guide for Ground-Fault Circuit Interrupters* (see Section 7, Field Test Devices, and Section 8, Field Troubleshooting), 1990.

NEMA AB 3, *Molded Case Circuit Breakers and Their Application*, 2013.

NEMA GD 1, *Evaluating Water-Damaged Electrical Equipment*, 2016.

NEMA ICS 1.3, *Preventive Maintenance of Industrial Control and Systems Equipment*, 1986, reaffirmed 2015.

NEMA ICS 2.3, *Instructions for the Handling, Installation, Operation, and Maintenance of Motor Control Centers Rated Not More Than 600 Volts*, 1995, reaffirmed 2008.

NEMA ICS 7, *Adjustable — Speed Drives*, 2014.

ANSI/NEMA MG 2, *Safety Standard for Construction and Guide for Selection, Installation and Use of Electric Motors and Generators* (see Section 8.3, Maintenance), 2014.

NEMA PB 1.1, *General Instructions for Proper Installation, Operation and Maintenance of Panelboards Rated 600 V or Less*, 2013.

△ M.2.8 NSC Publications.
National Safety Council, 1121 Spring Lake Drive, Itasca, IL 60143-3201.

Electrical Inspection Illustrated, 3rd edition, 2011.

M.2.9 US Army Publications.
US Army Corps of Engineers, 441 G Street, NW, Washington, DC 20314-1000.

TM-5-682, *Electrical Safety, Facilities Engineering US Army*, November 1999.

TM-5-683, *Electrical Interior, Facilities Engineering US Army*, November 1995.

TM-5-684, *Electrical Exterior, Facilities Engineering US Army*, November 1996.

TM-5-685, *Operation, Maintenance and Repair of Auxiliary Generators US Army*, August 1996.

TM 5-686, *Power Transformer Maintenance and Acceptance Testing*, November 1998.

TM 5-688, *Foreign Voltages and Frequencies Guide*, November 1999.

TM 5-691, *Utility Systems Design Requirements for Command, Control, Communications, Computer, Intelligence, Surveillance, and Reconnaissance (C4ISR) Facilities*, December 2000.

TM 5-692-1, *Maintenance of Mechanical and Electrical Equipment at Command, Control Communications, Computer, Intelligence, Surveillance, and Reconnaissance (C4ISR) Facilities-Recommended Maintenance Practices*, April 2001.

TM 5-692-2, *Maintenance of Mechanical and Electrical Equipment at Command, Control Communications, Computer, Intelligence, Surveillance, and Reconnaissance (C4ISR) Facilities-System Design Features*, April 2001.

M.2.10 Other Publications.

Power Quality Analysis, NJATC, 2010.

M.3 References for Extracts in Informational Sections.

NFPA 70®, *National Electrical Code®*, 2020 edition.
NFPA 70®, *National Electrical Code®*, 2023 edition.

Shaded text = Revisions.   △ = Text deletions and figure/table revisions.   • = Section deletions.   *N* = New material.

2023 Edition

Index

Copyright © 2022 National Fire Protection Association. All Rights Reserved.

The copyright in this index is separate and distinct from the copyright in the document that it indexes. The licensing provisions set forth for the document are not applicable to this index. This index may not be reproduced in whole or in part by any means without the express written permission of NFPA.

-A-

Adjustable Speed Drive
Definition, 3.3.1, A.3.3.1
Administration, Chap. 1
Application, 1.3
Equivalency, 1.4
Purpose, 1.2
Scope, 1.1
Units of Measurement, 1.5
Primary Units, 1.5.1
Secondary Units and Conversions, 1.5.2
Unit Application and Enforcement, 1.5.3
Appliance
Definition, 3.3.2
Approved
Definition, 3.2.1, A.3.2.1
Arc Flash Hazard
Definition, 3.3.3
Authority Having Jurisdiction (AHJ)
Definition, 3.2.2, A.3.2.2

-B-

Battery Energy Storage Systems, Chap. 32
Documentation, 32.3
Frequency of Maintenance, 32.2
Periodic Maintenance Procedures, 32.4
Cleaning, 32.4.2
Electrical Testing, 32.4.5
Mechanical Servicing, 32.4.4
Visual Inspections, 32.4.1
Scope, 32.1
Bonded (Bonding)
Definition, 3.3.4
Bonding Conductor (Bonding Jumper)
Definition, 3.3.5
Bonding Jumper, Equipment
Definition, 3.3.6
Busway
Definition, 3.3.7
Busways, Chap. 14
Frequency of Maintenance, 14.2
Periodic Maintenance Procedures, 14.3
Cleaning, 14.3.2, A.14.3.2
Electrical Testing, 14.3.5, A.14.3.5
Lubrication, 14.3.3, A.14.3.3
Mechanical Servicing, 14.3.4
Visual Inspection, 14.3.1, A.14.3.1
Scope, 14.1, A.14.1

-C-

Cable Tray, Chap. 19
Frequency of Maintenance, 19.2
Periodic Maintenance Procedures, 19.3
Cleaning, 19.3.2
Electrical Testing, 19.3.5
Visual Inspections, 19.3.1
Scope, 19.1
Cable Tray System
Definition, 3.3.8
Case Histories, Annex L
Clogged Cooling Ducts Cause Motor Failure, L.4
Explosion in an Electrical Room, L.9
Failure to Have Entire Critical System Acceptance Tested Results in $5.2 Million (US) Loss, L.7
Failure to Maintain Extension Cord Causes Fire, L.3
Hospital Electrical Panel Fire, L.6
Hospital MCC Fails and Air Conditioning Down, L.12
Infrared Inspection Prevents Potential Failure and Outage of 20 MVA Transformer, L.10
Lack of Cleaning Program Causes Switchgear Damage, L.2
Lack of Maintenance Causes Failure of Multiple Circuit Breakers, L.5
Office Building Drive System Loose Connection Results in Arcing Fault, L.11
Oil Contamination Causes Transformer Failure, L.1
Refrigeration Compressor Fails Unexpectedly as a Result of Improper Maintenance, L.8
Circuit Breaker
Definition, 3.3.9, A.3.3.9
Circuit Breakers, Low- and Medium-Voltage, Chap. 15
Frequency of Maintenance, 15.2
Periodic Maintenance Procedures for Low-Voltage Power Circuit (LVPCB), Molded Case Circuit Breaker (MCCB), and Insulated Case Circuit Breakers (ICCB), 15.3
Cleaning, 15.3.2
Electrical Testing, 15.3.5, A.15.3.5
Lubrication, 15.3.3
Mechanical Servicing, 15.3.4
Visual Inspections, 15.3.1
Periodic Maintenance Procedures for Medium-Voltage Power Circuit Breakers, 15.4
Cleaning, 15.4.2
Electrical Testing, 15.4.5
Lubrication, 15.4.3
Mechanical Servicing, 15.4.4
Scope, 15.1
Commissioning
Definition, 3.3.10
Condition of Maintenance
Definition, 3.3.11

Continuous Monitoring
Definition, 3.3.12
Coordination Study
Definition, 3.3.13
Corona
Definition, 3.3.14, A.3.3.14

-D-

Definitions, Chap. 3
Diagrams, Annex D
Disconnecting Means
Definition, 3.3.15

-E-

Electric Vehicle Power Transfer Systems and Associated Equipment, Chap. 33
Documentation, 33.3
Frequency of Maintenance, 33.2
Periodic Maintenance Procedures, 33.4
Visual Inspection, 33.4.1
Scope, 33.1
Electrical Disaster Recovery, Annex K
Catastrophic Event Categories, K.2
Developing a Safety Plan, K.2.4
Documentation, K.2.7
Equipment Tag, K.2.7.2
Equipment Tracking Sheet, K.2.7.6
Field Sketch, K.2.7.5
Labeling of Wires, K.2.7.3
Photographs of Equipment, K.2.7.4
Repair or Replace, K.2.7.7
Industry Standards and Guidelines, K.2.7.7.3
Repair or Replace Decisions, K.2.7.7.1
Repair or Replace Factors, K.2.7.7.2
Service Shop–Related Activities, K.2.7.1
Equipment, K.2.8
Balance of Plant Electrical Repair, K.2.8.5
Electric Motors, K.2.8.3
Low-Voltage Distribution Equipment, K.2.8.2
Medium-Voltage Equipment, K.2.8.1
Power and Control Wiring, K.2.8.4
Project Summary, K.2.8.8
Re-energization of the Facility, K.2.8.6
System Commissioning, K.2.8.7
Initial Damage Assessment, K.2.6
Drawings, Schematics, Equipment Documentation, K.2.6.1
Priority Assessment, K.2.6.2
Mobilization of Recovery Personnel, K.2.3
In-House Personnel, K.2.3.1
Notification to Insurance Carrier, K.2.3.3
Outsourced (Contract) Personnel, K.2.3.2
Securing the Facility to Limit Damage, K.2.2
Temporary and Emergency Power Generation, K.2.5
The Initial Event, K.2.1
Introduction, K.1

Electrical Maintenance Program (EMP)
Definition, 3.3.16, A.3.3.16
Electrically Safe Work Condition
Definition, 3.3.17
EMP Coordinator
Definition, 3.3.18
Energy Storage System (ESS)
Definition, 3.3.19, A.3.3.19
Equipment Storage and Maintenance During Construction, Annex H
Busway and Associated Fittings, H.3
Cables, H.6
Equipment, H.2
Switchgear, Switchboards, Motor Control, and Other Control Equipment, H.2.1
Introduction, H.1
Motors and Generators, H.4
Storage Batteries, H.7
Transformers, H.5
Primary Disconnect Switches, H.5.6
Transformer Gas Blanket, H.5.5
Transformers Filled with Insulating Liquid, H.5.4
Equipment, Mobile (Mobile Equipment)
Definition, 3.3.20
Explanatory Material, Annex A

-F-

Fault Current, Available (Available Fault Current)
Definition, 3.3.21, A.3.3.21
Field Testing and Test Methods, Chap. 8
Condition of Maintenance Indication, 8.7, A.8.7
Conditions of Maintenance, 8.7.1
Limited Service, 8.7.1.2, A.8.7.1.2
Nonserviceable, 8.7.1.3, A.8.7.1.3
Serviceable, 8.7.1.1
Introduction, 8.1
Qualifications of Testing Personnel, 8.4
Risk Assessment Special Considerations, 8.2
Test Equipment and Tools, 8.5
Test Record, 8.6
Testing Category Types, 8.3, A.8.3
Category 1 — Online Standard Test, 8.3.1
Category 1A — Online Enhanced Test, 8.3.2
Category 2 — Offline Standard Test, 8.3.3
Category 2A — Offline Enhanced Test, 8.3.4
Forms, Annex E
Fundamental Tests, Chap. 7
Bolted Bus Connections, Conductor Terminations, and Conductor Connectors, 7.2
Newly Installed Threaded Hardware Torque Values, 7.2.2
Fundamental Tests, 7.1
Infrared Thermography, 7.4
Insulation Resistance Quality, 7.3
Fuses, Chap. 16
Frequency of Maintenance, 16.2
Periodic Maintenance Procedures, 16.3
Cleaning, 16.3.2
Electrical Testing, 16.3.5, A.16.3.5

Mechanical Servicing, 16.3.4
Visual Inspections, 16.3.1, A.16.3.1
Scope, 16.1

-G-

General, Chap. 4
Acceptance Test Report, 4.6
Electrical Maintenance Program (EMP), 4.2
Condition of Maintenance, 4.2.3
EMP Audit, 4.2.7
EMP Controls, 4.2.5
EMP Principles, 4.2.4
General, 4.2.1
Incident Investigations, 4.2.6
Inspection, 4.2.2
Equipment Cleaning, 4.8, A.4.8
Cleaning Personnel, 4.8.1
General Requirements, 4.1
Impact of Additions/Rework to Retrofitting Equipment, 4.7
Personnel, 4.3
Electrical Maintenance Training, 4.3.3
EMP Coordinator, 4.3.1
Maintenance Personnel, 4.3.2
Planned Inspections, 4.5
Survey and Analysis, 4.4
Ground
Definition, 3.3.22
Ground Fault
Definition, 3.3.25
Ground Loop
Definition, 3.3.33, A.3.3.33
Ground-Fault Circuit Interrupter (GFCI)
Definition, 3.3.26, A.3.3.26
Ground-Fault Circuit Interrupter, Special Purpose (SPGFCI).
(Special-Purpose Ground-Fault Circuit Interrupter)
Definition, 3.3.54, A.3.3.54
Ground-Fault Circuit Interrupters and Ground-Fault Protection of
Equipment Systems, Chap. 21
Frequency of Maintenance, 21.2
Periodic Maintenance Procedures, 21.3
Ground-Fault Circuit Interrupters (GFCIs) and Special-
Purpose GFCIs (SPGFCIs), 21.3.1, A.21.3.1
Electrical Testing, 21.3.1.5
Low-Voltage Ground-Fault Protection Systems, 21.3.2,
A.21.3.2
Cleaning, 21.3.2.2
Electrical Testing, 21.3.2.5
Mechanical Servicing, 21.3.2.4
Visual Inspections, 21.3.2.1
Medium-Voltage Ground-Fault Protection Systems, 21.3.3
Cleaning, 21.3.3.2
Electrical Testing, 21.3.3.5
Mechanical Servicing, 21.3.3.4
Visual Inspections, 21.3.3.1
Scope, 21.1, A.21.1
Ground-Fault Protection of Equipment
Definition, 3.3.27, A.3.3.27

Grounded (Grounding)
Definition, 3.3.23
Grounded Conductor
Definition, 3.3.24
Grounding and Bonding, Chap. 20
Frequency of Maintenance, 20.2
Periodic Maintenance Procedures, 20.3
Electrical Testing, 20.3.5, A.20.3.5
Visual Inspections, 20.3.1, A.20.3.1
Scope, 20.1
Grounding Conductor, Equipment (EGC)
Definition, 3.3.28
Grounding Electrode
Definition, 3.3.29
Grounding Electrode Conductor
Definition, 3.3.30
Grounding Electrode System
Definition, 3.3.31
Grounding Terminal
Definition, 3.3.32

-H-

Harmonics
Definition, 3.3.34
Hazardous (Classified) Location Electrical Equipment, Chap. 10
Bolts and Screws, 10.7
Conduit and Equipment Seals, 10.6
Elimination of Hazardous Atmospheres, 10.3
Elimination of Ignition Sources, 10.4
Equipment Reassembly, 10.5
Field Modifications, 10.9, A.10.9
General, 10.1, A.10.1
Handling of Equipment, Components, and Tools, 10.8, A.10.8
Maintenance Personnel for Hazardous (Classified)
Locations, 10.2

-I-

Informational References, Annex M
Interharmonics
Definition, 3.3.35, A.3.3.35

-L-

Labeled
Definition, 3.2.3
Lighting, Chap. 22
Frequency of Maintenance, 22.2
Periodic Maintenance Procedures, 22.3
Cleaning, 22.3.2
Maintenance Program, 22.3.3, A.22.3.3
Servicing, 22.3.4
Visual Inspections, 22.3.1
Scope, 22.1
Listed
Definition, 3.2.4, A.3.2.4
Long-Duration Undervoltage
Definition, 3.3.36, A.3.3.36

-M-

Maintenance Interval
Definition, 3.3.37

Maintenance Intervals, Chap. 9
Equipment Condition Assessment, 9.3
Criticality Condition of Equipment, 9.3.2, A.9.3.2
Operating Environment Condition of Equipment, 9.3.3
Physical Condition of Electrical Equipment, 9.3.1
Nonconforming Equipment, 9.3.1.5
Nonserviceable Equipment, 9.3.1.4
Frequency of Maintenance, 9.2
Scope, 9.1
Continuous Monitoring and Predictive Techniques, 9.1.1, A.9.1.1
Maintenance Frequency Modifications, 9.1.2

Motor Control Center
Definition, 3.3.38

Motor Control Equipment, Chap. 28
Frequency of Maintenance, 28.2
Periodic Maintenance Procedures, 28.3
Cleaning, 28.3.2
Electrical Testing, 28.3.5
Lubrication, 28.3.3
Mechanical Servicing, 28.3.4
Visual Inspections, 28.3.1
Scope, 28.1

-N-

NEMA Configurations, Annex F
Noise
Definition, 3.3.39
Noise, Common Mode
Definition, 3.3.39.1

-O-

Overcurrent
Definition, 3.3.40

Overcurrent Protective Device, Branch-Circuit (Branch-Circuit Overcurrent Protective Device)
Definition, 3.3.41

Overload
Definition, 3.3.42

-P-

Panelboard
Definition, 3.3.43

Panelboards and Switchboards, Chap. 13
Frequency of Maintenance, 13.2
Periodic Maintenance Procedures, 13.3
Cleaning, 13.3.2
Electrical Testing, 13.3.5
Lubrication, 13.3.3
Mechanical Servicing, 13.3.4
Visual Inspection, 13.3.1
Scope, 13.1

Personnel Safety, Chap. 5
Introduction, 5.1

Photovoltaic Systems, Chap. 30
Documentation and Labeling, 30.3
Frequency of Maintenance, 30.2
Periodic Maintenance Procedures, 30.4
Cleaning, 30.4.2, A.30.4.2
Electrical Testing, 30.4.5, A.30.4.5
Mechanical Servicing, 30.4.4
Visual Inspections, 30.4.1, A.30.4.1
Scope, 30.1, A.30.1

Portable Electrical Tools and Equipment, Chap. 29
Frequency of Maintenance, 29.2
Periodic Maintenance Procedures, 29.3
Cleaning, 29.3.2
Electrical Testing, 29.3.5, A.29.3.5
Lubrication, 29.3.3
Mechanical Servicing, 29.3.4
Visual Inspection, 29.3.1
Scope, 29.1

Portable Equipment
Definition, 3.3.44

Power and Distribution Transformers, Chap. 11
Frequency of Maintenance, 11.2
Periodic Maintenance Procedures, 11.3
Cleaning, 11.3.2
Electrical Testing, 11.3.5, A.11.3.5
Mechanical Servicing, 11.3.4
Visual Inspections, 11.3.1
Scope, 11.1

Power Cables and Conductors, Chap. 18
Chapter Scope, 18.1, A.18.1
Frequency of Maintenance, 18.2
Periodic Maintenance Procedures, 18.3
Cleaning, 18.3.2
Electrical Testing, 18.3.5, A.18.3.5
Lubrication, 18.3.3
Visual Inspections, 18.3.1, A.18.3.1

Power Quality
Definition, 3.3.45

Power Quality, Annex J
Harmonics, J.2
Causes of Harmonic Distortion, J.2.2
Harmonic Surveying and Testing, J.2.3
Harmonic Symptoms/Effects, J.2.1
Solutions/Measures to Harmonic Problems, J.2.4
Inadequate Grounding, J.7
Monitoring and Testing for Inadequate Grounding, J.7.3
Solutions for Inadequate Grounding, J.7.4
Interharmonics, J.9
Causes of Interharmonics, J.9.2
Monitoring and Testing of Interharmonics, J.9.3
Solutions for Interharmonics, J.9.4
Symptoms of Interharmonics, J.9.1
Introduction, J.1
Long-Duration Undervoltages and Sustained Voltage Interruptions, J.5
Causes of Long-Duration Undervoltage, J.5.2
Causes of Sustained Voltage Interruption, J.5.6

Monitoring and Testing of Long-Duration
  Undervoltages, J.5.3
  Solutions for Long-Duration Undervoltages, J.5.4
  Solutions for Sustained Voltage Interruptions, J.5.7
  Symptoms of a Sustained Voltage Interruption, J.5.5
  Symptoms of Long-Duration Undervoltage, J.5.1
Noise in Electrical and Electronic Systems, J.8
  Causes of Noise, J.8.2
  Monitoring and Testing of Noise, J.8.3
  Solutions for Noise, J.8.4
  Symptoms of Noise, J.8.1
Power Quality Audit, J.11
Transients (Surges), J.3
  Causes of Transients, J.3.2
  Solutions to Transient Problems, J.3.4
  Transient Monitoring, J.3.3
  Transient Symptoms and Effects, J.3.1
Unbalanced Voltages and Single Phasing, J.6
  Causes of Unbalanced Voltages, J.6.2
  Monitoring and Testing of Unbalanced Voltages, J.6.3
    Measuring, J.6.3.1
  Solutions for Unbalanced Voltages, J.6.4
  Symptoms of Unbalanced Voltages, J.6.1
Voltage Fluctuations and Flicker, J.10
  Solutions, J.10.4
  Voltage Fluctuations Causes, J.10.2
  Voltage Fluctuations Monitoring and Testing, J.10.3
  Voltage Fluctuations Symptoms, J.10.1
Voltage Sags and Swells, J.4
  Causes of Voltage Sags and Swells, J.4.2
    Sag Causes — Facility Power Systems, J.4.2.3
    Sag Causes — Transmission Systems, J.4.2.1
    Sag Causes — Utility Distribution Systems, J.4.2.2
    Swell Causes, J.4.2.4
  Monitoring and Testing for Sags and Swells, J.4.3
  Solutions for Sags and Swells, J.4.4
  Symptoms of Sags and Swells, J.4.1
Predictive Techniques
  Definition, 3.3.46
Primary Contact Matrix, Annex G
  Primary Contact Matrix, G.1
Protective Relays, Chap. 35
  Frequency of Maintenance, 35.2
  Periodic Maintenance Procedures, 35.3
    Cleaning, 35.3.2
    Electrical Testing, 35.3.5
    Mechanical Servicing, 35.3.4
    Visual Inspections, 35.3.1
  Scope, 35.1
Public Pools, Fountains, and Similar Installations, Chap. 34
  Frequency of Maintenance, 34.2
  Periodic Maintenance Procedures, 34.3
    Electrical Testing, 34.3.3
    Mechanical Inspections, 34.3.2
    Visual Inspections, 34.3.1, A.34.3.1
  Scope, 34.1

-Q-

Qualified Person
  Definition, 3.3.47

-R-

Reconditioned
  Definition, 3.3.48, A.3.3.48
Referenced Publications, Chap. 2
Reliability Centered Maintenance, Annex I
  Benefits of RCM, I.2
    Increased Availability, I.2.2
    Reduced Costs, I.2.1
  Definitions, I.1
    Availability, I.1.1
      Function of Uptime, I.1.1.1
      Inherent Availability, I.1.1.3
      Operational Availability, I.1.1.2
    RCM Maintenance, I.1.2
      Condition-Based Maintenance, I.1.2.3
      Corrective Maintenance, I.1.2.1
      Preventive Maintenance, I.1.2.2
    Reliability, I.1.3
    Reliability-Centered Maintenance (RCM), I.1.4
  FMECA Procedure as Part of an RCM Program, I.6
    Example of FMECA, I.6.6
      Detection Method, I.6.6.1
      Occurrence, I.6.6.2
      RPN Calculations and Ranking Methods for Flexible
        Analysis, I.6.6.4
        Results — System X, I.6.6.4.3
      Severity, I.6.6.3
  Relationship of RCM to Other Disciplines, I.3
    Reliability, I.3.1
      Basic Reliability, I.3.1.3
        Environmental Concerns, I.3.1.3.2
        Maintainability, I.3.1.3.3
        Safety, I.3.1.3.1
      Inherent Versus Operational Reliability, I.3.1.1
      Mission-Critical or Functional Reliability Versus Basic or
        Logistics Reliability, I.3.1.2
  Reliability, Inherent Availability, and Operational Availability
    Data, I.5
  Supporting Data, I.4
Risk Assessment
  Definition, 3.3.49
Rotating Equipment, Chap. 27
  Frequency of Maintenance, 27.2
  Periodic Maintenance Procedures, 27.3
    Cleaning, 27.3.2, A.27.3.2
    Electrical Testing, 27.3.5, A.27.3.5
    Lubrication, 27.3.3, A.27.3.3
    Mechanical Servicing, 27.3.4, A.27.3.4
    Visual Inspections, 27.3.1, A.27.3.1
  Scope, 27.1, A.27.1

-S-

Sag
Definition, 3.3.50, A.3.3.50

Service Point
Definition, 3.3.51, A.3.3.51

Servicing
Definition, 3.3.52, A.3.3.52

Shall
Definition, 3.2.5

Single-Line Diagram
Definition, 3.3.53

Single-Line Diagrams and System Studies, Chap. 6
Coordination Studies, 6.4, A.6.4
Electrical Maintenance-Related Design, 6.8, A.6.8
Incident Energy Analysis (Arc-Flash Study), 6.7, A.6.7
Introduction, 6.1
Load-Flow Studies, 6.5, A.6.5
Reliability Studies, 6.6, A.6.6
Short-Circuit Studies, 6.3, A.6.3
Single-Line Diagrams, 6.2

Standard
Definition, 3.2.6

Stationary Standby Batteries, Chap. 36
Documentation, 36.3
Frequency of Maintenance, 36.2
Periodic Maintenance Procedures, 36.4, A.36.4
Cleaning, 36.4.2, A.36.4.2
Electrical Testing, 36.4.5, A.36.4.5
Visual Inspections, 36.4.1, A.36.4.1
Scope, 36.1, A.36.1

Stationary Standby Battery
Definition, 3.3.55, A.3.3.55

Substations and Switchgear, Chap. 12
Frequency of Maintenance, 12.2
Periodic Maintenance Procedures, 12.3
Cleaning, 12.3.2
Electrical Testing, 12.3.5, A.12.3.5
Lubrication, 12.3.3
Mechanical Servicing, 12.3.4, A.12.3.4
Special, 12.3.6
Auxiliary Apparatus, 12.3.6.2
Miscellaneous Equipment, 12.3.6.1
Visual Inspection, 12.3.1, A.12.3.1
Scope, 12.1

Suggestions for Inclusion in a Walk-Through Inspection Checklist, Annex B
General, B.1
Appliances, B.1.5
Electrical Equipment Rooms and Motor Control Centers, B.1.13
Emergency Equipment, B.1.17
Enclosures of Electrical Parts (e.g., Motor Control Equipment, Junction Boxes, Switches), B.1.15
Equipment Grounding, B.1.10
Extension Cords, B.1.3
Flexible Cords (Including Those on Appliances), B.1.1

Grouped Electrical Control Equipment (Such as Might Be Mounted on Walls), B.1.14
Hazardous (Classified) Location Equipment, B.1.16
Luminaires, B.1.9
Multiple Current Taps, B.1.4
Office Equipment, B.1.6
Plugs and Connectors, B.1.2
Portable Equipment (Tools, Extension Lamps, and Extension Cords), B.1.8
Receptacle Outlets, B.1.7
Services, B.1.12
Yard Transformer Stations, B.1.11

Survey
Definition, 3.3.56, A.3.3.56

Sustained Voltage Interruption
Definition, 3.3.57

Swell
Definition, 3.3.58

Switchboard
Definition, 3.3.59, A.3.3.59

Switches, Chap. 17
Frequency of Maintenance, 17.2
Periodic Maintenance Procedures, 17.3, A.17.3
Cleaning, 17.3.2
Electrical Testing, 17.3.5, A.17.3.5
Lubrication, 17.3.3, A.17.3.3
Mechanical Servicing, 17.3.4
Visual Inspection, 17.3.1
Scope, 17.1

Switchgear
Definition, 3.3.60, A.3.3.60

Symbols, Annex C

-T-

Tests
Acceptance Tests
Definition, 3.3.61.1, A.3.3.61.1
As-Found Tests
Definition, 3.3.61.2
As-Left Tests
Definition, 3.3.61.3
Definition, 3.3.61
Enhanced Tests
Definition, 3.3.61.4, A.3.3.61.4
Standard Tests
Definition, 3.3.61.5

Transformer
Definition, 3.3.62
Transformer, Power
Definition, 3.3.62.1

Transients
Definition, 3.3.63, A.3.3.63

-U-

Unbalanced Voltages
Definition, 3.3.64

Uninterruptible Power Supplies (UPS), Chap. 25

Frequency of Maintenance, 25.2
Periodic Maintenance Procedures, 25.3
    Cleaning, 25.3.2
    Electrical Testing, 25.3.5
    Lubrication, 25.3.3
    Mechanical Servicing, 25.3.4
    Visual Inspections, 25.3.1
Scope, 25.1
Special Procedures, 25.4
    Equipment Software Upgrades and Revisions, 25.4.1
    Load Transfer and Load Testing, 25.4.2
    Output Stability, 25.4.2.2
      Low Battery Voltage Shutdown, 25.4.2.2.3
    System Test Conditions, 25.4.2.1

Utilization Equipment
    Definition, 3.3.65

-W-

Wind Power Electric Systems and Associated Equipment, Chap. 31
    Frequency of Maintenance, 31.2
    Periodic Maintenance Procedures, 31.3
      Electrical Testing, 31.3.5
      Visual Inspection and Mechanical Testing, 31.3.1, A.31.3.1
    Scope, 31.1

Wiring Devices, Chap. 24
    Frequency of Maintenance, 24.2
    Periodic Maintenance Procedures, 24.3
      Cleaning, 24.3.2
      Electrical Testing, 24.3.5
      Mechanical Servicing, 24.3.4
      Visual Inspections, 24.3.1
    Scope, 24.1, A.24.1

Sequence of Events for the Standards Development Process

Once the current edition is published, a Standard is opened for Public Input.

Step 1 – Input Stage

Input accepted from the public or other committees for consideration to develop the First Draft
Technical Committee holds First Draft Meeting to revise Standard (23 weeks); Technical Committee(s) with Correlating Committee (10 weeks)
Technical Committee ballots on First Draft (12 weeks); Technical Committee(s) with Correlating Committee (11 weeks)
Correlating Committee First Draft Meeting (9 weeks)
Correlating Committee ballots on First Draft (5 weeks)
First Draft Report posted on the document information page

Step 2 – Comment Stage

Public Comments accepted on First Draft (10 weeks) following posting of First Draft Report
If Standard does not receive Public Comments and the Technical Committee chooses not to hold a Second Draft meeting, the Standard becomes a Consent Standard and is sent directly to the Standards Council for issuance (see Step 4) or
Technical Committee holds Second Draft Meeting (21 weeks); Technical Committee(s) with Correlating Committee (7 weeks)
Technical Committee ballots on Second Draft (11 weeks); Technical Committee(s) with Correlating Committee (10 weeks)
Correlating Committee Second Draft Meeting (9 weeks)
Correlating Committee ballots on Second Draft (8 weeks)
Second Draft Report posted on the document information page

Step 3 – NFPA Technical Meeting

Notice of Intent to Make a Motion (NITMAM) accepted (5 weeks) following the posting of Second Draft Report
NITMAMs are reviewed and valid motions are certified by the Motions Committee for presentation at the NFPA Technical Meeting
NFPA membership meets each June at the NFPA Technical Meeting to act on Standards with "Certified Amending Motions" (certified NITMAMs)
Committee(s) vote on any successful amendments to the Technical Committee Reports made by the NFPA membership at the NFPA Technical Meeting

Step 4 – Council Appeals and Issuance of Standard

Notification of intent to file an appeal to the Standards Council on Technical Meeting action must be filed within 20 days of the NFPA Technical Meeting
Standards Council decides, based on all evidence, whether to issue the standard or to take other action

Notes:

. Time periods are approximate; refer to published schedules for actual dates.
. Annual revision cycle documents with certified amending motions take approximately 101 weeks to complete.
. Fall revision cycle documents receiving certified amending motions take approximately 141 weeks to complete.

Committee Membership Classifications[1,2,3,4]

The following classifications apply to Committee members and represent their principal interest in the activity of the Committee.

1. M *Manufacturer:* A representative of a maker or marketer of a product, assembly, or system, or portion thereof, that is affected by the standard.
2. U *User:* A representative of an entity that is subject to the provisions of the standard or that voluntarily uses the standard.
3. IM *Installer/Maintainer:* A representative of an entity that is in the business of installing or maintaining a product, assembly, or system affected by the standard.
4. L *Labor:* A labor representative or employee concerned with safety in the workplace.
5. RT *Applied Research/Testing Laboratory:* A representative of an independent testing laboratory or independent applied research organization that promulgates and/or enforces standards.
6. E *Enforcing Authority:* A representative of an agency or an organization that promulgates and/or enforces standards.
7. I *Insurance:* A representative of an insurance company, broker, agent, bureau, or inspection agency.
8. C *Consumer:* A person who is or represents the ultimate purchaser of a product, system, or service affected by the standard, but who is not included in (2).
9. SE *Special Expert:* A person not representing (1) through (8) and who has special expertise in the scope of the standard or portion thereof.

NOTE 1: "Standard" connotes code, standard, recommended practice, or guide.

NOTE 2: A representative includes an employee.

NOTE 3: While these classifications will be used by the Standards Council to achieve a balance for Technical Committees, the Standards Council may determine that new classifications of member or unique interests need representation in order to foster the best possible Committee deliberations on any project. In this connection, the Standards Council may make such appointments as it deems appropriate in the public interest, such as the classification of "Utilities" in the National Electrical Code Committee.

NOTE 4: Representatives of subsidiaries of any group are generally considered to have the same classification as the parent organization.

Submitting Public Input / Public Comment Through the Online Submission System

Following publication of the current edition of an NFPA standard, the development of the next edition begins and the standard is open for Public Input.

Submit a Public Input

NFPA accepts Public Input on documents through our online submission system at www.nfpa.org. To use the online submission system:

- Choose a document from the List of NFPA codes & standards or filter by Development Stage for "codes accepting public input."
- Once you are on the document page, select the "Next Edition" tab.
- Choose the link "The next edition of this standard is now open for Public Input." You will be asked to sign in or create a free online account with NFPA before using this system.
- Follow the online instructions to submit your Public Input (see www.nfpa.org/publicinput for detailed instructions).
- Once a Public Input is saved or submitted in the system, it can be located on the "My Profile" page by selecting the "My Public Inputs/Comments/NITMAMs" section.

Submit a Public Comment

Once the First Draft Report becomes available there is a Public Comment period. Any objections or further related changes to the content of the First Draft must be submitted at the Comment Stage. To submit a Public Comment follow the same steps as previously explained for the submission of Public Input.

Other Resources Available on the Document Information Pages

Header: View document title and scope, access to our codes and standards or NFCSS subscription, and sign up to receive email alerts.

Current & Prior Editions	Research current and previous edition information.
Next Edition	Follow the committee's progress in the processing of a standard in its next revision cycle.
Technical Committee	View current committee rosters or apply to a committee.
Ask a Technical Question	For members, officials, and AHJs to submit standards questions to NFPA staff. Our Technical Questions Service provides a convenient way to receive timely and consistent technical assistance when you need to know more about NFPA standards relevant to your work.
News	Provides links to available articles and research and statistical reports related to our standards.
Purchase Products & Training	Discover and purchase the latest products and training.
Related Products	View related publications, training, and other resources available for purchase.

Information on the NFPA Standards Development Process

I. Applicable Regulations. The primary rules governing the processing of NFPA standards (codes, standards, recommended practices, and guides) are the NFPA *Regulations Governing the Development of NFPA Standards (Regs).* Other applicable rules include NFPA *Bylaws*, NFPA *Technical Meeting Convention Rules*, NFPA *Guide for the Conduct of Participants in the NFPA Standards Development Process*, and the NFPA *Regulations Governing Petitions to the Board of Directors from Decisions of the Standards Council.* Most of these rules and regulations are contained in the *NFPA Standards Directory.* For copies of the *Directory*, contact Codes and Standards Administration at NFPA headquarters; all these documents are also available on the NFPA website at "www.nfpa.org/regs."

The following is general information on the NFPA process. All participants, however, should refer to the actual rules and regulations for a full understanding of this process and for the criteria that govern participation.

II. Technical Committee Report. The Technical Committee Report is defined as "the Report of the responsible Committee(s), in accordance with the Regulations, in preparation of a new or revised NFPA Standard." The Technical Committee Report is in two parts and consists of the First Draft Report and the Second Draft Report. (See *Regs* at Section 1.4.)

III. Step 1: First Draft Report. The First Draft Report is defined as "Part one of the Technical Committee Report, which documents the Input Stage." The First Draft Report consists of the First Draft, Public Input, Committee Input, Committee and Correlating Committee Statements, Correlating Notes, and Ballot Statements. (See *Regs* at 4.2.5.2 and Section 4.3.) Any objection to an action in the First Draft Report must be raised through the filing of an appropriate Comment for consideration in the Second Draft Report or the objection will be considered resolved. [See *Regs* at 4.3.1(b).]

IV. Step 2: Second Draft Report. The Second Draft Report is defined as "Part two of the Technical Committee Report, which documents the Comment Stage." The Second Draft Report consists of the Second Draft, Public Comments with corresponding Committee Actions and Committee Statements, Correlating Notes and their respective Committee Statements, Committee Comments, Correlating Revisions, and Ballot Statements. (See *Regs* at 4.2.5.2 and Section 4.4.) The First Draft Report and the Second Draft Report together constitute the Technical Committee Report. Any outstanding objection following the Second Draft Report must be raised through an appropriate Amending Motion at the NFPA Technical Meeting or the objection will be considered resolved. [See *Regs* at 4.4.1(b).]

V. Step 3a: Action at NFPA Technical Meeting. Following the publication of the Second Draft Report, there is a period during which those wishing to make proper Amending Motions on the Technical Committee Reports must signal their intention by submitting a Notice of Intent to Make a Motion (NITMAM). (See *Regs* at 4.5.2.) Standards that receive notice of proper Amending Motions (Certified Amending Motions) will be presented for action at the annual June NFPA Technical Meeting. At the meeting, the NFPA membership can consider and act on these Certified Amending Motions as well as Follow-up Amending Motions, that is, motions that become necessary as a result of a previous successful Amending Motion. (See 4.5.3.2 through 4.5.3.6 and Table 1, Columns 1-3 of *Regs* for a summary of the available Amending Motions and who may make them.) Any outstanding objection following action at an NFPA Technical Meeting (and any further Technical Committee consideration following successful Amending Motions, see *Regs* at 4.5.3.7 through 4.6.5) must be raised through an appeal to the Standards Council or it will be considered to be resolved.

VI. Step 3b: Documents Forwarded Directly to the Council. Where no NITMAM is received and certified in accordance with the *Technical Meeting Convention Rules*, the standard is forwarded directly to the Standards Council for action on issuance. Objections are deemed to be resolved for these documents. (See *Regs* at 4.5.2.5.)

VII. Step 4a: Council Appeals. Anyone can appeal to the Standards Council concerning procedural or substantive matters related to the development, content, or issuance of any document of the NFPA or on matters within the purview of the authority of the Council, as established by the *Bylaws* and as determined by the Board of Directors. Such appeals must be in written form and filed with the Secretary of the Standards Council (see *Regs* at Section 1.6). Time constraints for filing an appeal must be in accordance with 1.6.2 of the *Regs*. Objections are deemed to be resolved if not pursued at this level.

VIII. Step 4b: Document Issuance. The Standards Council is the issuer of all documents (see Article 8 of *Bylaws*). The Council acts on the issuance of a document presented for action at an NFPA Technical Meeting within 75 days from the date of the recommendation from the NFPA Technical Meeting, unless this period is extended by the Council (see *Regs* at 4.7.2). For documents forwarded directly to the Standards Council, the Council acts on the issuance of the document at its next scheduled meeting, or at such other meeting as the Council may determine (see *Regs* at 4.5.2.5 and 4.7.4).

IX. Petitions to the Board of Directors. The Standards Council has been delegated the responsibility for the administration of the codes and standards development process and the issuance of documents. However, where extraordinary circumstances requiring the intervention of the Board of Directors exist, the Board of Directors may take any action necessary to fulfill its obligations to preserve the integrity of the codes and standards development process and to protect the interests of the NFPA. The rules for petitioning the Board of Directors can be found in the *Regulations Governing Petitions to the Board of Directors from Decisions of the Standards Council* and in Section 1.7 of the *Regs*.

X. For More Information. The program for the NFPA Technical Meeting (as well as the NFPA website as information becomes available) should be consulted for the date on which each report scheduled for consideration at the meeting will be presented. To view the First Draft Report and Second Draft Report as well as information on NFPA rules and for up-to-date information on schedules and deadlines for processing NFPA documents, check the NFPA website (www.nfpa.org/docinfo) or contact NFPA Codes & Standards Administration at (617) 984-7246.

NFPA LINK

Your window to productivity

LPG Bulk Plant Site

This situation covers:

💡 **LP-Gas Container Awaiting Use** ①

Requirements for containers not connected for use

💡 **LP-Gas Cylinder Storage** ②

Storage requirements of cylinders awaiting use, re...

💡 **LP-Gas Cylinder Filling** ③

WITH NFPA LINK® YOU HAVE ACCESS TO NFPA® CODES AND STANDARDS, EXPERT COMMENTARY, VISUAL AIDS, AND MORE—ALL IN THE PALM OF YOUR HAND.

LEARN MORE AND GET STARTED AT
NFPA.ORG/LiNK